Marriage Counseling in Medical Practice

A SYMPOSIUM

Edited by

Ethel M. Nash, *M.A.*

Lucie Jessner, *M.D.*

D. Wilfred Abse, *M.D.*

Preface

"Health, in its broadest aspects, includes four components, physical, mental, social, and genetic, and recent trends in the teaching and practice of preventive medicine include attempts to incorporate all these features into the broad field of public health. As optimum health must include adequate adjustment of the individual to family life, marriage counseling must certainly have a place in the program." [2] Thus wrote Dr. C. Nash Herndon in 1954. This book owes much to him, for he has contributed not only the Foreword, but unstintingly of his time, his knowledge, and editorial skills.

The field of marriage counseling as it relates to medical practice owes an unrepayable debt to the lives and writings of an obstetrician and a urologist, both of whom died during the 1950's.

Robert Latou Dickinson (1861-1950) in the Preface of his memorable *Atlas of Human Sex Anatomy* wrote: "The first principle of sex education and marriage counseling gives attitudes precedence over anatomies. Yet function has structure for its machinery, and evasion of instruction concerning anatomy in action is in part responsible for the physical discords alleged by the participants to be the original cause for half the marital maladjustments and three-fourths of the divorces and desertions. We in medicine, therefore, are called upon to do our part to persuade morals to wed normals, to induce theology to adopt biology, to integrate within a workable code of ethics a sane science of sex." [1]

Abraham Stone (1896-1959) lecturing in 1946 at the Pennsylvania

State College's Annual Institute on Marriage and Home Adjustment said that "while marital maladjustments may be in the background of many obscure physical symptoms and illnesses, organic diseases may be in the background of marital and personality disturbances." [3]

These quotations epitomize a philosophy developed primarily by Dickinson and Stone and contributed to by others. This philosophy provided the foundation upon which rest our present concepts of marriage counseling and sex education. We, the editors, gladly acknowledge our indebtedness to this philosophy, which has provided the starting point for this book.

Ethel M. Nash, M.A.
Lucie Jessner, M.D.
D. Wilfred Abse, M.D.

References:

1. Dickinson, Robert Latou. 1933. *Atlas of Human Sex Anatomy*. Baltimore: Williams and Wilkins.

2. Herndon, C. Nash. 1954. "Medical Genetics and Marriage Counseling," *Marriage and Family Living*, 16(3):207-11.

3. Stone, Abraham, 1946. "Psychosomatic Factors in Marriage." Lecture at The Annual Institute on Marriage and Home Adjustment, The Pennsylvania State College.

Foreword

C. Nash Herndon, M.D.

Marriage is a great institution; no family should be without it. However, marriage is also a two-edged sword. On the one hand, a reasonably happy and successful marriage can be a source of the deepest personal satisfaction and inspiration to the married couple and their children and can provide a tangible *raison d'être* in a frenzied world where standards of lasting value are hard to find. On the other hand, an unsuccessful or "sick" marriage can initiate a surprisingly long and complex series of reactions and interactions, with a wide range of social, psychologic, and psychosomatic effects on the married couple, their children, and even the innocent bystander.

It is unfortunate that most physicians have largely ignored the medical implications of marital conflict and maladjustment. Too many physicians remain blissfully unaware of the marital problems of their patients until called upon to sew up the lacerations resulting from personal combat. They may then offer the fatherly suggestion that the couple should "get along better" and return to have the stitches removed. Other physicians may wonder why peptic ulcer, or hypertension, or many other ailments are so refractory to treatment in some patients and never realize that chronic marital tensions continue to aggravate the symptoms and counteract therapy. They may also accept the fact that their office visits include a high proportion of "crocks" with multiple complaints and no detectable organic disease without suspecting that a proportion of these are casualties of the war between the sexes. Most physicians simply accept the depressing statistics on the rates of illegitimate pregnancies, forced marriages, and divorces as evidence of social problems, without considering that perhaps the medical profession has some obligation for prevention of such personal disasters. It seems safe to say that only the unusual physician has a real appreciation of the medical implications of marital and premarital problems and remains alert to recognize the etiologic and contributory effects of these on his practice.

A number of reasons or excuses for this state of affairs can be adduced, but several of these seem specious upon closer examination. The excuse is often offered that busy physicians simply do not have time to inquire into the state of marital adjustment of each patient. This is another way of saying that there is a demand for methods that reduce the time required of the physician in obtaining the history, physical examination, and ancillary studies. Complete omission of the collection of data that may be useful in arriving at a complete and accurate diagnosis can scarcely be defended, but the use of time-conserving procedures, such as health and social questionnaires to be completed by the patient, and of the services of ancillary personnel (nurses, secretaries, laboratory technicians, social workers, marriage counselors) can be commended. Occasional physicians have maintained that marital problems are not a proper concern of the physician. This argument fails completely in the face of clear evidence that such problems can be of major etiologic importance in disease. Many physicians will admit that they are made personally uncomfortable by discussion of intimate marital problems and by premarital counseling situations. This objection certainly has validity for the individual physician, but this reaction has deeper roots that may be recognized and can be amenable to correction.

There is reasonable evidence, discussed later in this volume, that much of the apparent indifference of many physicians to marital problems has its roots in their recognition of a lack of special knowledge and professional preparation in this field. In most medical areas the doctor is secure in the knowledge that he knows much more about the topic in question than does the patient and that he can speak and act from a position of authority. In the area of marital adjustment and sexual problems this is usually not true. The physician may actually be in the position of having personal problems of his own similar to those of his patient, and he may have as little idea as the patient about how to resolve them. If a physician recognizes that he has a deficiency in some other professional area (biochemistry, microbiology, genetics, etc.) he will usually arrange to take an appropriate post-graduate course or at least undertake some home study. It is unfortunate that opportunities for post-graduate training in marital problems are few and far between, and good books on the subject are also scarce. It is painfully obvious that there is little in the usual medical school courses and house officer training programs that prepares the physician to face the medical aspects of marital and premarital problems with any degree of self-assurance. The better residencies in obstetrics and in psychiatry should be at least partly exempted from this blanket indictment.

If the reader has not been completely outraged by the heretical suggestion that there is an important facet of medical practice about which physicians are generally poorly informed and that this hiatus in training has produced a common psychological "blind spot," he will recognize that this deficiency can and should be corrected. Five specific areas can be defined in which remedial efforts are badly needed:

1. *Undergraduate Medical Instruction.* There is now a considerable body of factual scientific knowledge about marital and sexual problems, some of which is summarized in this book. This is essentially basic science information to which the medical student should be introduced. A few medical schools are now offering courses of instruction that are still in experimental and formative phases (see Part IV). This seems to be the beginning of a healthy trend that should spread to all medical schools eventually.

2. *House Officer Training Programs.* The habits for a lifetime of practice are usually formed during internship and residency. The house officer should form the habit of including an assessment of marital and sexual status in his evaluation of each patient. This can be done only if the chief of service encourages this practice, and if some type of family service facility is readily available.

3. *Training in Counseling.* At some point in undergradate or graduate training the physician needs to acquire some skill in counseling techniques. It should be emphasized that it is the essence of counseling, whether marriage, genetic, or of other types, to gently guide the pa-

tient into making his own decisions. This is the antithesis of the usual medical treatment, where the physician issues orders and instructions that the patient is expected to follow. Counseling cannot be successfully approached from an authoritarian viewpoint. The therapeutic value of getting the patient to assume enough responsibility and attain enough maturity to reach his own decisions, rather than to depend on the all-knowing father image of the physician, cannot be overemphasized.

4. *Post-graduate Courses and Publications.* There are now few opportunities for the practicing physician to acquire the knowledge and skills mentioned above, but those courses that have been offered recently have been well attended. This volume has grown out of two post-graduate courses and represents an effort to provide a publication that will be useful to the practitioner. It is certainly to be hoped that continuing education programs will give more attention to marital problems in the future.

5. *Training of Marriage Counselors.* It is a well-established principle of medical practice that the physician should make efficient use of ancillary or paramedical personnel (nurses, technicians, psychologists, public health workers, rehabilitation specialists, etc.). In most of these areas there is a reasonable supply of well-trained specialists, and the physician is accustomed to the idea that these people are skilled in special techniques and possess specialized knowledge that is not a part of the professional armamentarium of most physicians. However, the physician knows the scope and limitations of the available services, knows when and how they can be helpful in the management of a specific patient, and has no hesitation in arranging for the patient to obtain the special studies or special therapeutic effects that such specialists can offer. The physician should think of the well-trained marriage counselor in this same light, as a member of the medical team. Unfortunately, the supply of specialists in marriage counseling is at present very limited, and there are simply not enough people with adequate training to provide the consultation and referral services needed by physicians. A few good training programs exist, but many more are needed. There are also some very inadequate programs, and some people masquerading as marriage counselors whose competence to deal with disturbed patients is open to serious doubt. A supply of well-trained specialists in marriage counseling competent to work with

physicians will develop only if physicians themselves create a demand for these services. Evidence is appearing that a demand for medically oriented marriage counselors is developing, and new training programs are at least in the planning stage. As physicians become more familiar with the problems and with the beneficial results that can be obtained by professional counseling services coordinated with the over-all medical management of the problems of appropriate patients, the supply of trained marriage counselors can be expected to increase.

A brief word on the origins of this book seems in order. The idea that such a book is needed grew out of discussions at two symposia on medical aspects of marriage counseling. These meetings, to which practicing physicians of the area were invited, were held at Greensboro, N.C., in October of 1961 and at Chapel Hill, N.C., in October of 1962, the first sponsored jointly by the three North Carolina medical schools (Bowman Gray School of Medicine of Wake Forest College, Duke University Medical School, and The University of North Carolina School of Medicine) and the second sponsored by The University of North Carolina School of Medicine, The American Association of Marriage Counselors, and the North Carolina Neuropsychiatric Association. Well-known speakers from many states were invited, and the sponsors were pleased and even a bit surprised by the enthusiastic response of the rather large audiences in attendance. The editors of this volume were stimulated to obtain expanded versions of manuscripts of many of the talks presented and to obtain additional manuscripts to cover certain aspects of problems not considered in the original sessions.

The present volume therefore represents an effort to approach the general topic of marital problems in medical practice on a broad front and from the viewpoint of the practicing physician. The editors are aware that this effort will not provide all the answers to all the problems. There are many aspects of marital problems upon which even the experts can only express opinions and educated guesses, because reliable and critical data have not been collected and subjected to rigorous analysis. Here, as in most areas of basic and applied science, the trite remark that "more research is needed" is especially applicable. However, the many contributors to this symposium have conscientiously and successfully surveyed the present state of knowledge in this area and have provided a "survey course" that we hope will prove to be useful and stimulating to physicians.

Contents

Part Two · Premarital Medical Counseling

PART ONE

Marriage Counseling
by the Physician

Marriage Counseling
and the General Practitioner

Rex W. Speers, M.D.

These days, with so much specialization in the field of medicine, the general practitioner is often concerned about his training background and competence in meeting problems related to one or another of the special disciplines. Uncertainty frequently arises when he is confronted by patients in marital conflict. However, inasmuch as doctors have always been counselors to patients who are emotionally disturbed, the general practitioner feels obliged to deal with these situations as far as his competence permits. Here an attempt is made to define the disorder, discuss the symptoms, and establish ground rules for management and treatment.

Marital Conflict and Marriage Counseling: An Aspect of Medical Practice

When either or both spouses enter the doctor's office and declare they are having marital difficulties and wish some assistance, there is little doubt of the diagnosis, and the ensuing action on the part of the physician comes under the heading of marriage counseling. However, such behavior on the part of marital partners is relatively uncommon in a physician's office. By far the majority of cases present themselves as medical problems for which medical or surgical treatment is sought.

There is little need to repeat the evidence indicating the relevance of psychological factors in the production of medical disorders. This has been presented many times. Most physicians recognize and accept the existence and importance of such factors, and the scientific validity of taking them into consideration. It is curious that many doctors who publicly deny the importance of the psychological factors utilize their intuitive and experiential knowledge of these factors in their private dealings with patients. Thus, if we accept the importance of psychological factors in our medical practice theory, we can cease permitting the dichotomy between the psychological and the physical and resolve to view the patient in the light of his total being. It is in this frame of reference that we shall encounter the problem of marital conflict and the dilemma of marriage counseling.

For the past fifteen years, non-psychiatrist physicians have been repeatedly admonished to include emotional factors in the treatment of patients in their practice. The usual reply to such admonitions centers around the question of "the busy practitioner's insufficient time." It is likely that "insufficient time" is not the basic problem. On the contrary, perhaps the busy practitioner would find the time to deal with some of the emotional problems of his patients if he had some understanding of how one actually proceeds. When the busy doctor is confronted with a new test, a new surgical procedure, a new anesthetic, a new X-ray or cardiographic technique, the directions are explicit. The doctor usually finds the time to learn how to use the procedure or equipment in his routine practice. But, in the psychological area, explicit directions are few. Instead, the physician is bombarded with phrases like: "Treat the whole patient"; "Listen to the patient's entire story"; "Be aware of your own inner life and do not let yourself get too involved with the patient's problems"; "Understand the transference and the counter-transference." It is unlikely that such phrases assist the physician in coming to grips with the treatment of couples in marital conflict.

Training and Experience Which the General Practitioner Can Use to Gain Competence as a Marriage Counselor

The training of every physician has included important experiences upon which he can draw to gain competence in the field of marriage counseling. The most important is the physician's training in listening to a patient. He learned how to listen to the patient's complaints in terms of his present illness, its onset and its course. He learned how to listen to the patient's history, family history and operative history. Every doctor in training was admonished by his instructors to "let the patient tell his story in his own words," and in so doing, the physician learned how to be a good listener. Such listening was not one of passivity on the part of the doctor but rather a complicated process of sorting and sifting of the data in an effort to arrive at a differential diagnosis. The doctor asked the patient questions in order to clarify this point or that point, to eliminate this possible diagnosis or that one. He then focused on the relatively few remaining possibilities and asked further questions. As a result of this careful listening and the active questioning for clarification, the physician gained a picture of the patient before his present illness, the onset and course of the illness, and the probable causes. He obtained laboratory tests that ruled out this diagnosis and verified that one until he had ample evidence to assure himself he had an accurate diagnosis. Treatment could then begin. The doctor could tell the patient what he had found, what the corroborative evidence was for the diagnosis, and what had to be done to correct the disorder. Thus, he outlined the plan of action against the disease. He told the patient what to eat, how much rest to get, when to take this pill and when to take that one, and in short, partly took over the life of the patient for the period of time necessary to cure him of his disease. Throughout the entire medical school training, internship, and residency, this procedure was followed.

Initially, the length of the history taken by the medical student was extensive and represented an attempt at good listening. However, as the student progressed in his medical training, the histories became shorter and by the time he was a resident, the history was very brief. The doctor now found himself asking more questions and listening less to the patient's story. The doctor found himself focusing on the presenting complaint, with the past history limited to "childhood diseases and operations" and family history to "A & W" or "deceased from diabetes." The social history became limited to "married, father of three children, 38-year-old carpenter." The physician became skilled at listening to the answers to his questions which were focused on the presenting complaints. In learning this most admirable and necessary skill, the initial focus was on the system complained about, and ultimately, the organ involved in the system. Once the primary organ involvement was delineated, laboratory tests were ordered to ascertain the particular cellular pathology in that organ. From this procedure an accurate diagnosis was possible. In the treatment program that followed, most doctors included stereotyped knowledge about emotional factors in the production of the pathology. They often told the patient, "Slow down"; "Get out and play more golf"; "Stop the rat race at work"; or they might have told the spouse that the patient "needs love and affection."

In patients with marital conflicts, there may or may not be detectable structural changes. The basic "pathology" is in the interaction of the patient and his spouse; i.e., the marriage. It is not a diagnosis of exclusion rendered by ruling out "organic" pathology. It is a diagnosis arrived at in a manner very similar to the method used in the discovery of system, organ, or cellular pathology, i.e., by listening and asking questions for clarification. It is a diagnosis of the person and his interpersonal relationships with his spouse. The name of it is marital conflict. It may be a result of personality difficulties in the person designated as the patient, or in personality difficulties in the patient's spouse, but always there are difficulties in the interaction of these two people. The difficulties in the person designated as patient may be psychotic, neurotic, characterological, or organic disease producing personality disturbances. Or the difficulties may be in the spouse rather than the person designated as the patient. Or it may be the result of two relatively "normal" personalities interacting in a conflictual manner. At any rate, the auxiliary aids the doctor knows so well as related to system, organ, or cellular pathology are useless in this situation: the EKG, the X-ray, the complete laboratory facility, and the stethoscope. Not even the prescription pad and the pharmacological knowledge of the doctor will always be of great value in this condition.

The one skill that will be of great value is listening with the same investigative curiosity that worked so well in the doctor's early medical training. He asks questions for clarification and he sifts the material in his mind until a pattern is revealed. The physician is thus able to ascertain whether the problem is one involving psychosis, neurosis, character disorder, or organic pathology in the patient. He may make a similar investigation of the spouse and ultimately of the interaction between them. He is now in a position to render a diagnosis of the personality of the patient, of the spouse, and of the marital interaction.

In summary, it is important to emphasize that the non-psychiatrist physician has had experiences in his training which he can utilize to develop skill in dealing with the problem of marital conflict in his practice. This experience is to be found in the physician's training as a listener and the training that enabled him to sift the patient's verbalizations in such a manner as to catalogue and differentially diagnose. The difference, when confronted with marital conflict, lies in the doctor's directing his attention as much to the behavioral aspects of the patient in his interpersonal actions and reactions, as to the patient's systems, organs, or cellular interactions. It is the contention of most psychiatrists that this should be part of the routine history-taking from every patient and that to do so requires little more overall time than if the behavioral interaction of the patient is excluded.

It was earlier stated that the traditional role of the physician involves his partly taking over the patient's life for the period of time required to cure him of his disease, i.e., the patient has therapeutic things done to him by the physician and is required to carry out certain procedures outlined and ordered by the physician. In other words, the physician makes the diagnosis and orders the treatment that he believes to be the most effective towards curing the patient. It matters little whether the patient understands the intricate details of the treatment, although most medical men, in an effort to gain patients' cooperation, do not attempt to treat without giving the patient some understanding of what is being done. However, the treatment is done to the patient by the physician.

In the counseling process, the role of the physician is somewhat different. Instead of making a diagnosis and telling the patient what to do about it, the physician assists the patient to "see," "become aware of" his pattern of behavior, and then he urges the patient to decide what he would like to do about this pattern. Herein lies the art in counseling (in fact, in all psychotherapeutic endeavors), for it may be very difficult to alter one's habit in this regard. The image of the physician as one who does to and for his patient is a well-established image. It is a role of benevolent authority and is not only the role ingrained in the doctor but also the role ascribed to the doctor by the patient. This image is basically "The doctor knows best what is good for the patient."

It is quite true that doctors are authorities on what is best for the patient as regards most organic ailments, but there is nothing in a doctor's training that qualifies him as an authority as to what is *best* for any marital conflict. However, a doctor's training does qualify him to recognize conflict. It is true that the conflicts the doctor is accustomed to recognize are those pathological processes interacting with normal cells, tissues, organs, or systems. Similarly there are conflicts involving the interaction of marital partners. It is little more difficult to listen to the patient tell of "symptoms" concerned with his relationship to his spouse than to listen to symptoms concerned with his organ or system functioning. Just as each doctor has had (and continues to have) personal experiences with his own system functioning which permits empathy with the patient, each doctor also has had experiences with his spouse which permit a similar empathy with the patient's interaction with his spouse.

It need not be difficult for the doctor to encourage a patient to talk about the difficult situations he encounters in his relationship to his spouse. Nor need it be difficult for the doctor to get a patient to tell how the patient felt in these interactions. The difficult problem is perhaps related to the doctor's image of himself as one who ought to know how to correct these difficulties. Also, the doctor may have similar problems of his own in relating to his spouse and may be overzealous in his sympathy with the patient. In either instance, the doctor may find himself telling the patient how to cope with the interaction. It is important to repeat that when it comes to organic disorders, the doctor is "supposed to know" what the problem is and what to do about it. However, in his role as a counselor, the physician can learn what the problem is (just as he can learn what the problem is in organic ailments), but he should not supply the patient with an authoritative, ready-made solution to the problem. Rather than tell the patient what is wrong and what to do about it, a counselor tries to get the patient to see what is "wrong" with his marriage, perhaps as a result of the patient's own patterns of action in the marriage.

Just as a doctor directs his patient's attention to the symptoms of an organic disorder and assists him in being as thorough as possible in telling about these symptoms, he can similarly direct the patient's attention to his marriage. For instance the patient is encouraged to talk about some of the events that recently transpired between him and his spouse. In each of these vignettes of interaction, the doctor notes that the patient had expected the spouse to do a certain thing and when the spouse did not, an argument resulted. He might then question the patient as to whether or not he had specifically told the spouse exactly what it was he wanted and why he wanted it. The doctor may talk to the spouse and find out that she (or he, as the case may be) was not aware that the patient wanted *that* particular thing, in fact thought he wanted something else. By further questioning, the doctor discovers that this patient routinely fails to communicate to others exactly what it is he wants.

Once the doctor has seen this pattern of behavior repeat itself in several situations, he can draw the patient's attention to it by telling him that he has noted this particular pattern in his relationship to his wife, to his boss, and to the doctor. He can encourage the patient to get as curious about it as the doctor is. The patient can now see that this happens repeatedly and always with the same results. In drawing the patient's attention to the pattern, one need not be accusatory or even final in attitude. The doctor can simply state that this is something he sees and ask what the patient thinks about it. If the patient feels the doctor has his best interests at heart and is not being depreciatory or accusatory, he may see the pattern fairly clearly and decide there is something odd about his behavior. He may even decide that he is not too sure what it was he wanted. Once he decides what it is he really wants from his spouse, he may talk to the doctor about some way of getting this or a substitute for it. If the doctor happens to know a good way, it is perhaps all right to tell him, but usually one might let the patient try a few possibilities until he finds a way that is satisfactory to both him and his spouse.

All of this is done without the doctor's taking over the patient's life, or telling him what to do, or doing anything to his person. It is done by being a curious listener, asking questions for clarification, and focusing on the pattern of behavior, much as a doctor focuses on the functioning of the cardiovascular-renal system in patients suffering from pathology of those systems. It is, in a way, similar to a period of observation of a patient wherein the doctor listens more, asks more questions, and investigates further. The difference lies in the doctor's not telling the patient what he finds "wrong" and what to do about it. Instead, he tries to find out what is "wrong" with the behavior of the patient, then assists the patient to see it also, and finally, encourages the patient to decide what he wishes to do about it.

What has been described may not be the only, or even the best way of counseling, but it is a start. The two aspects of a medical doctor's training that will serve him best in his role as a marriage counselor are his ability to listen and his curiosity about human beings. The habit the doctor has to alter is the one involving his image and role as a benevolent parent who knows what is best, who tells the "child" what is "wrong" and what to do to make it "right." It is perhaps worthwhile repeating that the art of marriage counseling includes providing the patient with a forum upon which he can express his feelings in regard to his marriage. In such a permissive atmosphere, the patient becomes aware that he has an empathic listener who desires to assist him with his problem. Also, the patient will become aware that the physician respects his right to have such feelings and will not condemn him for their presence.

However, he also is seeking assistance from the physician in finding a solution to his conflict. As the physician listens, he sifts and sorts the verbalizations until he becomes aware of a repetitive pattern of behavior evident in most of the patient's interactions with his spouse. He can invite the patient to listen to himself as regards this particular pattern. No one is implying that this activity is easy, nor is it maintained that marriage counseling is as simple as herein outlined; but doctors are skilled in listening and have always been curious about human beings and their nature. They, therefore, have the basic prerequisites to tackle the problem of marital conflict. If the doctor can also learn to allow the patient to find his own solution to what both agree is the "problem," things will not go too badly. Most doctors will sometimes find it advisable to discuss some of their cases with a qualified marriage counselor or a psychiatrist so as to enhance their skill in dealing with marital conflict.

It was previously stated that "time" is not the vital factor in the general practitioner's reluctance to accept the role of counselor. All doctors will surely agree that to try to treat marital conflict with pills, shots, X-rays, EKGs, or by frequent hospitalizations adds up to much more time, in the long run, than whatever time would be spent solving the problem by the attentive listening and investigative curiosity technique outlined.

Clinical Cases

Short Term

A young woman, married for two years, with no pregnancies, entered the doctor's office complaining of general fatigue, loss of appetite, and sleeplessness. The symptoms had been present for the preceding two months and were now accompanied by considerable anxiety. Her own diagnosis was that she had "low blood," and she requested vitamins and liver shots. In obtaining the history of the onset and the course of the symptoms, the physician noted the patient calculated the appearance of each symptom in terms of the number of months since her wedding ceremony. After obtaining the entire history, in the usual manner of allowing the patient to tell her own story, the physician told the patient that he had noted she dated each symptom according to the time interval between its appearance and the date of marriage. He inquired if perhaps her marriage had been somewhat disappointing to her.

With this question, the patient broke down and cried inconsolably for a few moments and then between sobs and sniffles spoke of her disillusionment in marriage. She angrily contrasted her husband's behavior before marriage and his changed attitude after the first six or eight months. She talked of his kind and considerate behavior before marriage and the fact that he now failed to note her hair-do, her dress, or the cleanliness of the home. She spent the next fifteen minutes detailing the numerous complaints that seemed to justify her feelings that her husband had changed from a kind and considerate suitor to a callous, indifferent bore.

The physician listened sympathetically and encouraged her to express more of these feelings. He remarked that it seemed her hoped-for plans in marriage had gone astray because of the changed behavior of her husband. She again cried and spoke of the unhappiness she had experienced as a child in observing the way in which her father had shown callous indifference to her mother. She had fantasied a perfect and blissful marriage for herself with the resolve that a life similar to her mother's would be avoided at all cost. The doctor remarked that he could well understand how she would wish to have a marriage different from mother's if she believed her mother to have been unhappy.

He then inquired as to her estimate of her friends' marriages. She again vehemently criticized the males in the marriages with which she was acquainted and the foolishness of the wives in tolerating their husbands' indifference. The doctor now pointed out to her that it seemed she felt all married women had to put up with some pretty difficult behavior in their husbands. The young lady allowed that it seemed to her that all women were tricked by men in that the male behaved in a chivalrous manner before marriage but, once he had the female hooked, failed to continue this much desired behavior. He then asked the patient if she had inquired of her mother and her friends whether or not they were happy in their marriages or if they resented their husbands' attitudes towards them. The patient thoughtfully replied that this was surprising to her inasmuch as none of them seemed particularly disturbed about this problem. In fact, she felt that most of them, including her mother, acted quite happy.

The physician now took a few moments to ponder the situation. It was evident to him that the patient had maintained a child-like fantasy regarding marriage. He also suspected that the patient was unable to permit herself a happy marriage because of some guilt towards her mother, i.e., as though the patient found it necessary to believe that her mother's marriage was an unhappy one and that the patient, because of her conflict with her mother, could not permit herself to have a marriage better than mother's.

He now considered the best approach to the patient and decided he would point out her pattern of attempting to force the husband into a predetermined mode of response to her. He thus requested that she detail specific instances in which she had found her husband to be callously indifferent to her. She recited several incidents wherein she had spent considerable time with her dress and felt her husband to be indifferent to her endeavors. She compared his response in the present with his enthusiastic praise before marriage. The physician insisted on her detailing exactly how the husband did respond in the present. The patient replied in an off-hand manner that it was true the husband did comment on her dress but he did not display the enthusiasm shown in the courtship. The physician asked for more examples, and the patient reluctantly recited other instances in which the husband had made comments of praise. The physician now pointed out to her that it seemed she was trying to make her husband behave as he had before marriage and that she found herself unsuccessful in these attempts. In fact, that she was quite miserable in her attempts to force him to behave differently. She admitted this was true and stated that she thought maybe she would like everything the way it was before marriage. The doctor suggested that she really did mean everything. She replied to the effect that she knew that was impossible and that she really did not want everything the same.

The doctor now stated that it seemed to him she was making herself pretty miserable in her attempts to achieve a situation that she herself knew to be impossible. She admitted this seemed to be the case and the doctor wondered why she might want to continue this behavior. The patient after reflection replied that perhaps she was demanding more from her husband than necessary. The doctor said that it seemed to him the husband was responding to her endeavors though not in the way she had experienced before marriage. Since she had noted that other women did not seem to mind this much, maybe she would consider why it bothered her so much. She replied that she could see her demands were perhaps not too reasonable and yet she felt unwilling to permit her marriage to be like her mother's. The doctor now suggested that he perform a physical examination and that she might go visit her mother and talk to her mother about the parental marriage.

A routine physical examination and laboratory study did not indicate organic pathology, and both patient and doctor agreed that the problem in the marriage could well account for her symptoms. The doctor again suggested that the patient might discuss how her mother felt about her marriage and perhaps the patient could return in a week and the problem be discussed further. The patient failed to keep her return appointment but telephoned the doctor and stated that her symptoms had nearly disappeared and she felt she had behaved like a little child in the marriage. She assured the doctor that things were going well now and she saw no need to return to him. He asked if she had discussed her mother's feelings about her marriage. The patient laughed and said that mother had told her how gratifying the parental marriage had been and that she considered her husband (the patient's father) to have been a most considerate man. The patient said she felt chagrined that she had so misjudged the parental marriage. She felt she also had misjudged her own husband and now realized how really complimentary he had been to her. She said she could not figure out why she had been so convinced he was indifferent to her. The doctor stated that all girls are entitled to happiness in their marriages and that he felt she was no different in this regard from others. The patient thanked him for his help and stated that should she have any further trouble she would surely be back to see him. Although it is evident that this young woman had considerable guilt feelings arising out of her competitiveness with her mother, it seems likely that a re-evaluation of the total situation enabled the patient to permit herself more pleasure in her marriage.

The doctor had perceived that the patient's demands on her husband were child-like and thus unreasonable and was sufficiently curious to wonder why the patient had to make these demands on the husband. The patient's comments about the mother's marriage convinced him that her guilt feelings were preventing her from enjoying the fruits of the marriage and forcing her to believe that her marriage was not as good as the mother's. To assist the patient to see the unrealistic nature of her demands was insufficient for alleviating the situation. Had the mother of the patient detailed a life-time of suffering at the hands of an indifferent father, it is doubtful that the patient could have permitted herself anything any better. However when the mother spoke of the profound gratification she had obtained from her marriage, this permitted the patient to enjoy her own marriage to a much greater degree. In his final comment to the patient, the doctor attempted to reinforce this attitude by the general statement that all girls had a right to a happy marriage.

Long Term

A general practitioner, who had become aware of the emotional difficulties in the patients he saw, began setting aside time in which he could listen to some of the seemingly less malignant emotional problems in his patients. One day a big, healthy-appearing man came into his office and told the doctor of his symptoms of fatigue, nervousness, sleeplessness, loss of appetite, and urinary distress. In obtaining a history the doctor learned that the man's wife and two daughters lived in the town where the physician was practicing but the patient worked as a railroad engineer in Chicago. His symptoms had begun a year or so earlier and had gone from bad to worse in the preceding six months. He had reported to the company physician who sent him to one of the better hospitals in Chicago where he had numerous tests administered to him without finding organic causes for the symptoms. He was then referred to a psychiatrist. He reluctantly visited the psychiatrist and after a couple of hours of talking, the psychiatrist told him, "You hate your wife." The patient thought this was a crazy thing to say because he was convinced he loved his wife. He got quite angry and decided the best thing to do was to take sick leave and return to the home of his wife and daughters.

The physician examined the man in a routine, but careful, way and found nothing that might account for his symptoms. He told the patient he thought they ought to talk some more about his feelings and life in general and suggested he return the following week at noontime. The doctor set aside thirty minutes a week and over the next eighteen months saw the patient about seventy-five times. The patient told about his living in Chicago and how his wife would come and stay for a while and then take the children back home. This had been going on for some eighteen years, and all in all they had lived together as a family only about three years with the past five years being limited to visits at Christmas-time only.

The doctor felt this was quite interesting data and asked him some questions about how all this came about. The patient had a difficult time explaining to himself or to the doctor how this had come about, but one thing he was certain of was that there had been no fights or arguments. At another visit he told the doctor that he was "not too much on this sex stuff." The physician thought this was very interesting and suggested they talk some more about this feeling. He eventually told the doctor that he had thought a few times about a woman down the hall in the boarding house where he lived but had decided he would not step out with her because it might be unfair to his wife. The physician conveyed continuing interest and asked more questions about these urges and his feelings of not wanting to be unfair to his wife. The patient also talked about his everyday activities at home and the thing the doctor noted was that he did not seem very meaningfully involved with either his wife or his daughters, nor too much involved with the doctor. The doctor thought the two of them had not talked about much that was world-shaking, but he did think it evident that this man did not get very involved with people; he did not seem to like them very near him, but he also seemed a bit reluctant to hurt their feelings.

After the patient had given the doctor a good deal of evidence to support this idea, the doctor told him that it seemed that the patient was not very involved with his wife and daughters and wondered what he thought of this. The patient told of the many things he did not like in his wife, but that he did not like to hurt people's feelings, so he never said anything about them to her. The doctor and patient talked about this for a while and the doctor commented that maybe the patient's way of dealing with the things he did not like too well about his wife was to stay quite a distance from her. The patient thought about this and said it surely was true that he had some feelings against his wife he did not tell her about, and it was also true he had managed to live away from her most of their married life. He also admitted that even though he was living at home now, he still was able to remain quite a distance from her.

The patient did not return for several weeks after the consultation, but one day he came in the office and excitedly told the receptionist he had to see the doctor. He seemed very upset, so the receptionist told him to wait, for she was sure the doctor would see him. He ultimately got into the office and excitedly said, "Doc, I've found out what my trouble is. I hate my wife." He poured out a lot of feeling against his wife and said he had decided that his holding all his feelings inside, without telling her or anyone else about them, had been the cause of his distress. He said that he and his wife had had a discussion over the past few days and he had told her all the things he did not like about her, and she in turn, told him all the things she did not like about him. They both decided it would be best if he went back to Chicago to work. He returned to Chicago and his wife continues to live some thousand miles from him.

It is apparent that the patient made a realistic evaluation of the difficulty between him and his wife and also recognized this conflict to have been the cause of his symptoms. One might argue that this is a less than desired result, but it is perhaps best if the counselor accepts the solution proposed by the patient (if that solution is not a destructive one). In this instance it has to be concluded that the results were constructive in that the patient returned to his work and the situation in regard to marriage was restored to its pre-symptom level. In these instances the doctor must be careful not to impose his own standards of marriage on his patients. The solution proposed by this patient was his own solution and it apparently worked out fairly satisfactorily for both parties.

A chance meeting with this man seven years later revealed him to be healthy and happy. He and his wife traded visits two times yearly for one month to six weeks at a time. He felt they got along very well and had been able to quarrel on occasion without distress. He was looking forward to his retirement within five years after which he planned to return to the small town to live with his wife.

Technical Considerations

One of the questions that arises when one decides to try counseling is whether to see the spouses together or separately, or to refer one spouse to another doctor. There has been a good deal written about this point and an attempt should be made to simplify it if possible.

If the married couple come to their family physician and say they are having trouble with their marriage and want help with it, the "it" is the marriage and it takes two of them to have an "it." In those circumstances, it would seem preferable to see both of them and treat "it," meaning the marriage. In this instance, the physician might let each tell his side of the story and listen to the interaction of the two of them. It is this interaction that should be observed. If neither of them is psychotic or severely neurotic, the doctor might try to find the pattern of interaction that is giving them trouble and help them to see this pattern. A good many of these problems center around the failure to communicate, in that each often assumes the other knows what he or she wants without its being verbalized. Or, vice versa, one assumes the other wants a certain thing but fails to ask if this is true and proceeds on the assumption that it is. He is then very confused, angry, and upset when the partner fails to respond adequately to his actions.

Marital conflict involving competition is frequently seen wherein the dominance-submission theme is evident. In other words, these couples operate as though every situation were one of either dominating the partner or being submissive to him. Actions involving cooperation and sharing are infrequent.

It is of interest and importance to note the frequency with which "somatic language" is used in the complaints made against the spouse and the marriage: "Sick and tired of it all," "He hurts me in every way," "The pain he causes me," etc. In some instances the use of somatic complaints in an effort to control the spouse produces serious conflict.

Problems involving the couple's sexual behavior are frequent and vary from simple ignorance to severe problems in role identification. If one is certain the problem is basically one of ignorance, educative literature may be of some help. However, neurotic prohibitions and anxieties with some degree of sexual role misidentification are more frequent problems.

Problems involving profound dependency needs and the hostility resulting from frustration of such wishes create serious marital conflicts. These are often concomitants of neuroses in one or both partners and may require extensive psychotherapy.

Should the spouse be consulting a lawyer at the time the patient comes to see the family doctor and the spouses are not speaking to one another except via lawyers, it is necessary that the doctor see them separately until they agree to a joint interview. By the time they agree to such an interview, the doctor will have obtained each side of the story and can now bring them together and state what he understands the problem to be. He might ask if each agrees that this is the problem and, if not, will they correct the misunderstanding. This usually leads to a variety of charges and countercharges and the doctor can get some idea in this interchange whether or not either party wishes to preserve the marriage. He might eventually ask them how they feel about the possibilities of preserving the marriage versus the desirability of divorce. Assuming their answer involves a wish to preserve the marriage, the doctor can then delineate the problem as he now sees it, emphasizing the areas in which they disagree as to what the problem actually is. If the physician acts as some sort of neutral referee in this bout and makes sure that no physical harm comes to either partner, and if he keeps on prodding them into more and more discussion, all participants will ultimately agree as to the real conflict between them. This conflict can then be investigated as to its origin and the possibilities of resolving it.

If the doctor, in his preliminary investigations, finds that one or both partners have serious psychotic, neurotic, or characterological problems, he must decide whether he wishes to treat them individually, send one partner to another doctor, or send them both to a psychiatrist for treatment. Also, if the doctor finds that he is too uncomfortable treating the interaction, it may be better to treat the partners separately or refer one. It is likely, however, that sooner or later, the interaction needs discussion with both partners present.

The frequency of interviews varies according to the acuteness of the situation. In acute difficulties, a few interviews over a two-week period may suffice. In more chronic situations, weekly interviews over a long period of time are essential. If one sees a patient individually, at frequent intervals (two to three times a week), it would be wise if the doctor were to receive supervision by a psychiatrist because of the transference and counter-transference problems such treatment produces. Perhaps most marriage counseling by non-psychiatrist physicians should entail from one to a dozen spaced interviews. In acute situations two to four interviews should be sufficient. If the situation seems to require a good deal more, it is likely a professional counselor or psychiatrist should be consulted. Most interviews should last somewhere around an hour. It is unlikely that longer than an hour would be beneficial. There is nothing magic about an hour, but in our culture the clocks are marked in hours and it is an easy and convenient time interval. Most of all, it is likely the doctor loses his effectiveness after an hour in such charged situations. In other words, he tires and needs a short rest before seeing his next patient.

An adequate fee for the amount of time spent with the patient is an integral part of treatment itself. The prevailing time-fee schedule should usually be adhered to.

A Clinical Case

To illustrate some of the problems encountered in marital conflict, a more complicated case follows. About five years ago, a young lady was admitted to a psychiatric hospital with various conversion phenomena and hysterical anxiety. She was treated in analytically oriented psychotherapy over the next two and one-half years. Although an attempt was made to get her husband into concurrent therapy with another therapist, this met with little success. As the wife progressed in therapy and demonstrated a capacity for mature behavior, it became evident that her husband was becoming quite emotionally disturbed. He ultimately had a severe depression with suicidal manifestations and was admitted to a Veterans Administration Hospital where he received shock and pharmaco-therapy. A second attempt was made to get him interested in personal psychotherapy following discharge, but this also met with failure. The interaction between the marital partners became a subject for discussion in the wife's therapy and a fairly clear picture of the interaction was obtained. The wife eventually could see that her wishes to assume a child-like dependent role, with her husband becoming an all-giving mother, usually led to her protesting, partly because of the frustration of her more mature wishes. It also was apparent that the husband enjoyed being put in this mothering role until such time as he felt his masculine ideal was threatened by submergence in a feminine identification. At such time, he also rebelled. It appeared that the two became rebellious at approximately the same time and each blamed the other for their frustrations. A crisis of severe proportions usually resulted. The crisis was usually preceded by the wife making demands upon the husband to satisfy her previously inhibited sexual wishes, and in making these demands she implied that her husband was somewhat less than a man. The husband, smarting from his own feelings concerning his masculinity, found the barbs of his wife intolerable and usually ended up by showing her that he was quite capable of caveman tactics. This invariably included hitting her a few times on the jaw. This always resulted in her calling him various kinds of beasts and returning to the sanctuary of her mother's home. Once the wife was able to see clearly this interaction she began to alter the pattern by giving up many of these infantile needs, plus gratifying her mature sexual needs on a more nearly regular basis and being considerably less hostile and castrative towards her husband. This seemed like a fairly good solution and over the next three months it appeared to be working satisfactorily and no further crises developed. It was thus deemed advisable to terminate therapy and give the couple an opportunity to gain confidence in their own ability to live together happily. Over the next year and a half, the crises were few and much less dramatic and the patient was heard from infrequently. However, over the following six months, the crises became more frequent and finally a full-blown battle ensued wherein the patient left home, sought the local judge, and obtained a warrant for the arrest of her husband on assault and battery charges. The patient made her way to the hospital and insisted she be seen and help given her to obtain a divorce. An interview with her revealed that the crisis had recurred because she found it impossible to forget the times her husband had belted her in the jaw and she felt a great need to get even with him. She now insisted that the recent behavior on his part had proved her right to get even, inasmuch as he had belted her rather viciously the night before. It was evident that re-instituting therapy on the same basis probably would not convince her that her need to get even with this man was a detriment to the marriage. Interpretation of her anger at her former therapist was also to no avail. It was suggested that joint interviews with the husband be held over the next few months. The patient grabbed at this opportunity because of her conviction that the therapist would quickly see what a brute her husband was and would be on her side and thus grant her the right to get even. In the joint interviews the wife repeatedly listed the sins of the husband and her determination to get even with him at all costs. The husband was able to recognize that, regardless of what his day-to-day behavior might be, the wife would find excuses for obtaining her hoped-for revenge. He was also able to see how her innuendoes regarding his masculinity produced intense anger in him and also how his need to mother her brought on much of his sensitivity to these innuendoes. He now developed certain techniques that permitted him to avoid the need to reassure himself of his masculinity by the cave-man tactics he had used in the past and, in fact, was able to cope with his wife's revenge-driven behavior quite nicely. The question of divorce was proposed and thoroughly discussed with these two combatants and rejected as undesirable by both. The wife stated that she could see her hatred of all men and envy of their role in life as a basic drive in her behavior and that divorcing this man and finding another would not solve the problem. The husband, on the other hand, stated that he loved his wife and wanted to keep her as his wife regardless of the difficulties their marriage seemed to produce. He found that his techniques of avoiding her revengeful behavior and thus gaining better control over his retaliatory rage were quite effective. They both thus understood that these crises might continue to occur inasmuch as each had certain neurotic conflicts that would invariably produce difficulty in their marriage. Since making this decision, there have been no further crises although they report some very good arguments without a need for physical violence. The wife still expresses a wish for revenge but the vehemence seems to have lessened markedly. The husband speaks of his depression having completely lifted and states that he believes the guilt over his wishes to belt his wife had produced much of the depression he suffered for so many years.

The joint interview therapy of this couple could well have been carried out by a general practitioner with a moderate amount of consultation with a psychiatrist (the wife's therapist). The primary technical difficulty involved in the therapy would perhaps center around the physician's being able to tolerate the hostility shown by the wife. It was important, however, that the physician accept her hostility; for in so doing, he supported the husband and afforded him a model for identification. The husband could readily see that his wife's hostility in no way destroyed the physician and the physician had no need to counterattack the woman. The husband's competitive, masculine identification was thus furthered. It was an excellent object lesson for the husband inasmuch as he recognized that his previous response enhanced the problem. He now had a new way of interacting. Similarly, once the wife recognized her inability to provoke her husband into a sado-masochistic struggle she altered her own patterns of behavior. It would be obvious that the envy this

woman has of the male is basically unaltered, as is the feminine identification present in this husband. However, their interaction is much
less neurotic and they have been forced to develop new patterns that
conceivably could enhance their marital, as well as individual, growth.

Guiding Principles

In summary, some guiding principles that may be of value to the
general practitioner who wishes to undertake marriage counseling in
his medical practice follow. It is important to recognize that to become a proficient counselor it is necessary that one have a good deal
of supervised clinical experience. In order to gain such proficiency, a
physician should discuss his cases with an expert in the field. Most
psychiatric centers have a general practice liaison committee that is
available to groups of general practitioners for discussion of psychological problems in their practice.

The basic attitude of the counselor is perhaps best described as presenting an appropriate and varied mixture of sympathy and empathy.
This paper earlier alluded to the phrases with which the non-psychiatrist physician is bombarded, in an effort to caution him in treating
the emotional problems of his patients. Similar phrases are descriptive
of the physician's attitude towards all disease processes but they need
to be restated and understood. The physician's attitude is "diagnostic"; one of "active listening"; "involvement without over-identifi-
cation"; "detached but with personal interest"; and the physician encourages "free communication."

The many and varying personal problems that are brought to the
counselor invariably have an underlying structure of unpleasant emotions described in a multiplicity of ways, usually with the indications of such feelings as a sense of insecurity, helplessness, raw rage,
poorly directed eroticism, and frustrated longing. These feelings are
not always immediately expressible to the physician but are hidden
by a multitude of defenses that prohibit free expression. It is only in
the permissive and encouraging atmosphere of the attentive counselor
that the underlying feelings can be more fully expressed. The physician-counselor must patiently wait for and encourage the expression
of these feelings.

In any series of counseling sessions there is a certain sequence observable: an initial resistance and psychological defensiveness manifested as symptoms or complaints. This will usually give way gradually to the free expression of the underlying feelings along with more open expression of conflictual patterns. Such expression will only obtain in the permissive, unhurried, interested, and encouraging atmosphere provided by the physician-counselor. It is this emotionally laden material, exposed in the setting of the counseling situation, which gives the counselor the opportunity to offer new and hopefully useful points of view to his patients. One must not forget that people coming for counseling have magical and unrealistic expectations of the counselor-physician and these need to be put into a realistic perspective. But because of these unrealistic expectations and the image of the physician as an omnipotent parent, the patient will request (and even demand) that he be told what is wrong and how to change it. For the physician to offer solutions to the stated problem, without the patient having expressed the underlying affective components, will result in little or no change. Even should the underlying feelings be expressed, it is wise to remember that long-lasting, repetitious patterns, which began early in marriage and continue for years, are difficult to modify. In many instances if a spouse could gain a "feel" for his partner's point of view, this may be the most that can be expected. However, such a "feeling" for his partner may eventuate in a significant shift towards marital adjustment.

Although the problems encountered in counseling people in marital conflict are many, doctors, because of their interest and curiosity about human beings, have tackled difficult problems in the past and found reasonable solutions for them. Because of this same interest and curiosity, it is quite possible for the doctor to draw attention to marital problems that are creating symptoms and then to assist in their reasonable solution.

2

Sexual Symptoms
as Presenting Complaints

Cornelius Lansing, M.D.

The popular books on sex make it all sound so simple. One kind emphasizes a careful mechanical approach: a woman is a delicately balanced machine, trickier and more complicated than a man, but capable of control through mastery of anatomical, physiological, and psychological understanding and technique. All factors are taken into account: the calendar, the clock, the lights, the music, the menu, the words, the sighs. The evening is programed like a giant computer, all systems are "Go," the correct buttons are pushed, and the machine is marvelously in orbit. Still, it is also somewhat reminiscent of my uncle's account of the maneuvers used for winter starting of a capricious and headstrong Model T. When it comes to sex, is all this effort necessary? And if so, is it worth it? The books generally gloss over any functional problems that the *man* might have. Most of them are written by men, and there is an inescapable suspicion that the author is anonymously bragging about his own success with the ladies, implying: "Do as I do. Just be manly but patient, and you won't have a bit of trouble."

Another kind of book, giving much less space to How To Be a Great Lover, Even Though Married, emphasizes togetherness, communication, sympathy, understanding, and mutual consideration. If the husband is amorous, but the wife is tired, anxious, tense, and uninterested, the husband simply sets disappointment aside, summons up a modicum of sympathetic emotional maturity, and the problem is settled.

People who can profit from this sort of advice do not need it. Those who need it generally find the problems to be more stubborn and complicated than the books will admit, and some will seek medical or other professional aid. This is not easy for them: sex is quite a taboo subject for polite conversation, and if it is to be talked about at all, boasting is preferred to admission of difficulty, since the latter is often equated with failure or personal inadequacy. People who spend a fortune on their skin and hair, and are very kind to their stomachs, may let their libidos take an awful beating rather than run the risk of being mocked or scolded by revealing a "shameful" secret. Of course, many prefer self-medication to professional consultation anyway—note the widespread sale of anodynes, antacids, hypnotics, cold cures, and vitamins. Many people dislike having a doctor tell them what to do, unless they are seriously worried or hurting badly. But good health *is* socially approved, and there is no danger of loss of face if you get a regular physical examination, visit your dentist twice a year, eat a balanced diet, and get plenty of sleep, fresh air, and exercise. A man who gets a checkup from his doctor may publicly tell what a brave and conscientious fellow he is, how he took his medicine like a man, and so forth.

But no one can brag publicly about anything to do with sex, which in our culture is in a peculiar position. Its importance is openly acknowledged in print, but not in spoken words. If normal sex actually became taboo, advertising would be revolutionized, and products would have to be sold strictly on their intrinsic merits, instead of by association with the sensuous charms of professional models posing as consumers and displaying an almost perverse infatuation with the product. If abnormal sex likewise became taboo, much of the excitement would disappear from the local news, and the papers might be obliged to print more about world events. But the public importance of sex is always *officially* ignored or denied, playing down in words what is so heartily played up in pictures. Whatever its real importance, it cannot command an air of respectability; sober attention to the achievement of satisfactory sex life is not attended by the same high moral tone that accompanies correction of anemia or regulation of the bowels. Although sexuality is essential for the survival of the race, it is well known that lack of it poses no immediate threat to the life of the individual; sex is commonly regarded as a mildly nefarious self-indulgence, somewhere between coffee and tobacco, or between tobacco and dope, depending on social and religious affiliations.

In other cultures and other times, sexual interest, performance and satisfaction have been matters of public concern, and the subject of long (and even dull) scientific and religious treatises. Difficulties found no lack of professional practitioners sincerely devoted to restoring the sufferer to a state of health. But in our culture, prudery lays its chilly hand even on the medical profession, whose members, despite being *allowed* to know all about sex, often do not. In a paper at the Toronto meeting of the American Psychiatric Association in 1962, Dr. Harold Lief pointed out that doctors are "woefully ignorant about sex," which makes it difficult for them to help patients with problems in this area. Possibly because they assist in the birth process, doctors are reputed to know all about sex. Children think they do, and their early sexual explorations are commonly called the "Doctor Game." This myth of sexual omniscience lives on in popular literature, where the wily medical student gives the cavalryman and sailor a run for their money as champion in the art of seduction. This myth may also be fostered by the fact that some female patients become emotionally and sometimes sexually involved with male physicians. Even though this kind of situation is comparatively rare, it is still a possibility in the public mind and adds force to the notion of the doctor as a sexual expert. Yet in medical schools very little is taught on the subject beyond anatomy and purely automatic functioning, and I do not quite see how the physician is supposed to learn the rest without study, as his personal sexual experiences are in fact not much different from anyone else's, and the possession of more detailed anatomical knowledge adds little to his capacity as performer or advisor. A century ago, when ignorance and prudery were rampant, perhaps the doctor's routine anatomical knowledge really did put him ahead of properly brought-up people; he actually *did* know where babies came from, and quite a few otherwise intelligent people were not quite sure about it.

I think this myth of sexual omniscience is a heavy burden on our profession, and cramps our style. Many doctors, as students, believe the stories and assume that *only they* are somewhat ignorant of the ramifications of sex, and to all their colleagues they ascribe the standard myth of sexual omniscience. Hence they do not like to ask questions about it, or even to be caught reading about it, since this would seem to be admitting an exaggerated or perverse interest, or worse yet, a childish ignorance and naïveté. Yet how else can one learn except by study and reading? Personal experience, however extensive and varied, is not enough to cover the whole field. We all eat, but we are neither dietitians nor nutritionists. We breathe, but we are not respiratory physiologists. We eat, digest, and defecate, but this does not qualify us as gastroenterologists. Hopefully, we provide sterling examples of reasonably normal and satisfying sex life, but that does not give us leave to pose as experts on the subject.

There is certainly no reason for physicians to think that they deserve a monopoly on advising people about sexual problems. They do not advise people on dancing, gymnastics, piano duets, or contract bridge, all activities requiring skill and cooperation for maximum enjoyment. But since physicians do concern themselves with the structure and function of the human mind and body, their scientific training provides an excellent background for expert counseling in the field, although they can hardly expect to become proficient without study. Physicians and medical students should be encouraged to study the subject of sex. There are a great many books written about it, some good, some bad, some unbelievably tedious. The last word has not been said, and the safest literary diet is a varied one. A briefly annotated bibliography is appended to this chapter. The comments represent no official position, merely the author's personal opinions.

I will now specify and describe a few varieties of sexual problems, interpret their possible significance, and outline some ideas about treatment. Since this volume deals with the problems of married people, I will similarly restrict myself to sexual symptoms arising in this group. The problems of the unmarried are interesting and important, especially to those concerned, but they do not ordinarily involve permanent interpersonal relationships. The problems of a married person, on the other hand, impinge continuously on the spouse, affect the total interpersonal relationship, and are affected by it. It is this interpersonal aspect on which I would like to lay particular emphasis.

Another restriction on the topic is that the symptom must be such that one or both members of the married pair consider it a problem for which they may be seeking some sort of help. People often settle sexual problems by compromises that would not appeal to you or me, but as long as they are satisfied with the solution, we as physicians are not going to hear about them. Let me give an example. Although it has been shown that a substantial number of elderly people retain sexual interest and potency into the seventies and some even into the eighties, nobody is concerned that a great many do give up most sexual activity in the sixties. Now, if a couple in their late twenties decided to give up sex, it would be most unusual, yet if both were *really* in agreement about it and remained otherwise harmonious and devoted, it would not constitute a medical problem, and one would only hear about it inadvertently. This couple obviously does have a personal problem, but they have dealt with it (I shall not say solved it) in their own way. As long as the method actually works and does not lead to some kind of disabling symptom, such as hysterical or psychosomatic manifestations, it is not our business to *insist* on change. In the same way, we do not interfere by brute force with phobic, hysterical, or compulsive symptoms, which may represent the best adjustment the patient is capable of at the time.

Another example of a "sick" solution to a marital sexual problem is one in which a man deals with frustration or anger at his wife by having affairs with other women. No man is going to seek medical help about this unless he feels guilty about it, or his wife finds out and is angry, or he becomes involved in some sort of publicly disreputable behavior. Presumably such behavior is based on some kind of a personality problem in husband or wife or both, but the unprofessional solution of taking a mistress may be highly effective, albeit sometimes risky. Many people cope with their sexual problems without seeking advice, or even thinking of it. Some go to lawyers seeking divorce, and I understand that many lawyers try to get the warring couple to settle their differences. And some people wind up talking to the district attorney, so to speak, as in the famous case of Frankie and Johnnie.

Let me summarize by saying that I am going to discuss problems involving the sexual aspect of relationships and activities of married couples which are *perceived* as problems by one or both partners, or where neurotic "solutions" to the problem create social difficulties in the family or community.

I would now like to specify the conditions or broad diagnostic categories under which sexual problems may come to the attention of the physician. I am considering the problems as *symptoms*. I cannot emphasize too strongly that although the patient may have nothing on his mind but his sexual problem, it should always be considered as one aspect of a potentially more complex situation requiring diagnosis, and not simply as an isolated problem requiring blind treatment. I have made four categories, which I think cover all situations, although a case might come under more than one category. These categories are convenient aids to thinking in the course of taking a history and, if kept in mind, will prevent one from missing the obvious. While the patient goes on giving a perhaps too meticulous description of the malfunctioning of his genitalia, the physician can be thinking, "Could this fellow be psychotic? Has he a neurosis? Does he beat his wife, or vice versa? Or does he really have gonorrhea?" The categories I have chosen are:

1. Symptoms associated with physical disease.
2. Symptoms associated with psychosis.
3. Symptoms associated with neurosis.
4. Symptoms arising predominantly in the framework of a neurotic marital relationship.

Physical Disease: Sexual incapacity may be associated with physical diseases such as local acute or chronic inflammation, trauma, infection, or tumor; neurological disturbances; toxic, systemic, and metabolic disorders. The preponderance of sexual disorders are psychological and functional in origin, and in my opinion it would be fatuous to indulge in a heroic hunt for organic disease in every case, but thorough history-taking, a careful routine physical and neurological examination, routine laboratory work including serology, and meticulous examination of the affected parts are certainly in order.

Psychosis: Sexual symptoms, or some alteration of sexual habits, may be early manifestations of a psychotic disorder. Along with fatigue, insomnia, loss of appetite, and general slowing of physical activity, loss of libido is a common symptom of depressive reactions. Not all depressive reactions are psychotic, but it would be important to keep the possibility of this diagnosis in mind, since early discovery and appropriate treatment may forestall more serious developments. A manic or schizophrenic process may be ushered in by an increase in sexual activity or orgastic capacity, or by peculiar or bizarre ideas about sex or the sex organs. In such cases, diagnosis of the mental disorder can be made on the basis of the mental examination and many other aspects of the history. It should be remembered that bizarre ideas about sex do not necessarily imply psychosis. Such a condition is normal in children, even when they are adequately educated, and some individuals shy away from getting better information in later life. A colleague recently told me of seeing a college student who was disappointed by his discovery that Comparative Anatomy is not the study of the difference between the sexes!

Neurosis: In this category I would like to include sexual problems of psychogenic origin which are symptomatic of intrapsychic conflict, but where psychosis is not present or imminent. Obviously people whose problems arise within the marital relationship also fall within the neurotic category, but I would like to make a somewhat arbitrary distinction here, between cases where the inciting cause lies *within* the marital relationship, and those where it lies *outside* it. The latter category would include people with neuroses and personality disorders that might give rise to symptoms in the sexual area. It would for instance include all sexual deviations, such as exhibitionism, fetishism, sadism, masochism, homosexuality, etc. People with personality disorders generally do not suffer from much anxiety and so do not often seek help spontaneously, but they may come in at the behest of their spouses, or if their actions are detected and defined as criminal by public authority. If their "abnormal" actions are successfully concealed and if the "normal" sexual role is adequately performed, there is no complaint, and they do not seek help.

Neurotic disturbances such as hysteria, phobia, and anxiety reaction may be manifested by sexual difficulties, usually associated with such unpleasant emotions as fear, anxiety, guilt, and shame, and are manifested less by action than the lack of it. In the case of women, frigidity and dyspareunia come readily to mind, while impotence and premature ejaculation are chief among such problems in men. These are basically related to emotional immaturity, and the persistence of fearful or negative childhood attitudes into adult life. In our culture sex is officially an adult game, like automobile driving, and children are forbidden in no uncertain terms to play it. If they are "sat on" often enough and hard enough, and scared enough into the bargain, they may not realize that they have grown up even when they reach physical and legal maturity, and the fears and taboos may persist despite all logical efforts to dislodge them. Sometimes, of course, this leads to avoidance of marriage, but commonly such people do marry and some sooner or later discover that they are missing something that others enjoy or that the spouse is disappointed that they *do not* enjoy. In addition to the persistence of childhood fears, orgastic impotence or lack of enjoyment may be associated with envy and hostility toward the opposite sex, poor sexual-role identification, or excessive self-love that precludes actually loving another person.

Let me give some examples of cases in which neurotic intrapsychic conflicts gave rise to sexual problems:

1. A young man has had difficulty in breaking away from his domineering but neurotically helpless mother, who uses physical symptoms and "hysterics" to control her children. He marries a more stable woman, but whenever she becomes ill or at all emotional, he suffers anxiety and premature ejaculation. Her actions are not neurotic, but they remind him unconsciously of the complex and disagreeably close relationship with his mother, and although he loves his wife, under such conditions he wants to get out of there fast.

2. A woman marries a man somewhat like her father. She becomes frigid whenever her relationship with her husband evokes certain feelings which remind her of an erotically tinged situation with her father, repressed since she was a little girl. Guilt over forbidden childhood sexual wishes prevents her from enjoying her perfectly lawful marital relationship at times.

3. A normally aggressive man encounters unexpected success in his professional work. As a child he had a strong wish to compete

with and surpass his father, but he never really expected to do so. Since his field of work is entirely different from his father's, he now feels as though he had won a victory by stealth and anticipates some horrid but unspecified doom, like a teenager who has been caught smoking his father's cigars and drinking his brandy, but whose fate has not yet been decided. After a time, his anxiety culminates in impotence, which irritates his wife.

4. A young woman marries an older man, a widower, and although she is apparently devoted to him she finds sexual intercourse painful and disgusting. Her "devotion" is rather like that of a little girl for a parent, and she actually wants to be treated not as a real wife but like a princess or a favorite child. She is too immature and self-centered to be capable of adult love and sexuality.

5. A man loses his father, with whom he had never gotten along well. He feels as though his failure to answer a letter had somehow hastened his father's death. He feels depressed and has loss of libido out of proportion to the depression. Much of his hostility had been engendered by his father's virtual abdication of family responsibility and his many extramarital affairs. While disapproving of this, the patient had unconsciously envied his father's seductive skill and happy-go-lucky attitude, especially during adolescence.

In most of these cases, the sexual symptoms have not been the only complaints, and I have tried to present them as strictly *neurotic* problems, in which interference with sexual function or enjoyment is simply one aspect and may or may not be the presenting complaint. Much depends on the attitude of the spouse. In Victorian days it was not ladylike to enjoy sex, and many men who liked a lusty wench would nonetheless have been shocked if their *wives* became "involved" sexually; *they* hardly complained of a wife's frigidity, but nowadays it is often quite a different story. In the third example, above, where the man first had anxiety symptoms, the later impotence was an hysterical symptom, and for *him* giving up sexual activity "solved" his internal dilemma nicely. His wife did not like it a bit, however, and nagged him into getting help. If she had been frigid, or strongly inhibited sexually, or afraid of pregnancy, his symptom might have suited her fine, and he might not have sought help until he himself got tired of being impotent. We must also keep in mind that his impotence might have subsided spontaneously in time.

Neurotic Marital Relationship: The last category of marital sexual difficulties are those which are related to the neurotic elements in the relationship of a married couple. In addition to specific strengths, virtues, and other admirable qualities that stir up enough mutual admiration to lead to the altar, each spouse brings to the marriage his own conflicts, sensitivities, and special needs. Significant incompatibilities may be present, which do not manifest themselves until some time after the marriage has begun, which may appear so insidiously that they are hard to recognize as such until both partners are suffering from profound irritation, and which make adjustment and compromise all the more difficult. Perhaps the state of "being in love" is responsible for much of this, the marvelous self-deception that persuades the young man that he has found the girl of his dreams, and the same for the young lady. Dream girls and boys do not exist this side of the Pearly Gates, yet young people in love insist on attributing the most angelic qualities to each other and expecting the same of themselves, a happy delusion that must somehow be worn away if they are ever to create a workable adult human relationship. Where mutual expectations are unrealistic, the letdown is cruel, and disillusion is painful when couples are confronted too abruptly with each other's frailties.

Some couples attempt to avoid acknowledgement of childish feelings and utilize deficiences of character to escape the pain of facing these. Instead of living, they try a kind of play-acting. The man may assume the role of the tyrannical husband if his partner will play the hysterical wife. Or vice versa. From his side of the stage, the husband is being the sick little boy, casting his wife in the role formerly occupied by his controlling, aggressive mother. On her side, the wife is engaged in portraying to herself the long-suffering neglected girl, while assigning to her husband the role of her coarse, lazy, incompetent father. Neither is aware that the other is writing a different play, and neither has access to the real list of characters, which shows both of them as overgrown children trying to be adults, unable to escape from their past family relationships and busily and tragically recreating them in the present. The saddest part of all is that each resists maturing tendencies in the other and tries to coerce the partner into truly living the assigned role. If the husband achieves more stature, the wife uses her knowledge of his sensitivities to cut him down to size; if the wife becomes less bitchy, the husband does all he can to provoke her to return to the neurotic status quo.

The actual manifestations of this problem are the same as those mentioned under the heading of neurosis; the difference is that *both* partners are neurotically involved, and the difficulty lies more between them than within either one. It is somewhat like a *folie à deux*, in which two people participate in the same psychosis and share the same delusions about people in the outside world. The neurotic couple usually see the outside world clearly enough but have strongly distorted perceptions of each other, which they tend to perpetuate rather than amend.

Let me give an example of a typical complicated interaction involving sex in a relatively normal couple. It begins with a common source of confusion, the normal difference between the sexual urges of men, which are fairly steady, and those of women, which tend to vary with the menstrual cycle. The husband has been away on a trip, feeling a bit sexy, looking forward to fun in bed on his return, and recalls what a delightful time he had with his wife the night before he left, just a week ago. She is very glad to see him back, and they are quite romantic at dinner. They have some wine and are both relaxed, in fact he is quite tired after his long day's journey. She is feeling cuddly but not sexy, but he does not know this, and when he makes a lazy pass at her, she is suddenly revolted. It reminds her of mashers and the lecherous uncle who used to feel her up slyly at family reunions when she was a teenager. She reacts with disgust, and he is quite taken aback, so sudden and unexpected is this turn of events, which was definitely not on his program for the evening. He feels like a child arbitrarily and unjustly cut off in the midst of innocent fun, and he reacts in one of his characteristic ways, by turning away, hurt and pouting. This in turn makes his wife feel anxious and guilty. Her father used to act like this when angry, and she always felt it was somehow her fault. Although she is actually quite angry, she assumes an air of remorse and artificial friendliness and tries in a babyish way to be "nice." This unconsciously reminds the husband of certain contradictory attitudes of his mother, which always used to confuse and bother him, and he now becomes angrier still. At this point either of two things might happen: the husband becomes totally uninterested in sex and retreats nursing a grudge surprisingly reminiscent of an adolescent's feeling of not being understood, thwarting his wife's guilty and highly ambivalent attempts to act loving or sexy; or, alternatively, his anger takes an active form, in which he aggressively shows the little bitch that she is not going to treat *him* like a kid, and she responds spontaneously to his now ruthless ardor, and they have a fine time, and later recall that they have gotten into this bind on previous occasions. Where honest communication of feeling is possible, unpleasant situations like this can often be resolved in a way that leads to more realistic mutual perception. Where such communication is lacking, a stalemate ensues, often followed by endless repetition of the same dreary sequence.

It sometimes happens that in couples whose attitude toward sex is healthy, difficulty may nevertheless arise as a by-product of conflict in other areas. Sexual passion is frequently aggressive, and the emotion of love lies very close to that of hate. Where one or both partners have strong conflicts about hostility and aggression, sexual activity may have to be kept rather tame in order to prevent the adjacent feelings from getting out of control. A husband who needs such control may be a frustration to a wife who would like him sometimes to be a caveman. If she can communicate her wishes convincingly, they may find common ground; if not, he may merely think that her messages constitute a trap of some kind and remain all the more vigilantly calm.

Treatment: As in all other areas of scientific medicine, accurate diagnosis is the cornerstone of therapeutics. Once the underlying disturbance is recognized, therapy can proceed rationally. In the *physical* category, appropriate physical treatment is of course indicated; however, one must keep in mind that physical disease does not confer immunity against emotional problems, which may either be coincidental or secondary to the disease itself.

With patients in whom *psychosis* is suspected, psychiatric consultation should be considered, to verify the diagnosis and find what form of treatment is indicated. However, if the situation is chronic and stable, and the amount of social disturbance is slight, it may not be necessary to refer the patient elsewhere. Sympathetic support, or modest drug therapy, may provide all the stabilization that is needed. It must be kept in mind that even though the patient complains of something—in this case presumably a sexual problem—he *may* not really want to get rid of the symptom. If the symptom departs, well and good; if it does not, this is no reason to send the patient elsewhere or smother him with medicine, unless he is becoming otherwise more disturbed and hard to manage. If he maintains his job and family life and keeps coming to see you, let him complain as much as he wants. The symptom may represent the "ticket of admission" that permits him to maintain therapeutic contact with the physician.

There are many different ways in which *neurotic* patients can be treated, depending on the particular case. Simple reassurance as to the benign nature of the symptom may help a great deal. People are always worrying that they might be abnormal in some way, especially in regard to sexual feelings and fantasies. Reassurance and sex education, both by discussion and having the patient read a book, may bring great relief from guilt and anxiety. Of course the physician should be well acquainted with the wide range of what is "normal," which may not coincide with his personal view of what is optimal. The "Kinsey Reports" are good sources of information for physicians, but are not recommended for patients.

A "talking-out" type of psychotherapy may be very helpful, and this is well within the capacity of the average practitioner in many cases, if he can arrange the time. Patients with bothersome symptoms and relatively healthy personalities are the best motivated for formal intensive psychotherapy and can profit the most from it. Such patients also have the best chance of spontaneous recovery and can be greatly assisted by the tolerant understanding and non-interfering sympathy of a family doctor, especially if the problem is a fairly acute one. This is particularly true of male patients, who are aided not only by having a patient listener but by identification with a mature and healthy male, such as most doctors are. Neurotic female patients with sexual problems are trickier, since some will be prone to develop complex emotional attachments to a male physician and may indulge in highly seductive maneuvers, all of which are difficult to deal with unless you have had special training or happen to be personally skilled in avoiding entanglement without rejecting the patient. The most trying developments can be minimized by referring such patients to a female physician, but since these patients are often very immature, they tend to develop strong, sticky, dependent attachments that may be equally tedious to deal with, if less alarming. I do not recommend the use of drugs for patients with isolated sexual complaints. If the symptom is merely one aspect of a more complex neurotic problem, or if the measures already suggested are of no avail, psychiatric consultation is in order.

Patients with neurotic personality disturbances, who translate their conflicts into action (such as "running around") instead of perceiving them as feelings or symptoms, are very difficult patients to treat. Although some may seek psychiatric help, often they are poorly motivated and are merely complying with somebody's pushing. As in the case of alcoholism, family pushing may be 50 per cent pulling. A masochistic wife may foster philandering at the same time that she is complaining of it, to maintain her status as a woman wronged. If you can see the interaction of such people and tell them about it quite bluntly, it may be of some help. Psychiatric treatment will be of little avail unless the patient sees himself as actually sick and wants to change. It will be a waste of time to insist that a truly reluctant person visit a psychiatrist. Those whose actions have gotten them in trouble with the law are still harder to treat, but the unambiguous quality of the threat of legal prosecution may be helpful.

In the case of *neurotically interacting couples*, the family physician may have as good a chance as anyone else in ferreting out the distortions and irrational elements in the relationship. The simple presence of an impartial referee sometimes enables couples to get things off their collective chest and resume normal communication. After talking to both alone and hearing some of the complaints, the doctor might get them together, and say, "I have the impression that you're both rather angry at each other, and afraid to admit it. Now why don't we talk about this?" This is really a way of saying, "Why don't you stop pouting and try to settle your problems like grown-ups?" while at the same time providing physical presence and moral prestige as a reassurance that nobody is going to get maimed in the discussion. Psychiatrists, social agencies, and marriage counselors often handle problems of this sort, and the physician should feel free to call on them. No doctor should try to do work of this sort unless he really wants to, but it can be highly interesting and rewarding.

In closing, let me reiterate my "permission" and exhortation to all physicians to read up on the subject of sex, if they wish to be able to help patients who come with such problems. Many patients have sexual problems that they would like help with, except that they wait to be asked about them. Many physicians feel embarrassed asking patients about sex, probably because they do not feel themselves well-grounded in the subject. If the patient brings it up, well and good, he has taken the responsibility himself. If the physician brings it up, the patient *might* become angry or offended. However, the possibility of such a reaction never seems to stop doctors from asking patients about their excretory functions in the course of history-taking. If the patient is alarmed, the doctor can usually reassure him that such questions are scientific, necessary, and routine. There is really no reason why sex should not be given an equally important place on the list of pertinent questions.

Bibliography

Eisenstein, Victor W. 1956. "Sexual Problems in Marriage," in Victor W. Eisenstein (ed.), *Neurotic Interaction in Marriage*. New York: Basic Books, Inc.

Ellis, A. 1951. *The Folklore of Sex*. New York: Boni.
Interesting survey of "public" attitudes toward sex as displayed in contemporary mass media.

Ford, C. S., and F. A. Beach. 1951. *Patterns of Sexual Behavior*. New York: Harper & Brothers and Paul B. Hoeber.
An important treatise on various kinds of sexual activities in primates and lower animals, including the natural occurrence of what human beings often call "perverse." A relatively short book, well-written and readable.

Gebhard, P. H., W. B. Pomeroy, C. E. Martin, and C. V. Christenson. 1958. *Pregnancy, Birth, and Abortion*. New York: Harper & Brothers and Paul B. Hoeber.
This is the third of the celebrated "Kinsey Reports," sober statistical studies of sexual attitudes and practices, based on extensive surveys. They have been criticized on technical grounds by statisticians, some of whom feel the sampling procedure to be biased; nevertheless, these will remain definitive studies until something better comes along. Being crammed with

facts, charts, tables and "statistics," they make heavy reading, and will not be especially helpful for laymen, unless there is a need to convince a patient that something is "normal" to the extent of being prevalent. A good antidote for pious moralizing. Enormous bibliographies.

Herndon, C. N., and E. M. Nash. May, 1962. "Premarriage and Marriage Counseling: A Study of Practices of North Carolina Physicians," *J.A.M.A.*, 180:395-401.

Survey of attitudes and practices of 514 physicians in a variety of specialties, regarding premarital examinations, contraceptive advice, counseling about marital problems. Statistics in easily assimilable form.

Kinsey, A. C., W. B. Pomeroy, and C. E. Martin. 1948. *Sexual Behavior in the Human Male*. Philadelphia: W. B. Saunders Co.

Kinsey, A. C., W. B. Pomeroy, C. E. Martin, and P. H. Gebhard. 1953. *Sexual Behavior in the Human Female*. Philadelphia: W. B. Saunders Co.

Lewinsohn, R. 1958. *A History of Sexual Customs*. New York: Harper & Brothers.

A thorough and interesting survey of sexual attitudes and customs in various parts of the world. The historical approach permits valuable insight into some of our ancestors' aberrations and some contemporary "tribal customs." Suitable for intelligent patients seeking explanations.

Prange, A. J., Jr., M. G. Sandifer, C. R. Vernon, and D. R. Hawkins. June, 1959. "A Brief Appraisal of Pain and Normal Sexual Behavior as Subjects of Medical Instruction," *N. Carolina Med. J.*, 20:222-25.

Brief survey of small sample of students from many medical schools, regarding presence or absence of instruction in sexual behavior; 90% had instruction on sexual behavior in children, but only 45% were instructed regarding adults.

Robinson, M. N. 1959. *The Power of Sexual Surrender*. New York: Doubleday & Co. Also published as a paperback (P 2100) by Signet Books.

An important book, written by a woman analyst, explaining the psychology of frigidity and offering sensible "self-help." It can be recommended equally for physicians, patients, and husbands. Very well-written, easy to read, and free of jargon.

Van de Velde, T. H. 1930. *Ideal Marriage: Its Physiology and Technique*. New York: Covici, Friede.

Excellent book for married people, leisurely and respectful; an "old standby" for many years, but by no means outdated. Emphasis on love and sentiment may not appeal to some, but will be welcomed by those who find mere mechanics rather sterile.

3

Sexual Disorder and Marriage

D. Wilfred Abse, M.D.

Introduction

Herbert Spencer,[29] in an interesting passage, referred to nine components of the love of man for woman—the physical impulse of sex, the feeling of beauty, affection, respect, approbation, self-esteem, proprietary feeling, extended liberty of action from the absence of usual personal barriers, and exaltation of the sympathies. "This passion," he concludes, "fuses into one immense aggregate most of the elementary excitations of which we are capable." The developed love of adults is, indeed, highly complex, and lust becomes coordinated among many other elements in the loving relationship. When there is a deficient integration of many qualities, especially when "the physical impulse of sex" is more or less dissociated, the love relationship of marriage founders.

One of the most fundamental of Freud's books, his *Three Contributions to the Theory of Sex,*[17] is concerned with the deviations of the sexual instinct and the development of adult sexuality from the elementary excitations of infancy through the changes that come about at the time of puberty. The psychoanalytic investigations that Freud initiated led him to views that were first outlined in this book, namely that sexual development is of a complicated nature and begins in infancy, coming to a standstill about the age of four or five, after which no further progress is made until puberty when further development ensues. He showed how the final stage of genital primacy is reached only through many evolutionary changes in the elementary components that comprise the beginnings of sexuality. These changes are influenced both by the inborn sexual constitution and by the experiences of life, especially early life, and they are thus subject to many inhibitions, fixations, and deviations in the course of development.

In another early essay, Freud [15] reported his clinical findings in cases of men showing disturbances of potency. He stressed the importance as etiological factors of infantile fixations, the barrier of incest, and the later privations during adolescence. The common difficulty encountered in these cases was that of fusing feelings of tenderness, such as are empathic toward a loved mother, with sensual urges that are regarded by these patients as incompatible. Freud boldly asserted that this kind of difficulty in fusion of tender and sensual feelings is general in our civilization. Indeed, he thought that no civilized man is completely potent in the sense that he can enjoy a fully developed love relationship with the maximum of sensual pleasure. Respect for the partner in varying degrees inhibits sensual pleasure, so he thought, and consequently many men are only capable of intense physical pleasure with a woman who is socially, morally, or aesthetically of a lower order. Certainly in the southern region of the U.S.A. now, in the latter half of the twentieth century, this difficulty is quite outspoken in many men who for one or another reason apply for psychiatric consultation. Certainly too, especially because of existing adolescent sexual mores including "going steady," the whole question of adolescent frustrational relationships must be raised to an adequate level of discussion that would include the issue of medical instruction in contraception.

Nearly twenty years later than the essay just referred to, Freud [14] again expatiated upon this theme in a contribution to sociology which has wider implications and which now, because of the prevalence of thermonuclear fear, has even more urgency. Freud saw civilized society as perpetually menaced with disintegration through the primary hostility of men towards one another. Against the aggressive instincts of men, society erects barriers; these are reinforced by policies by means of which men are driven to identifications and aim-inhibited love relationships that deplete the libido available for their wives. As long as men knew no other form of life in common but that of the family, the ever-present conflict between love and hate expressed itself in the Oedipus Complex, caused by the development of conscience and created feelings of guilt. But when man tried, as he has been obliged to do more and more, to institute wider forms of communal life, the same conflict is intensified and society in its aim to bind men into a closely knit mass foments an ever-increasing sense of guilt in order to further check aggressiveness. This leads into a vicious cycle until the sense of guilt swells to a magnitude that is insupportable for the individual—or for a peaceful society. In particular, and this is relevant here, the socially induced oppression with guilt and suppression of aggressiveness is a factor of importance in disabling the sexual life of modern man.

The common difficulty of fusion of tender and sensual feelings that Freud found in so many of his male patients was often expressed in disturbed potency in the marriage bed, whereas outside of it sensual satisfaction was obtained. This difficulty is also related to the ascendancy of the ascetic Christian ideal in the Occident, as indeed it is to other similar monastic ideals in the Orient.* Once celibacy was elevated to the position of *summum bonum* in the hierarchical system of values, the antisexual forces of the psyche were considerably reinforced. Jung [22] has given particular attention to the history of certain regularly recurring forms of attitude toward the world, invoking Nietzsche's fundamental pair of opposites, the Apollonian-Dionysian. From the pagan art deities, Apollo and Dionysus, we discern that this opposition already existed in the Grecian world reflected in the art of the shaper, the Apollonian, and the Dionysian non-plastic art of music. By Apollonian tendency, Nietzsche refers to measure, number, limitation, the mastery of everything savage and untamed. The Dionysian, on the contrary, represents the freeing of the unmeasured

---

* Many of the oriental religious systems revolve around the axis of detachment from the world of the senses, rather than directly discountenancing the physical impulse of sex. In the more extreme forms, or advanced stages, of the religious process, the obsessive concern with detachment is translated into a more massive withdrawal and abnegation of those ego forces which are object-related. Then the knife-edged attitude of the psyche is poised between the dilemma of withdrawal from and participation in the external world, a dilemma beautifully portrayed in the Celestial Poem of The Bhagavad-Gita.

instinct, the breaking loose of the unbridled dynamics of the animal and divine nature; hence in the Dionysian choir, man appears as a *satyr,* God above and goat below. It represents horror at the annihilation of the principle of individuation and at the same time rapturous delight at its destruction. The Dionysian is, therefore, comparable to frenzy; individuality is suspended in orgies of exuberant sexual license and in religious mysteries that issue in ecstasies. Jung discusses the battle of the early Christian church with pagan practices and with the gnosis, contrasting the characters of Tertullian and Origen, the influential fathers of the second century. Tertullian was a pagan who yielded himself to the lascivious life of his city until about his thirty-fifth year when he became a Christian, creating the church Latin that lasted for more than a thousand years. The passion of his thinking was so inexorable that his ethical code was bitter in its severity. Martyrdom he commanded to be sought, not shunned; he permitted no second marriage and required the permanent veiling of persons of the female sex. The gnosis, a passion for thought and cognition, he attacked with unrelenting fanaticism, including both philosophy and science which are so closely linked up with it. To him is ascribed the sublime confession: *Credo quia absurdum est* (I believe because it is against reason). The self-mutilation achieved by Tertullian in the *sacrificium intellectus* led him to the complete rejection of philosophy and science. Origen, in contrast to Tertullian, remained a philosophical theologist but before 211 A.D. actually castrated himself. The Christian process of development encountered in Origen a type whose bedrock foundation was his relation to other people. His self-castration was thus the expression of the sacrifice of his most valuable function. It is characteristic of Tertullian that he should perform the *sacrificium intellectus,* whereas Origen was led to the *sacrificium phalli,* since the Christian process at that time demanded a complete abolition of the sensual hold upon the object.

The anti-sensual direction given by the early church in its embattlement with paganism was augmented in the Middle Ages. The ascetic ideal flourished and monasticism became the refuge of many of the finest minds. There came into being as a consequence a conception of woman as the supreme temptress, the most dangerous of all obstacles in the way of salvation. At the same time, ambivalence became manifestly heightened in a counter-doctrine of the superiority of women, an adoration of the Virgin in Heaven, and of the lady upon earth. The latter resulted in ideals of chivalry. As Trethowan [31] has recently emphasized, the persecution of witches was attributable to the ferocious asceticism and was therefore largely a result of the sexual urge being directed away from its natural context. It was believed that these women had given up their immortal souls to the prince of evil for the privilege of enjoying the services of his demons. Especially, witches were accused of hindering husbands from performing the sexual act and wives from conceiving. The leading ardent persecutors of witches were, of course, those sworn to celibacy.

Innocent VIII, elected to the papacy in 1485, became sincerely alarmed at the profusion of witches. In his celebrated bull of 1488, he called the nations of Europe to the rescue of the church, imperiled by the arts of Satan, and he set forth the horrors that were rampant, including the blighting of the marriage bed. Sprenger and Kramer shortly published the *Malleus Maleficarum,* or *Hammer to Knock Down Witches*. In this, the authors laid down a regular form of trial and appointed a course of examination by which inquisitors might best discover the guilty. Mackay [25] gives a vivid account of the ensuing exacerbation of the witch mania all over Europe.

In both the *Malleus* and in the later *Compendium Maleficarum* (Guazzo, 1608) there is a classification of impotence, which Trethowan [31] points out is in certain respects related both phenomenologically and psychodynamically to modern knowledge. There is evidence of appreciation of the part played by inner (unconscious) mental processes, it being held that these, by deceiving the senses, can give rise to the illusion of genital deprivation; a phenomenon that can probably be equated with castration anxiety and conviction. Trethowan sums up as follows: "Viewed retrospectively, the persecution of witches in medieval times seems to have stemmed from several sources. Because Ritual Witchcraft represented the persistence in Europe of the pre-Christian pagan religion or Dianic cult, those who practised it were regarded as heretics. Further impetus was given to this persecution by knowledge of certain sexual rituals probably akin to primitive fertility rites. This in the setting of misogyny attendant upon the Christian ascetic ideal, led to the emergence of a delusional belief that witches had power to interfere with sexual relationships."

Male Potency Disturbances

It is a widely held clinical impression (see, for example, Eisenstein [11]) that the average duration of intercourse is from one to five minutes from the act of insertion until the completion of orgasm. Ejaculation is usually accomplished following some thirty to fifty frictional movements, lasting about three minutes. *Premature ejaculations* is a common potency disorder; erection is attained but ejaculation occurs either prior to penetration of the vagina or within a minute after intromission. This may be only a transient manifestation, without denoting serious pathology in orgastic potency, or it may be persistent.

CASE EXAMPLE 1. A married man, aged forty years, usually without potency disturbance, returned from a business conference on the West Coast where he had been for ten days, and two months later sought an appointment. While away, he explained in interview, he had attempted intercourse with a call girl and this had failed—he had ejaculated before intromission. Since returning home, the same thing had occurred with his wife on several occasions, since when he had refrained from intercourse. This led to complications with his wife, who was now loudly demanding to know what had upset him during his trip. The patient, who had at first appeared calm in interview, became progressively more excited, demanding a cure before there was more trouble for him with his wife. He had gone to his own doctor several times. The physician had referred hm for psychiatric consultation after medication had failed to relieve the precocious ejaculation. In the course of several interviews it became evident that he feared that he might have contracted venereal disease as a punishment for his sexual digression. Following examination, including the usual laboratory tests, by another specialist to whom I referred him, he was firmly reassured and sent back to discuss this matter further with me. In the course of ensuing interviews, which included discussion of his restrictive upbringing in childhood, of his excursions to a brothel with other college students, and the later development of a steadfast devotion to his church like his father's, the patient came to fear my disapproval. This, it became increasingly clear, was partly the result of a transference-projection upon me of his own conscience insofar as this had been formed on the model of his father. This too was brought into the field of discussion, so that it became possible to reduce his castration-anxiety and to alleviate his sense of guilt. At this time, the patient was able to discuss his secret struggle with masturbation during adolescence and his fear of and anger against his father during high school and college years. Shortly, the patient recovered his potency with his wife and showed no further desire to continue in investigative psychotherapy, which anyway he regarded as too expensive—although he insisted upon his gratitude in terminating therapy.

Complete impotence denotes an inability to attain or to maintain an erection during an attempt at intercourse. This too may be transient and only occur as a result of special conditions evoking an acute mental conflict. In his diary, Goethe describes the following events: Returning from a sojourn away from home, he was faced with a long delay when the wheel of his carriage broke. The poet was thus forced to spend the night at a nearby inn. Here he became involved in a flirtation with a young and attractive chamber-maid and arranged with her a midnight rendezvous in his room. She told him that she was a virgin but was so impressed with him that she wanted to give him her first love. Goethe's sexual excitement immediately subsided and he became quite impotent. He was baffled and thought of the enjoyment he always had with his wife whereupon he became aware of a strong erection. His sexual arousal disappeared promptly, however, when he attempted to approach the girl again. Meanwhile the girl fell asleep, and Goethe left his bed to write in his diary the following words to his wife:

"I was approaching my home, when the last hours threatened to move me away from you, my beloved. But then, in a peculiar place, and under peculiar circumstances, I have found back my faithful heart. You may not understand this and the following inference, beloved; but note the mysterious final verse: Often it is illness that helps preserve our health."

When impotence is persistent, however, it betokens severe neurotic disorder. Moreover, when the patient is a young man this symptom requires psychiatric consultation. Often, in such cases, secondary depression is severe and there is risk of suicide. This situation contrasts markedly with its counterpart of persistent frigidity in young women which is so often accepted without severe depressive reaction, as will be discussed later.

CASE EXAMPLE 2. A young man of twenty-two years who had attempted suicide by hanging himself was in treatment for severe depression, and this treatment was continued on an outpatient basis for a further eighteen months with sessions four times a week. The son of a wealthy business man, he had flunked out of college despite his high intelligence and had spent a good deal of his time racing around the country in his sports car, keeping his parents anxious and intimidated. His father had attempted thrashings and severe coercion during his defiant early adolescence but had later not found it possible to control him; and psychiatric evaluation indicated that he had not yet emerged from late adolescence. Moreover, there was evidence of obsessive neurotic disorder as well as of pronounced schizoid problems. Early in the treatment of his depression, I had discovered that the suicide attempt had followed a sexual fiasco and that he had attempted intercourse many times previously without success, at different times his sexual disability varying from precocious ejaculation to complete impotence. The ensuing intensive analytically-oriented psychotherapy revealed severe castration anxiety defended against by an attempted identification with a brutal, sadistic father, an identification which, however, was shattered by his experiences in a number of sexual involvements with different young women. Moreover, as part of his apparent strong attachment to his mother, it shortly became clear that his hostility toward her was so severe that this too impeded his relationships with other women. In particular there was an unconscious equating, represented in phantasy, of ejaculation with defecation and urination. In the work with this patient, problems of acting out were particularly difficult to deal with. His more openly expressed hostility to his parents at home resulted in his father's attempting to control the therapy both by threats of terminating it (he paid the bills) and by trying to bribe me by means of increasing my fees. At a later stage in therapy, without bringing it to my notice for a long time—at this time, he was compliantly remembering details of his childhood—he seduced his father's secretary (an attractive woman in her forties who was his father's mistress, as he knew) and became deeply involved in a love affair with her, during the course of which he discovered his potency. During the further course of the therapy he rid himself of this woman and began an attachment to a younger woman and made good progress. Treating this individual was a hair-raising experience for his therapist, both because of his reckless driving in which he expressed his self-destructive trends and because of his brinkmanship with his father's mistress. The handling of the defiant and guilt-ridden father transference was thus an especially thorny problem.

This vignette may draw attention to the severe underlying problems encountered in dealing with potency disturbances psychotherapeutically. Even in rather less severe cases, the potency disturbances are built upon complicated developmental foundations and are but symptoms of a neurosis. Adequate treatment in such cases thus has to be directed not to the sexual symptom itself but to the underlying neurotic problems. Usually adequate treatment, even in younger men, requires several years of Freudian psychoanalysis. On the other hand, transient potency disturbances are often readily responsive in brief psychotherapy consisting of distributive discussions. In the course of these discussions, it is necessary to elucidate the leading mental conflicts and to provide adequate opportunity for the patient to ventilate his feelings. Certainly, as far as the single man is concerned his sexual disorder should be treated before marriage is contemplated. Marriage should never be recommended as a deliberate part of therapy.

As already indicated in the introduction, a common type of selective impotence is but an exaggeration of a prevalent form of reduced potency in marriage, whereas with female partners who are not respected, potency is more adequate. This *selective impotence* may be, or become, more or less complete, the result of an unconscious identification of the wife with sister or mother, leading to the assertion of the incest taboo and severe inhibiting castration anxiety. The following case illustrates starkly this common phenomenon, and has been reported elsewhere.[2]

CASE EXAMPLE 3. A married man came for treatment because of impotence with his wife. With other women he had experienced no such difficulty. His wife was eight years older than he was, and they were devoted to one another; this last attested by the fact that their marriage had lasted for four years, despite his persistent symptom, and his wife's longing for a child. The youngest of a large family, he had been very indulged by his mother in childhood and had never adequately emancipated himself from her influence. The source of his trouble was found to be deep-seated. His wife had eventually been chosen on the model of his mother after a protracted courtship. This so-called "anaclitic choice," based on his over-dependent need for mothering, was associated with an unconscious identification of his wife with his mother resulting in selective impotence with her. As long as he was refueled, as it were, in his day-to-day emotional life with his wife, outside the home he presented an aggressive attitude in his business affairs and in his occasional affairs with other women, with whom he had orgastic sensual pleasure in coitus. This patient had, of course, provoked his difficulties by his marriage as much as he had solved the eventual separation from his mother. The conflict between his sexual urge and his sense of guilt remained unconscious and was itself the result of an unconscious provocation. The neurosis was referable to an unsettled Oedipus situation in early life, as became increasingly clear in analysis. Moreover, pronounced oral dependency problems required to be worked through in the treatment before the selective impotence abated: anxious and jealous emotions related to the possibility of his wife's becoming pregnant emerged; especially he was afraid of a baby deviating her attention—after all, he insisted, *he* was "her boy."

From the foregoing considerations, it should be apparent that sexual impotence has varying bases and refers to a number of symptoms all of which are characterized by some disturbance, transient or more permanent, in performing the act of intercourse with orgasm. The last example discussed, selective impotence, at the level of symptom-observation already shows the dissociation characteristic of hysterical phenomena. Sometimes, rather than selective impotence, one perhaps should speak of *selective potency*, for some men are potent only when certain specific love conditions are fulfilled, and these may be of apparently bizarre nature. Total lack of sexual interest in the sexual act sometimes has its basis in an underlying incipient depressive or other psychotic disorder, and in such cases the physician is confronted by a patient whose former sexual interest has disappeared. Sometimes when the lack of interest has been long-standing there may be a compulsive neurotic basis. In these cases investigative psychotherapy may reveal a secret "chastity clause" by means of which the individual wards off guilt. This chastity commitment may have been forged during adolescence as an attempted solution to the struggle with masturbation and later forgotten. Strong incestuous attachments are always involved in such instances, and sometimes actual incestuous relations with a sister in childhood or youth. The sacrifice of interest in sexual intercourse is often a self-punitive device that satisfies the sense of guilt sufficiently so that moderate success and enjoyment in other areas of living is possible. *Retarded ejaculation* and *intercourse and ejaculation without orgasm,* are less frequent manifestations of disturbance in potency. These symptoms are often associated with underlying severe neurotic character disorder and radical treatment requires prolonged psychoanalysis. Sometimes a patient complains of *distressing spontaneous ejaculations,* a problem briefly discussed elsewhere.[4]

In all these manifestations, there is underlying castration anxiety or, more exactly, unconscious apprehension of injury to the penis, in some instances equated with or reinforced by fear of death. Associated with this underlying anxiety are a number of other psychodynamic factors of varying importance in different instances. Always of primary importance is the influence of the character structure of the individual as this is related to the pregenital organization of his libido—that is to say, the relative dominance of oral, anal, urethral, skin, and other bodily areas in the childhood sexual history. This history includes both the actual experiences, and the fantasies with which early sexual theories are associated. These often have a profound influence on the later development and manifestations of the sexual drive. They usually consist of notions of birth by the bowel and a sadistic misconception of coitus.

Female Frigidity

Just as male potency disturbances comprise various symptoms that are usually the expression of different neurotic problems or sometimes of underlying psychotic disease, so the general term frigidity has been applied to a number of symptoms of sexual disability in woman. Impairment of a woman's capacity to enjoy heterosexual genital intercourse may be partial or total, and partial impairment is a common symptom. In 1912, Freud [15] wrote that the adult sexual life of women is also adversely affected by the prevalent conditions of upbringing in civilized society. Both the strong incestuous fixations of childhood and the frustration by reality suffered during adolescence, factors operative in impairing the sexual life of modern man, also affect modern woman. Further, women are strongly affected by the reaction upon them of the sharp contrast between the "mother" and the "harlot" in the attitude of men. Commonly the outcome has a different emphasis from that in men and Freud [15] stated this as follows:

In my opinion the necessary condition of forbiddenness in the erotic life of women holds the same place as the man's need to lower his sexual object. Both are the consequence of the long period of delay between sexual maturity and sexual activity which is demanded by education for social reasons. The aim of both is to overcome the psychical impotence resulting from the lack of union between tenderness and sensuality. That the effect of the same causes differs so greatly in men and women is perhaps due to another difference in the behavior of the two sexes. Women belonging to the higher levels of civilisation do not usually transgress the prohibition against sexual activities during the period of waiting, and thus they acquire this close association between the forbidden and the sexual. Men usually overstep the prohibition under the condition of lowering the standard of object they require, and so carry this condition on into their subsequent erotic life.

As a result of this association, women often desire to keep even legitimate relations secret for a time, and some women frigid in legitimate relations recover the capacity for full sensation as soon as the condition of prohibition is restored by a secret intrigue with a lover. Partial frigidity in marriage is a common phenomenon caused often, or in part, by this paradoxical need for "forbiddenness" in order to achieve maximal sensual pleasure resulting from correspondence with fantasy. However, should the "forbiddenness" assume a stronger quality, frigidity once again is manifest.

The following is a case which illustrates a common problem encountered in psychiatric practice.

CASE EXAMPLE 4. A woman of thirty years of age was referred for psychiatric consultation by a gynecologist following her complaint of frigidity and his finding nothing physically amiss. Discussion disclosed that since the birth of her baby two years previously, she had felt increasingly aversive to sexual intercourse and had enjoyed it less and less, until one year before her complaint to the gynecologist, she had total vaginal anesthesia. In this first interview, it became evident that her reaction to motherhood was quite positive and that the pregnancy and delivery had been without any considerable problem. Moreover, the early few years of marriage had been characterized by an active and pleasurable sexual life. Pregnancy had been delayed by contraceptive measures because she and her husband had been concerned with establishing reasonable economic security. She had helped him in his business of trucking, supervising in the office at the yard, figuring the accounts, and checking the return of the men from their journeys, and so forth. Now at home she continued to help him with the accounts of his expanding business. Meanwhile her husband had been getting busier and busier in the prosperous business. Following a further interview, this attractive and intelligent woman elected to come to psychotherapeutic sessions three times a week, and this continued for four months, after which the frequency of sessions was reduced to once a week for a further two months.

Early in psychotherapy, she confessed to an involvement with a young man working at her husband's business. She had had frequent contact with him while she worked at the yard, and they had conversationally flirted from time to time, often enough in the presence of her husband. After the birth of her son, on occasional visits to the yard a few miles from her home she had again encountered this young man, and on these few occasions her husband was away on business. The young man was married too, but he had expatiated on how much he had missed her during her pregnancy and later occasionally during the day he drove his truck on one pretext or another to her home. Still later, he turned up in the park where she perambulated her baby. The affair had come to consist in romantic protestations and love-making short of actual intercourse and had persisted into the present; and now she was worried about this, although she enjoyed so much the thrill of their secret assignations. It became obvious to both of us that this affair had developed *pari passu* with her increasing aversion to sexual intercourse with her husband and with the onset of vaginal anesthesia.

The anamnesis in psychotherapy came to center around her attachment to her father, apparently usually a grim character, who, however, became especially relaxed with her and cheerfully played with her during her childhood; and she had been an especially amusing child, in this way gaining her father's attention. She also discussed her ambivalence toward her mother, acute during adolescence, but the picture outlined was generally of a warm, affectionate mother with whom she had identified. The transference to me became erotically tinged, and during discussions of this, erotic fantasies relating to her father and abounding in adolescence were remembered. She saw that her husband had been, and continued to be, seriously concerned with his job like her father, and she admired his progress in establishing a large enterprise. Now the husband's moments of relaxation seemed to be centered around his interaction with his son, and she felt his attitude to her since she had become a mother was less playful. As her transference to me developed further, her interest in her meetings with the young man subsided, she came to the decision to terminate the involvement, and did so after a discussion with him. Her curiosity and erotic fantasies about me were uncovered following the analysis of defensive inhibited silences that became a feature of our sessions. She became indeed more concerned about her relationship with me than with the sexual problem in her marriage. The blushing, embarrassed silences were replaced by tearful sessions in which we came to discuss the stringencies of the doctor-patient relationship and its relevance to the sensual barriers between her and her father. Also discussed at this time was the equating of her psychotherapeutic sessions with forbidden and secret assignations, and these were brought into conscious connection with her games with her father and her elaboration of them in fantasy. Shortly the sexual incapacity with her husband diminished, though it fluctuated as we discussed the termination of therapy and the preliminary reduction of frequency. Six months after the termination of therapy, this lady brought me a small gift and gave an account of a happy relationship with her husband.

In this analytically oriented brief psychotherapy of a woman of basically sound personality afflicted with an hysterical type of frigidity disorder, the factors mentioned by Freud as of outstanding importance were obvious—the incestuous fixation in childhood, the need for a certain degree of replication of "forbiddenness," and the delay of adequate sexual experience during adolescence. Obvious also was the need for love and her anxiety about maintaining my approval as well as that of her father, a need that was utilized though not analyzed in this brief psychotherapy. This anxiety in women corresponds with the castration anxiety encountered in men, and her frigidity in intercourse with her husband was also related to self-punishment connected with guilt about her extramarital involvement, an involvement which she felt might cost her the love of her husband. It will also be noticed that her husband's reactions to her becoming a mother had played an important part in the ensuing circadian marital interactions issuing in total vaginal anesthesia. In this particular case, in brief psychotherapy, no obtrusive problems relating to penis-envy found conscious expression. The hints of these problems that were evident to me were not interpreted at all.

In more intense degrees of frigidity than the example discussed above, anxiety results in dyspareunia (painful intercourse) in which the vaginal sphincter muscle closes tightly and obstructs, or partially obstructs, the entry of the penis into the vagina (severe vaginismus). This too may, however, be merely transient. When more permanent, the basic significance usually is associated with deep-seated guilt as well as anxiety, the guilt connected with repressed sadistic impulses, such as revenge upon the penis and the man, and the anxiety connected with masochistic anticipations of genital injury. Even this severe form of frigidity, though more often exhibited in relation to any sexual partner, sometimes is dissociated inasmuch as it occurs within the marriage, the marital partner having assumed incestuous meaning and having absorbed the greater force of reactions to penis-envy, whereas extra-marital affairs may yield a measure of satisfaction. Such women have often induced the husband to attempt manual stimulation of the clitoris or oro-genital contact or both as well as demands for unduly prolonged forepleasure to enable them, they rationalize, to become more receptive to the act of penetration itself. Often enough these rationalizations have been initiated or reinforced by reading "enlightened" instructions about technique in sex manuals. Analysis, however, reveals that *inter alia* these demands are motivated by an attempt to disparage the penis as a pleasure-giving organ and that the rationalizations are in the service of unconscious hostility to and envy of men. At any rate my clinical experience supports the statement of Bergler [7] that "the opinion is false that the man must have a certain technique or even a knowledge of perverse tricks to produce orgasm in the woman. The healthy woman only permits coitus if she loves tenderly too. . . . It is true that the graph of excitement in coitus shows a more rapid rise and fall in the man than in the woman, so that pre-pleasurable acts are in many cases necessary, but this implies by no means that special subtleties are required. . . ." The husband in some instances is further humiliated by his wife's infidelity becoming known to him, if it is not directly announced by the wife, whereupon she insists upon the sexual satisfaction obtained with the other man and blames him for his sexual incompetence. Abraham [1] described this type of woman, the revengeful or vindictive type, who encounters so many difficulties in erotic life, and he emphasized the neurotic manifestations of penis-envy, perhaps to some extent overlooking other contributory earlier experiences of jealousy within the family drama which lend a paranoid tendency, or hostile-world outlook, to the entire personality.

It will at this time perhaps be recalled that in my definition of frigidity I did not specifically call attention to those involuntary contractions of the vagina which follow upon pleasurable sensation and which are characteristic of vaginal orgasm. The obsessional concern nowadays of some women who have a more diffuse rather than focused experience of orgasm is, it seems to me, often a disguised expression of unsurmounted penis-envy and a concern misleadingly reinforced by some sexologists. However, here is the statement of an eminent woman analyst [10] (pp. 218 ff.): "The road to the feminine woman as a sexual object leads through the psyche, and all the four fundamental factors . . . must be taken into account if her conditions are to be met. Her inhibition can be strengthened by her narcissism, masochism, tie to former objects and motherliness; and each of these four factors, if present to an excessive degree, can become a source of frigidity. Especially in favour of the last-named component does the feminine woman often renounce orgastic gratification, without the least suffering in her psychic health. But even if motherliness is not involved, she often tolerates her own sexual inhibition without losing her all-embracing warmth and harmony."

Misconceptions based on crude ideas about Freud's libido theory, not as he developed it and as it has become elaborated by Freudian analysts, often result either in a notion of imperfection if focused genital discharge is not regularly achieved as in the obsessional concern of some modern women, or else in a total rejection of libido theory which can, it seems to me, only be achieved by lack or gross denial of clinical psychoanalytic experience and inference. Perhaps it will be useful to state here that for both men and women orgastic experience is not a guarantee of psychic health and that orgastic experience occurs often under conditions of psychic disturbance. Phyllis Greenacre [18] discusses the automatic vaginal orgasm of "latent psychotic" patients as part of a revival of an intense polymorphous perverse period. In early life, the incapacity of the weak infant to endure overstimulation to which it is subjected can cause a discharge through many channels, including the genitals; and later vaginal sensation in such women may be readily elicited with orgasm. One borderline psychotic patient in treatment with me for a number of years for other than sexual symptoms, and for whom sexual acting out was a problem, had intense orgastic experience in sexual intercourse. In addition to evidence of severe oral fixation, her childhood history included a vehement struggle between her mother and her constipation, with the frequent giving of enemas. For another example, the reader is referred to Fenichel's paper on "Defense Against Anxiety, Particularly by Libidinization" [13] in which he discusses at some length a cyclothymic woman patient who was "by no means frigid" and who used sexuality, as indeed did the patient just mentioned, as a defense against anxiety. It is, anyway, in my opinion difficult or impossible to distinguish between so-called true orgasm and counter-phobic orgastic experience. Before drawing conclusions in regard to sexual normality, the context in which heterosexual intercourse takes place as well as the psychic life in general of the individual require careful and detailed study. Then it is possible to decode, as it were, the manifest sexual behavior that certainly then is a further key to understanding the total defense struggle of the individual patient.

Freud [16] pointed out that the girl's development to womanhood is more difficult and complicated than that of the boy's development to manhood. The girl has two additional burdens: in the phallic phase, the clitoris is the dominant erotogenic zone and with the change to decisive femininity, the clitoris must give up to the vagina its sensitivity wholly or in part; then again, the first love-object, the mother, is relinquished in large measure in favor of the father in the Oedipus phase of development. These changes in erotogenic zone and in the first object-cathexes are additional since the boy from the phallic phase keeps both of them unchanged. For many neurotic women, the husband who had in the first instance inherited his position from the father, comes in the course of time to inherit the position of the mother as well. Whereupon the conflicts of the pre-Oedipal attachment to the mother become re-enacted in marriage. In this way, it is in many instances the case that the second part of a woman's life is taken up with a struggle against her husband, just as the shorter earlier part was occupied with rebellion against her mother. If the man is himself burdened through his neurosis with sadomasochistic problems, the resulting interactive hostility, partly displayed in sexual conflict, may come to resemble a Strindberg play. Staged on the domestic scene, often in reality hidden from any audience, and often enough "expressionistic" inasmuch as the emotions involved are not adequately represented in words or objective situations, the drama unfolds in the psychiatrist's office with the complaint of frigidity. As Therese Benedek [5] tersely expresses an important aspect of this situation: "Since the social and emotional significance of frigidity is different from that of impotence, women can use the suppression of their own sexual needs as a weapon against their husbands." This aspect is the obverse of the obsessive preoccupation now more prevalent with deficient orgasm, used as a hitching post for inferiority feelings; and sometimes both these facets are illuminated in the course of the first psychiatric consultation.

Paraphilia and Marriage

The word "perversion" has many connotations, some of which readily transform its meaning to that of a persuasive definition of sin inappropriate for scientific and medical discussion. On this account, following the terminology in this respect of Wilhelm Stekel,[30] the word "paraphilia" is employed here instead. A severe paraphilia may exist within marriage, causing more or less disturbance to marital relations.

CASE EXAMPLE 5. A soldier was sent for psychiatric treatment because of a manifest severe anxiety state impeding the performance of his duties. Discussions disclosed that this young married man had the habit in youth of periodically donning feminine attire at home and after marriage continued occasionally to strut around, sometimes partially inebriated, in this garb under the conditions of domestic privacy. His wife shared his secret, had indeed been apprised of this habit before marriage, and had been tolerant of it. During the few years of marriage the habit had diminished considerably. Later during army service, he became more and more uneasy with little opportunity to indulge in his parade as a woman; and then his special possessions were confiscated by a sergeant resulting in the onset of manifest neurotic disturbance. In one interview, the patient talked as follows:

"My first recollection of having worn women's clothing dates back to my fifth year.

"My sister had just been born, and for various reasons, I had to sleep with my grandmother. When she got up in the mornings, very often I would wake up, and then I would be awake and watch her dressing. One morning after she had left the room, I jumped out of bed, wrapped one of her corsets around me and put on a pair of her knickers. Neither garment fitted me; my grandmother was stout, I was rather small. From then on, I indulged in this whim whenever the inclination came and circumstances permitted.

"My father was often, during the early part of my life, away at sea for long periods, and I, therefore, spent most of my time with the women of the family. I was the third son, my sister the only girl. Of the other two, one died before my birth, the other a few years after my sister's birth. My father died when I was fourteen.

"During my childhood I had all the usual illnesses, plus dysentery, a mastoid, and a weak heart. All of this tended to keep me away from the normal pursuits of a young male and draw me more closely to the womenfolk around me. Living with women it was always easy for me to get the clothing with which to satisfy my impulse. Unbeknown to them, however.

"At sixteen I had my first affair with another boy, who though younger was physically bigger. It lasted for some weeks, but there was no great intimacy; he used to fondle the upper part of my body.

When it first started I took the part of the 'girl' quite naturally. It seemed to be accepted that I would. (At this time, there was, and had been for some time, an open discussion among my male friends, as to my sex—because of my heart, I was not allowed to swim; the people in question suggested that the real reason for my non-appearance in a bathing costume was due to my having feminine breasts.)

"I did not masturbate until well into my sixteenth year. This happened when I was wearing feminine clothing, but not always.

"At eighteen I took up bicycle racing and women. This did not influence my desire for femininity in any way. My relationship with girls, and I had a continual stream of affairs, all reached a point of intimacy just short of seduction. My reason for not having intercourse was economic rather than moral or lack of ability. My only attempt at actual sexual intercourse, which took place in a French brothel, was a failure; not that I was sorry. I could not get an erection, due partly I think, to a slight state of inebriation, lack of any preliminary love play, and disgust.

"In January, 19—, I joined the army. I was barely twenty and still not fully aware of the implications of my passion for feminine attributes. For the greater part of my life in the army, I was lucky enough to be within easy reach of my home, or living in circumstances where I could give vent to my impulse with little difficulty. In any case I was never away from my source of supply for more than three months. During my service in the U.K., I met and married my wife. To me she is the personification of everything I would like to be. She is aware of my peculiarity and we have a perfect understanding regarding it, and its practice. With my marriage I had my first experience of coitus. I had no difficulty; I do not suffer from premature ejaculation, but can maintain an erection for a considerable period; I need no stimulation other than normal love play, and I enjoy it. However, I do at times like to play the passive role in feminine clothing. I think that I become sexually more excited in women's clothing, but it is not necessary for me to wear it when performing my function as a male.

"For the first year of my service overseas I repressed my impulse whenever it occurred, and in doing so began to find, for the first time, its force and compelling nature. During this period my only satisfaction came in dreams and daydreams. Those at night often ended with an emission, in the day with onanism. Eventually I was unable to restrain myself any longer and went out and bought myself some undies; the only things I could wear. Although I derived a great deal of pleasure from this, I was not wholly content. Life in a barrack room gives very little privacy, and I had no illusions as to the outcome, if anyone found me out. All this naturally rather took the edge off things and worried me a little; I had one or two rather anxious moments. I'm rather fussy with feminine clothing, I like to keep my things clean and pressed and tidy, all of which I found very difficult to do. These underthings were actually the first I had bought for myself; before, for various reasons chiefly financial, I had satisfied myself with the clothing of my wife, sister, etc. With the hot weather my activities were considerably restricted owing to the wearing of shorts or less clothing. I began to get depressed again. In this connection, it has always been a source of sorrow to me, that I have been unable to indulge in the expression of my femininity openly. I resent having to do it in secrecy, with my reflection in a mirror as my only company. With my wife I enjoy my whim in freedom and find the utmost happiness and contentment.

"I find it impossible to describe or explain my feelings when wearing feminine clothes. It is only then that I feel properly dressed, as if I am what I want to be, a woman. At times, when so dressed, I look at my body and feel utterly miserable, I want to cry, my body is all wrong. It is at such moments I find my peculiarity very hard to bear. At other times I accept it, and making most of what I can from my femininity, I enjoy myself and do feel really happy. When I wear a brassiere, or corset with a brassiere top, I always have to pad myself: I feel nicer then.

"In my imagination my female self has various roles: with my wife, as another girl; or as I'm very fond of helping my wife, as her personal maid; with a man (usually one of my friends). In this instance my daydreaming is typical of what actually would occur, if I gave myself to a man. The man has to return my affection, he has to call me by a feminine name, and above all treat me exactly the way in which he would a girl. In our intimacy I would permit anything but physical entry into my body, and possibly *fellatio*. I do not think that my relationship with men, however, will ever be other than in imagination.

"My other role is that of a ballerina. I'm very attracted to classical music. My favorite form of entertainment is the ballet, and above all things I'd like to look like my wife and be a ballerina, perhaps, because my world like that of ballet is a lot of make believe, and because I'd like to be admired by thousands, male and female.

"Women affect me in two ways, either from a purely masculine standpoint, or my feminine self which is intensely envious of them, because they have what I want.

"After some sixteen months overseas of repression and partial satisfaction, my impulse for femininity became so powerful as to make me think in terms of two, my masculine self and my feminine self of whom I think as Freda. Being predominately male, I have always tried to subjugate my other side to my maleness, but at last it had become so strong as to get the better of me. As Freda I entertain little thought of my masculine self, but as I, I have continual reminders of Freda. I pick up a magazine, my attention is drawn to all things feminine. I have little or no interest in male clothing but marked views on female dress. I know what I like to wear: satin cami-knickers embroidered in silk, a suspender belt, fully fashioned silk stockings, and wedge-heeled shoes, a silk, satin or taffeta blouse, and a tailored costume. I know exactly how I'd dress my hair, the type of cosmetics I'd use. All my clothing would be carefully tended.

"As Freda I was recently very much attracted to one of the men among my associates. He once asked me if there was any chance of me changing my sex, maybe he sensed my femininity. Apart from calling me, rather jokingly on his part I suspect, 'Darling' on various occasions, which I rather liked, nothing developed, but had he been inclined to pursue the matter, I, with a struggle, think I could have resisted him. Fortunately he was not inclined and I keep him in my imagination. I say fortunately because above all other things I place my wife and my duty to her as a man. In all things she and her happiness must come first. It must be nice to be loved as a woman by a man and have a baby.

"When I married, I believed that I would in married life grow out of my peculiarity, maybe one day I will. And yet is it possible for me to ever forget that feminine undies are so much more pretty and pleasing than men's, even if made from silk?

"Because of all this, my worries and depression and nervous state, I decided to seek advice, after I could work up enough courage to tell my story.

"In one of my dreams physical assault took place. I dreamed I was asleep in the barrack room; someone got under my mosquito net, pulled my knickers down (I was actually sleeping in silk knickers), and tried to wake me. I jumped up but not in time to see who it was. I switched on the light, wakened everyone, and said what had happened, pointing out for the benefit of all that I was not homosexual.

"This nightmare caused me to wake up, I was very hot and frightened.

"I mention this because it illustrates, or does to me, my views on my relationship with men. As my female self I'm inclined to view my associations with women as Lesbian, rather than homosexual with men. . . ."

This case discloses the early feminine identification as well as the developing anxiety about homosexuality, from which his marriage had protected him to a considerable extent. When the schizotypical solution was no longer possible, his anxiety became overwhelming and he was then referred for psychiatric examination. It is of interest that the "Freda" component approaches closely one kind of hysterical feminine character disorder.[27] Quite starkly, too, this case of transvestism (Hirshfeld) or eonism (Ellis) [12] displays in the verbatim sample record the envy that some men have of women and that can sometimes enter into the pathology of disturbed marital relations just as the "penis-envy" of women often does. It should also be clear from this case illustration that the structure of a paraphilia is often complex and bears to a varying extent an inverse relationship to neurotic disturbance. In this case, for example, the suppression of acting out of paraphilic impulses resulted in an exacerbation of symptoms of anxiety. The acting out can, however, itself lead to neurotic disturbance, especially if the expression of pregenital impulses and fantasies becomes less and less disguised and then conflicts with countermanding personality trends. Or, as in the case of overt male bisexuality to be discussed below, homosexual practices come into conflict with actual social regulations.

Homosexuality and Marriage

The last case illustration draws attention to the fundamental bisexuality of the human being, and the fact that in the process of individuation sexual identification is an important variable interacting with other factors in the integration of identity formation. In this individual, a feminine ideal or aspiration competed with a masculine one; in fact, in psychotherapy he spoke of "perfect femininity" represented for him by the Madonna and her relationship with the Child. Into these complexities of personality development we can go no further here, except to note that the partial personality of Freda represented only a larval stage of feminine development, and one which impeded his masculine identification despite his efforts to sequestrate these components. Usually without adequate motivation a practicing homosexual does not progress in psychoanalysis to a heterosexual adaptation adequate for a genuinely productive and emotionally enriching marriage. However, as the following case illustration briefly demonstrates, so many factors are, or become, involved in psychotherapy, that even under conditions of legal and social coercion, considerable progress can occur in treatment.

CASE EXAMPLE 6. A prominent professional man, married, with one child, had continued episodic homosexual activity during the ten years of his marriage. Sometimes, he undertook lengthy automobile journeys to professional meetings in distant parts of the country, and one of the ways in which he made contact with male sexual partners was by picking up hitchhikers. One of these occasions led to police intervention and later public scandal and court proceedings. He came into psychotherapy through coercion and had to make monthly visits to a probation officer to whom he had to report that he was in treatment with me. Under these inauspicious conditions psychotherapy thrice weekly for six months apparently made no great progress. In regard to homosexual activities, however, the patient was in a condition of forced abstinence. During the first six months, he spent most of the time moaning about his fate, expressing his resentment, his views about regulations of society which impinged upon personal freedom, and then about my expensive fees and my complicity in a conspiracy "to take him to the cleaners." He came to think that he might as well use his time more productively, as I would not release him from the treatment with a certificate of cure, and in the ensuing six months elaborated his history and his feelings about his parents and siblings as well as those concerned with his current situation. Especially, he came to express his resentment against a dominating mother who, following his father's demise, had come to live in his home. His work with me led to a considerable emotional emancipation from this mother and more positive attachment to his wife who, it became apparent, was a masochistic character quite the opposite of his mother in many features of her personality. The hostility he had formerly displayed toward his wife was considerably reduced, and his sexual interest and satisfaction with her became progressively enhanced. He soon commenced to see the benefits of treatment, which he continued in the absence of further social coercion. In the course of further therapy he made remarkable progress, including no longer experiencing any homosexual temptation and improving his friendly relationships with both men and women in his social milieu. During the latter part of treatment, his mother decided to live away from his hometown.

Since Lesbianism is not legally punishable in general, the female homosexual avoids anxiety in this respect. Moreover our culture permits a good deal of homo-erotic behavior between women, kissing and hugging being quite readily accepted. This is the cultural counterpart of the early female pre-Oedipal attachment to the mother which thus in a way receives some degree of recognition.

Both manifest homosexuality and excessively pronounced latent homosexuality can be, or become, very destructive to a marriage; even in those cases where the marriage escapes destruction, the means whereby stability is achieved always results in the impoverishment of the marital relationship. Underlying excessive latent homosexuality is often part of the neurotic or psychotic problem that lurks beneath the rationalized complaints of one or both partners to the marriage. Following the menopause, partly directly as a result of and partly in psychological reaction to the hormonal changes of this time, there is considerable regression with underlying increased homosexual orientation in some women and this may issue in open marital conflict. In the more severe instances, the somatic and psychic symptoms of involutional depressive and paranoid disorder are sufficiently obvious to the physician.[8] With adequate psychiatric treatment, the outlook is generally good. As a rule, even with conservative treatment, there is a tendency for marital homeostasis to be regained after a period of psychological fluctuation that partly depends upon the temporary endocrine disturbance. Similarly, with some men in their fifties, jealous and paranoid reactions or depressive periods often disturb marital relations. When severe these take the form of a temporary psychotic disorder, the so-called *forme fruste* paranoia of French authors.[9] In this involutional period, both for men and for women, one of the essential underlying factors is a regression that accentuates homosexual libido, a regression that may be energetically defended against in ways that put additional strains upon the marriage.

Other Paraphilias

Besides the deviations discussed above, other paraphilias include those in which children are chosen as sexual objects (*pedophilia*). Only exceptionally in these instances are children the exclusive sexual objects; sometimes a married person becomes involved in this particular problem, a sure indication of inhibition and frustration of adequate gratification in the marriage. Many such instances, where a man or woman in varying degrees finds sexual gratification in the caresses of children, are associated with the invalidism of the spouse. *Zoöphilia*, an unusually strong attraction to animals, can become associated with *zoöerasty* or sexual intercourse with an animal, a case of which in investigative psychotherapy [3] demonstrated the release of repressed unconscious rebellion and regressive acting out of infantile sexual and sadistic ("polymorph perverse") incestuous fantasies. This patient also demonstrated the guilt and shame reactions to such release and the wide ramifications of erotic symbolism.

In other paraphilias, there are pronounced deviations in respect to the sexual aim. Freud [17] stated, ". . . there are certain intermediate relations to the sexual object, such as touching or looking at it, which lie on the road towards copulation and are recognised as being preliminary sexual aims. On the one hand these activities are themselves accompanied by pleasure, and on the other hand they intensify the excitation, which should persist until the final sexual aim is attained" (pp. 149-50). In the sexual aims of paraphilia, though the partner may be of the opposite sex, one or more of the pregenital impulses substitute for genital intercourse or else overshadow the act of coitus. Oral activities such as the apposition of the mouth to the penis (*fellatio*) or the apposition of the mouth to the vulva (*cunnilingus*) are common manifestations. The sexual use of the anal orifice is by no means limited to the sexual expressions of male homosexuals, but may be a means of obtaining orgasm in heterosexual intercourse. In cases of *osphresiophilia*, when sexual pleasure is largely derived from the sense of smell, anal activities may predominate. *Voyeurism* and *exhibitionism, sadism* and *masochism* are other important paraphilias. The latter group, involving the desire to inflict pain upon the sexual object and its reverse, received these names from Krafft-Ebing [23] after the authors of *Justine* [28] and *Venus in Furs,* [32] two novels in which the major theme is sexual cruelty and pleasure in humiliating or being humiliated. Sadism and masochism are the most common of the paraphilias, and as Freud [17] writes, the roots are easy to detect in the normal, for the sexuality of males contains an element of aggressiveness, a desire to subjugate, whereas there is an irreducible masochism in female sexuality. It is where these components of the sexual instinct became independent and exaggerated and usurp the leading position in sexual interaction (as in the novels mentioned above) that sado-masochistic paraphilia arises. Sometimes associated with sado-masochistic activities, erotic excitation may be induced or produced by the act of urination. In *fetishism*, the fetish may completely replace the sexual partner, and in *mixoscopia*, excitement is found in witnessing the sexual behavior of others.

When any of these activities, or combinations of them, are absolute preconditions overshadowing in importance the act of coitus, or replace this as a means of obtaining orgasm, paraphilia may be diagnosed. On the other hand, the occurrence of such activities sometimes as a prelude to genital intercourse, or their occurrence sometimes to the exclusion of such intercourse, does not justify this kind of clinical appraisal. Sometimes, a psychiatrist may interview an outraged wife who complains of an unusual occurrence of this sort, often, in such an instance, dubbing her husband a "sexual maniac." Often enough, this wife may be partially frigid, and the occurrence of a sexual act definitely offensive to her is symptomatic of a worsening marital relationship and a developing severe neurotic interaction. However, in the event of some demands or activities persistently replacing or overshadowing genital intercourse on the part of one or other spouse, the question of paraphilia requires consideration. This may coexist alongside frank neurotic disturbance; anyway, it is an expression of neurotic character disorder. Often enough, married couples mutually participate in deviant sexual behavior, as, for example, sado-masochistic games, including flagellation or tying one another up with the bed-clothes, and only later when other developments in their total relationship bring about dispute, and then only with difficulty, does the doctor hear of these sexual events. It may later be clear that these activities, indicative of neurotic character disorder, were replaced by others that became too offensive to one or the other partner—as, for example, when sadistic sexual acts are replaced by marital infidelity paraded before the spouse. Another example is a wife's increasing demands for fore-pleasure, including manipulation of the clitoris, which brings about orgasm and disinterest in ensuing intercourse. Soon the husband gets the message of her disparagement of his penis, which anyway is also reflected in her attitudes about and toward him.

There are also men and women who engage in intercourse as part of their marital duty, but achieve more satisfaction from solitary sexual stimulation, perhaps masturbating after intercourse to the accompaniment of elaborate sado-masochistic fantasies. Such events are often disclosed in psychotherapy for neurotic problems that the patient had not formerly connected with his sexual behavior.

From this brief survey of paraphilic disorder, it will be apparent that the variable dissociation of tender and sensual feelings, so commonplace in the sexual life of modern man, may be complicated by deeper regressions issuing in the dissociation of components of the developed sexual instinct. Fixation or regression to the anal-sadistic phase is especially common in these disorders, and the reaction formations that defend against anal-sadistic strivings and that sustain a group-relatedness within the primary family, break down when heterosexual adaptation is attempted in marriage, or even before marriage is contemplated. The integration of the personality to a level at which sustained heterosexual love and companionship in marriage is possible, an integration that depends upon a predominantly genital libido organization, is defective in these disorders. Freud [17] made the following remarks in this connection: "The very remarkable relation which thus holds between sexual variations and the descending scale from health to insanity gives us plenty of material for thought. I am inclined to believe that it may be explained by the fact that the impulses of sexual life are among those which, even normally, are the least controlled by the higher activities of the mind. In my experience anyone who is in any way, whether socially or ethically, abnormal mentally is invariably abnormal also in his sexual life. But many people are abnormal in their sexual life who in every other respect approximate to the average, and have, along with the rest, passed through the process of human cultural development in which sexuality remains the weak spot. . ." (p. 149).

Sexual Disorder as a Medical Problem

From our discussion of the psychological aspects of sexual disorder, a discussion that laid emphasis on the psychogenic factors involved, it is obvious that the physician must look further than structural disease involving the genito-urinary system. At the same time, we have to keep in mind somato-psychic sequences, too, especially diseases of the endocrine, central nervous, and genito-urinary systems. Even mild systemic physical illness, exhaustion and fatigue, or pain from organic disease, can cause transient sexual disorder. Surgical operations, not only because of temporary direct physical effect but often because of the mobilization of mutilation fantasies, frequently are responsible for transient impotence or frigidity. It is especially important to keep in mind that the menstrual cycle affects pronouncedly the intensity of sexual desire, the sexual behavior, and the degree of gratification. Benedek and Rubinstein [6] made a detailed collaborative study of the relationships between endocrine functions in woman and psychological processes. Heterosexual interest is more prominent in general during the preovulatory phase of the sexual cycle when estrogen levels are relatively high than during the postovulatory phase when progesterone exerts its effects, including a shift of emotional concern to the body and its welfare in conformity with the somatic preparation for pregnancy. Upon the decline of progesterone production in the premenstrual phase, a regression of psychosexual integration takes place and very few women are free from mood changes and from discomfort during this time.

There are many disease conditions that can be diagnosed readily as the result of the careful routine examination including the nervous system, the lungs, and the urine, such as *tabes dorsalis,* tuberculosis, and *diabetes mellitus.* Mechanical defects such as malformation or cancer of the penis, or defects such as carcinoma of the cervix with pain, or infantilism shown in the form of the external genitalia are readily detectable on adequate physical examination. A history of alcoholism or drug addiction, even when gross physical effects are not immediately evident, is of importance as decreased genital sexual adequacy is associated with these conditions. Nowadays, too, it is especially necessary to have a good account of the medications a patient has been receiving because of the widespread use of psychotropic drugs; certain tranquilizers may markedly decrease sexual drive and, for example, thioridazine HCl sometimes inhibits ejaculation. I have mentioned here only a few conditions of organic disease that have been detected in patients who have presented themselves for psychiatric examination because of sexual problems within my own experience. These mentions should be sufficient to indicate that sexual disorder is always a medical problem, though impotence and frigidity caused by such conditions are infrequent in comparison with the incidence of these symptoms in the absence of organic disease. Apart from disease, some cases of frigidity may depend partly upon anatomical factors, such as the susceptibility of the clitoris to displacement during intercourse.[26]

Important too from the medical and public health viewpoint is the incidence of venereal disease. Syphilis and gonorrhea, even when they are not directly responsible for sexual disorder—and they often are—are themselves frequently the product of sexual disorder. So-called "hypersexuality" in the Don Juan type, a type often dominated by narcissistic needs and sadistic trends, and in the nymphomaniac type, a type often dominated by vindictive attitudes rationalized as an insistence on a single standard of sexual freedom, often results in the spread of these venereal diseases. At present, there is an increased incidence of these diseases, so that medical vigilance is especially necessary. From the medical and sociological viewpoint too, sex offenses are of increasing importance in a time of increasing velocity of social change. A recently published symposium [20] includes a contribution by Bernard Glueck, Sr., stressing the clinical aspects of the problem. Those sexual offenses that occur in the setting of severe personality disorder of psychopathic type may include rape, sexual assault, and mutilation. In such cases, the behavior disorder is often associated with electroencephalographic (EEG) abnormalities [21, 24] and "organicity" may also be a feature of the Bender-Gestalt protocol, even though the patient is apparently seizure-free. Gibbs and Gibbs [19] have shown that the type of seizures associated with EEG patterns of six- and fourteen-per-second positive spikes are among the more common forms of epilepsy and are usually responsive to medication. If sexually antisocial behavior is associated with similar EEG patterns or with other abnormal patterns, pharmacotherapy is an important part of treatment.

Finally, as has already been noted, sexual disorder is sometimes a symptom of incipient psychosis, and this sometimes is of an organic reaction type. All these considerations amply emphasize the need for complete medical examination of patients suffering from sexual disorder and the fact that treatment should proceed only with medical and psychiatric collaboration.

References

1. Abraham, Karl. March, 1922. "Manifestations of the Female Castration Complex." *Int. J. Psychoanal.*, 3 (1):1-29.
2. Abse, D. W. 1950. *The Diagnosis of Hysteria.* London: John Wright and Sons, Ltd., and Baltimore: Williams and Wilkins.
3. ———. Fall, 1955. "Psychodynamic Aspects of the Problem of Definition of Obscenity," *Law and Contemporary Problems*, 20(4):572-86.
4. ———. Nov., 1962. "Spontaneous Ejaculations," *J.A.M.A.*, 182(7): 820.
5. Benedek, Therese F. 1959. "Sexual Functions in Women and Their Disturbance," in S. Arieti (ed.), *American Handbook of Psychiatry.* New York: Basic Books, Inc.
6. ———, and B. B. Rubinstein. 1942. "The Sexual Cycle in Women," *Psychosomatic Medical Monographs*, Vol. III, Nos. I & II. Washington, D.C.: National Research Council.

7. Bergler, Edmund. 1946. "Sexual Conflict in Marriage," in *Unhappy Marriage and Divorce*. New York: International Universities Press.
8. Bigelow, Newton. 1959. "The Involutional Psychoses," in S. Arieti (ed.), *American Handbook of Psychiatry*. New York: Basic Books, Inc.
9. Cameron, Norman. 1959. "Paranoid Conditions and Paranoia," in S. Arieti (ed.), *American Handbook of Psychiatry*. New York: Basic Books, Inc.
10. Deutsch, Helene. 1944. *The Psychology of Women*, Vol. I, Chapter 5. New York: Grune and Stratton.
11. Eisenstein, Victor. 1956. "Sexual Problems in Marriage," in Victor W. Eisenstein (ed.), *Neurotic Interaction in Marriage*. New York: Basic Books, Inc.
12. Ellis, Havelock. 1936. *Studies in the Psychology of Sex*, Vol. III. New York: Random House.
13. Fenichel, Otto. 1953. "Defense Against Anxiety, Particularly by Libidinization," in *The Collected Papers of Otto Fenichel*, First Series, 27. New York; W. W. Norton & Co.
14. Freud, Sigmund. 1930. *Civilization and Its Discontents*, Joan Riviere (trans.), The International Psycho-Analytical Library, No. 17. London: Hogarth Press.
15. ———. 1950. "The Most Prevalent Forms of Degradation in Erotic Life" (1912), in "Contributions to the Psychology of Love," in *Collected Papers*, Vol. IV. London: Hogarth Press.
16. ———. 1933. *New Introductory Lectures on Psychoanalysis*, W. G. H. Sprott (trans.). London: Hogarth Press.
17. ———. 1905. *Three Essays on Sexuality* in *The Standard Edition of the Complete Psychological Works of Sigmund Freud*, James Strachey (ed.). The Hogarth Press, London, 1953.
18. Greenacre, Phyllis. 1952. "Special Problems of Early Female Sexual Development," in *Trauma, Growth and Personality*. New York: W. W. Norton Co.
19. Gibbs, F. A. and E. L. Gibbs. 1952. *Atlas of Electroencephalography:* Vol. 2, *Epilepsy*. Cambridge: Addison-Wesley Press, Inc.
20. Glueck, Bernard, Sr. Spring, 1960. "Sex Offenses: A Clinical Approach," *Law and Contemporary Problems*, 25(2):270-91.
21. Hill, D. and D. Watterson. 1942. "Electroencephalographic Studies of Psychopathic Personalities," *J. Neurol. Neurosurg. Psychiat.*, 5:47-65.
22. Jung, C. G. 1923. *Psychological Types*. New York: Harcourt, Brace and Company.

23. Krafft-Ebing, Richard. 1931. *Psychopathia Sexualis.* New York: Physicians and Surgeons Book Company.

24. Kurland, Howard D., Charles T. Yeager, and Ransom J. Arthur. 1963. "Psychophysiologic Aspects of Severe Behavior Disorders," *Arch. Gen. Psychiat.*(Chic.), 8(6):599-604.

25. Mackay, Charles. 1841. *Memoirs of Extraordinary Popular Delusions.* London: Richard Bentley.

26. Marmor, Judd. May-June, 1954. "Some Considerations Concerning Orgasm in the Female," *Psychosom. Med.,* 16(3):241-45.

27. Michaels, Joseph J. 1959. "Character Structure and Character Disorders," in S. Arieti (ed.), *American Handbook of Psychiatry.* New York: Basic Books, Inc.

28. Sade, Marquis de. 1791. *Justine or the Misfortunes of Virtue,* Collection "Le Ballet des Muses," Paris.

29. Spencer, Herbert. 1855. *Principles of Psychology,* Part IV, Chapter VIII.

30. Stekel, Wilhelm. 1930. *Sexual Aberrations.* 2 Vols. London: John Lane, The Bodley Head, Ltd.

31. Trethowan, W. H. May, 1963. "The Demonopathology of Impotence," *Brit. J. Psychiat.,* 109:341-47.

32. Von Sacher-Masoch von Lemberg, Leopold. 1947. *Venus in Furs.* New York: Sylvan Press.

Marital Stress in

Psychosomatic Disorders

Eric D. Wittkower, M.D.
Eva P. Lester, M.D.

The Concept of Psychosomatic Illness

Recent statistics in the U.S.A. and elsewhere indicate that, while the mortality rate has decreased, the general morbidity of the population has not been reduced appreciably. That is, the frequency of occurrence of disease in man has changed but slowly over the past decades. During this time, however, the *concept* of disease has undergone fundamental changes. The old concepts, viewing disease solely as the result of damage inflicted on the various body organs by microorganisms or physical agents, have been discarded. It is now accepted that disease in man is a complex phenomenon resulting from his unsuccessful attempt to adapt to his physical and psycho-social environment. Man reacts both to damaging forces from his biological milieu and to threats or dangers relevant to his relationships with other people. These latter dangers, whether real or symbolic, are extremely significant to man's adaptive efforts within his highly organized social system.

Chapman, Hinkle, and Wolff [3] have recently stated: "Disease is the end result of so many interacting factors that the concept of the 'cause' of disease in a specific instance becomes almost unmanageable. Inappropriate adaptive responses mediated through the central nervous system are implicated to some degree in diseases of many categories including infectious, degenerative, neoplastic, and psychiatric. Bodily illness on the one hand, and disturbances of mood, thought, and behavior on the other, are best seen not as causally related but as being a component of the individual's total response to his internal and external environment." Engel [7] writes along similar lines: "No linear concept of etiology is appropriate, but that rather the pathogenesis of disease involves a series of negative and positive feedbacks with multiple simultaneous and sequential changes potentially affecting any system of the body." Pavlov demonstrated that, in the living animal, all part functions are under the influence of central integrative action; his and Cannon's studies established the basis for the physiology of emotions. Physiological changes accompanying the various emotions probably occur in most, if not all, organ systems including the central nervous system. H. Wolff [18] and his associates have shown that marked functional changes may occur in any of the mucous membranes of the body during or after periods perceived by the individual as threatening. Thus vasodilatation, edema, erosion, diapedesis, hemorrhage, increased friability of tissue, and lowered pain threshold were observed in the mucous membrane of the nose, upper airways, eyes, stomach, colon, bladder, and vagina during experimentally induced stress. Furthermore, it was demonstrated that the cardiovascular and renal systems as well as the skin and skeleto-muscular systems show functional involvement in emotional situations. The alarm response, or preparation for action, has been shown to evoke pressor responses, to increase cardiac output, and to reduce visceral circulation.[11] Similarly, effective renal blood flow may be reduced 40 to 50 per cent during stress. Studies of essential hypertension indicated that mounting blood pressure and vascular disease are associated with increased psycho-social stresses in the life of the individual patient. Migraine, hypertension, syncope, cardiac arrythmias, and neurocirculatory asthenia have been the focus of extensive studies from a similar standpoint. Physiological changes in the skin resulting from various emotional states involve all functions of this important organ.[16, 17] Itching and abnormal skin sensation often have a marked emotional component. Cormia [4] has provided evidence that psychic trauma reduces the itch threshold in a given individual and that under specific emotional stress the wheal and flare produced by intradermal injection of histamine is larger and the ensuing itching more severe and prolonged. Extreme dilatation of both arterioles and minute vessels, i.e., the cutaneous changes associated with urticaria, were experimentally produced in humans placed in various stress situations. Similarly seborrhea (that is, excessive sebum secretion), as well as excessive sweating, were induced by experimental introduction of stress stimuli. In addition it was shown that analogous to the blush and flush of everyday life, pathological reddening of the skin, e.g. rosacea, is based on emotionally determined vasodilatations in the skin. The skeleto-muscular system also participates in the physiological expression of emotional states and the adaptive functions of the individual. Basic emotions such as fear and anger are accompanied by postural changes. The increased muscular tension associated with defensive or aggressive behavioral patterns may, if prolonged or exaggerated, produce pathologic conditions in the system.

As implied above, no organ or part of the body is immune from possible emotional response or inappropriate adaptive reactivity to situations of real or imagined threat. Discussing the underlying neurophysiological mechanisms, H. Wolff [18] states: "Despite undue popular emphasis on the role of the autonomous nervous system, the pathological reactions here described are not due solely to its dysfunction, its neurohumoral agents, or its diencephalic endocrine connections. In deed, the somatic nervous system, including both afferent and efferent pathways, is most importantly implicated. Dominant in the integration of all these reaction patterns are the cerebral hemispheres. However, it is erroneous to infer that any one specific area of the cerebral cortex is specifically related to one or another particular pattern or that only the cerebral cortex is implicated. Indeed, for these integrations, cortical, subcortical, and brain-stem aggregates are all essential."

The development of disease, then, should be viewed as a complicated psychobiosocial phenomenon. In this sense every illness is a psychosomatic illness and is determined by genetic, physicochemical, and experiential psychosocial factors. It is the individual's past (his genetic endowment, early life experiences, physical integrity, etc.), his present (improper interactions with his environment), and his future (through the real or symbolic future threat of an actual situation) that enter into the picture. Despite these changes in the concept of illness, however, the term "psychosomatic" is still used in its earlier context, i.e., to describe those clinical conditions in which the occurrence of relevant experiential-emotional factors are more readily observed than in others. The most common of these illnesses are peptic ulcer, ulcerative colitis, bronchial asthma and other allergies, essential hypertension, migraine, diabetes, obesity, and certain dermatoses.

Flanders Dunbar,[6] Wittkower,[16, 17] Alexander,[2] Weiss,[15] Mirsky,[12] and many others have extensively studied the emotional factors implicated in these illnesses. The personality of the patients, their psychological make-up and their specific conflictual situations were thoroughly investigated. Deviant bodily functions have been linked with specific unconscious conflict-states. It has been much debated to what extent psychosomatic illness can be understood as an affect concomitant, affect equivalent, or as a pregenital conversion.

The relevance of intrafamilial conflictual situations to the etiology of psychosomatic illness has, of course, been stressed by all writers on the subject but little has been written specifically on the effect of marital stress. Reference may be made in this connection to E. M. Goldberg's book *Family Influences and Psychosomatic Illness.*[9]

Marital Relationships and Marital Stresses

The marital situation has long been recognized as a potential source of stress for the individual. It is only during the last few decades, however, that the marital relationship has been studied and scrutinized by behavioral and medical scientists. And it is only recently that marriage or rather the marital relationship has been investigated as an important variable in the development of adaptive failures and illnesses in men and women. Ackerman[1] writes: "The interrelations of the individual and family group determine dispositions to illness and health at every stage of growth, infancy, childhood, adolescence, adulthood and old age. In the dimension of time, it is the longitudinal development which lays down the patterns of weakness and vulnerability, but it is the current interaction of the individual and family group which precipitates illness, molds its course, shapes recovery or brings the risk of relapse."

The marital union is admittedly the most challenging of all human relationships. It is within the marital situation that the integrity of the personality structure is fully tested and it is in the marital relationship that the significance of the early object relations is evaluated. It is usually through marriage and parenthood that an individual reaches emotional growth and maturity. A marriage is obviously not the sum of the two personalities that make it up. A marital relationship, by its nature, represents a new distinct level of organization possessing its own characteristics. The personalities of the spouses interact in the marriage situation according to patterns specific to this relationship and emerge through these interactions with new qualities that in turn shape the relationship further. The significance of the organization and its effect on the individual has long been recognized in biology. It is best exemplified in the well-known quotation of Eddington, a physicist whose initial insights into complex systems spurred great interest in the study of biological and social organizations. "We often think that when we have completed our study of 'one' we know all about 'two' because 'two' is 'one and one.' We forget that we have still to make a study of 'and,' that is to say, of 'organization.' "

In our western societies, and especially in the United States, the percentage of the population reported as "married and living with their spouse" is the highest in the history of the census.[13] Thus a proportionally large number of people are experiencing the stresses related to marriage.

The stresses in a given marital situation derive from the personal interactions of the two spouses (as well as parent-child interactions if children are present) and the social interactions between the marital unit and the social group. Understandably there is no clear separation between these two sets of interactions, but they interlock and overlap, and both are subjected to the continuous evolution of culture. During the last fifty years this evolution has been accelerated and the changes that have resulted in the cultural organization have profoundly influenced the character of the family. The "basic and irreducible functions" of the family as described by Talcott Parsons [13] are the socialization of the children and the stabilization of the adult personalities of the society. While these have remained unchanged through the centuries of human civilization, the last five or six decades have witnessed a great deal of change in the morphology and secondary functions of the family and the marital unit. These changes can be summed up as the transition from the large kinship family with its broad aims of promoting the security and the survival of the individual to the present-day nuclear family in which the emphasis is displaced to issues and values of interpersonal relationships. The shift from the numerous but simple and hierarchically organized kinship family, based on centuries of tradition, to the small isolated and precariously integrated family of today, lacking in values and directions, puts a tremendous burden on the marital relationship. Not only do the spouses depend on one another alone for the basic human gratifications, but they must also provide themselves and each other with direction and support to absorb the rapid social changes. Another change that needs to be stressed is that from the previous patriarchal family structure to the present companionship marriage. This shift, i.e., the progressive emancipation of women, has led to an uncertainty of social roles of husband and wife creating new sources of marital discord and resulting in an increase in psychosomatic illness, as J. Halliday [10] has pointed out.

Ackerman [1] points out that "disturbance of marital relationships is characterized by two salient elements: (1) failure of reciprocity of satisfactions and (2) conflict." He further states: "These central features are influenced by several processes: disturbance of empathic union and identification; defective communication; the failure of devices of restitution following an upset in the balance of the relationship; and a failure of complementarity in which the one partner no longer derives from the other satisfaction of needs, support of personal identity, and buttressing of necessary defenses against anxiety." Dicks,[5] in a study of married couples seeking help for various maladjustments, describes marital tensions as related to the following:

1. The importance of role expectations, namely, the fulfillment by each partner of the role of spouse "after the manner of some stereotype or figure in the fantasy world" of the other partner.

2. The power of past identifications. "Marriage and often marriage alone will cause a return in a spouse's own behavior of a re-

pressed bad internal object, which has been identified with in the past, however hard both partners may have attempted to develop a personal ego-ideal or pattern of behavior in denial or contrast to that of the bad internalized figure whom they had banished into the unconscious."

3. The partner as the "other half." Subjects may persecute in their spouses tendencies that originally attracted them, the partner having been chosen as a representation of lost or repressed aspects of the subject's own personality.

4. Dominance-submission conflicts. "Marital disharmony is frequently the expression of dominance-submission conflicts rooted in discrepancy between role and unconscious needs."

5. Failures in sexual functions.

Clinical Observations and Studies

Accepting Ackerman's observations that failure of reciprocity of satisfactions and conflict are the basic elements of marital disturbances, we proceeded to study the marital relationship of "psychosomatic" patients seen at the out-patient department of a large general hospital. Most of these patients suffered from various psychosomatic dermatoses. Patients with obesity, ulcerative colitis, bronchial asthma, and peptic ulcer were also included.

The outstanding finding of this study (which finding is presented here as a clinical observation rather than statistically validated research data) is that, in a large number of the patients examined, ungratified strong dependency needs formed the core of the marital disturbance. In all these patients we found overwhelming needs for being mothered, being taken care of and being protected. All patients had histories of severe affective deprivations and object losses in their early years and a life-long yearning for total unconditional love. Their personality make-up was indeed very similar to the infantile personality as described by J. Ruesch in his profile of the psychosomatic patient.[14] The marital partner in all of them represented a substitute for the idealized parent. Entering marriage with the unconscious expectation of a parent-child relationship, the marital "bliss" lasted only for a very short time and marital disharmony developed with disappointment, frustrations, and confrontation of reality. The onset and/or exacerbation of the psychosomatic illness was always precipitated with almost mathematical certainty by rejection, desertion, or withdrawal of the partner's love. The following two cases illustrate the dynamics, the psychosomatic interactions, and crucial significance of the marital relationship in the course of an illness.

1. The patient, Mrs. V. B., twenty-eight years old, mother of one child, was referred to the psychosomatic skin clinic because of atopic dermatitis resistant to standard treatment. The patient was described by the interviewing psychiatrist as a tense but agreeable, communicative, and eager-to-please young woman. "Funny thing about my skin. I had this very bad when I was a baby.

"Then a little on my arm until I was ten years old. Then my skin was OK for nine years. At nineteen I got married and the rash came back on my arms. Then I had trouble with my husband and it spread on my neck and face." (What kind of trouble?) "All kinds of trouble. He was going out with other women. Money trouble. He spent all his money in the taverns and we were starving. I tried everything. I tried to be soft with him, then I tried to be hard. Nothing helped."

The atopic dermatitis in this patient, as is often the case, had a familial character, her father and brother having had the same illness in varying degree. The brother, who was also a patient at the psychosomatic skin clinic, suffered from bronchial asthma as well. The father's sister was suffering from eczema and diabetes. The patient was the middle one of three children. She described her childhood as an endless series of frustrations, deprivations, fears, and punishments. She was never able to please her forbidding and rejecting mother. "She never praised us, never encouraged us to do anything. She was always saying how good other children were. I was always afraid of her; up to this day I cannot stand up and face her." The father, who died of leukemia at middle age, was a quiet man who "made little trouble" but gave no support to his children. He suffered from a severe depression that lasted on and off for about fifteen years. During this time he was once admitted to a mental hospital and was treated with electroconvulsive treatment.

The patient attended school up to the eighth grade. "I couldn't learn a thing. I had a block in my mind. I just couldn't bring myself to say anything. I thought I was stupid, everybody else was intelligent except me. Now I see I was not stupid but I was so emotional." She knew her husband for about two years before marriage. "I knew he was drinking but I did not care then. He was so good to me." The atopic rash appeared on the arms shortly after the wedding, but during the first two years of marriage it was not extensive and the itching was moderate. "Then everything changed. My husband started making more money and changed his way of life. He started going out with girls and was drinking again. I felt awful but I didn't say anything at first. I felt my pride was hurt. The rash spread on my face and my neck. I couldn't go to bed with my husband anymore. I felt ugly, terribly wounded. Maybe that had to do with his going out with other women." The patient became depressed, had suicidal ruminations, and was retarded. Her depression stirred some guilt feelings in the husband who, for a while, returned to her. For a period the situation was peaceful and the patient's skin cleared up again. She became pregnant and gave birth to a girl. The arrival of the child estranged the spouses again. For both it represented loss of gratification from each other. The husband turned again to his drinking and his women friends. The patient, restricted by her motherhood, felt again rejected. She made an attempt to return to her mother but was rebuffed by her. She then gave her child to foster parents and went out to work. There was a second short period of reconciliation with the husband. The child was taken back but proved to be a source of anxiety and guilt for the mother as she had by then developed serious behavioral problems. As soon as these two people were faced with any difficulty in their marital-parental roles, the marital situation would rapidly deteriorate and the two would draw apart. As a result the wife's skin condition spread and became active while the husband's social behavior became disorganized. Progressively this man entered into criminal activity that culminated in his arrest and being sentenced to a federal penitentiary. The wife obtained a welfare allowance as the mother of a young child without marital support and at the time of examination she was living alone with her daughter.

2. Mrs. Y. L., age forty-two. A housewife and mother of three children, she was referred to the psychosomatic skin clinic with a

generalized psoriatic rash with seborrheic elements. The rash was highly itchy and resistant to dermatological treatment. Besides the skin condition the patient presented various other somatic disorders that the attending physician had described in the past as psychogenic in origin. She was suffering from periodic attacks of bronchial asthma, vomiting and diarrhea, obesity, and anogenital pruritus. The examining psychiatrist described the patient as follows: "A short, obese woman, sloppy and careless in her appearance, looking about her stated age. Communicative but very tense and depressed. Her verbal productions are generally disorganized, fragmented, centered around her own self. Intelligence appears low average."

Similarly, as with the previous patient, this woman's psychosomatic history presents two clusters of illness—one during childhood and the other related to specific stresses in the marital relationship. The patient was the last of six children in a low-income family. Following her birth, and allegedly because of it, the mother suffered from some heart ailment from which she eventually died when the patient was four years old. Only a few months later the patient's father died from cancer. The six children were placed with various relatives and the patient went to live with an uncle who eventually adopted her. Two years later the adoptive mother died and the father delegated the care of the child (now six years old) to a woman who lived in the same apartment house. The patient stayed with this woman for six years, which she considers the most miserable and deprived years of her life. "I was hungry all the time. She put me to sleep on a suitcase. She gave everything to her daughter and nothing to me. She threatened to kill me if I said anything to my father. She was mean and cruel and heartless. I was so afraid of her, I didn't dare to take anything, even what was offered to me." It was at the very beginning of this arrangement that the patient developed severe bronchial asthma. "At twelve I looked like a girl of five. My father put me in a hospital." She was kept several months at the hospital and there she gradually recovered and gained weight. Following discharge the patient went to live with a sympathetic aunt and remained free of symptoms for a long time. Then she decided to work and found a job as a domestic. She lasted only a few months on the job and then developed vomiting and diarrhea and at sixteen she was readmitted to the hospital. "A good doctor took care of me. They built me up with vitamins." After discharge she was advised to go back to her aunt where she stayed until the age of nineteen when she got married.

The husband was a young plumber of nineteen who had courted her for a couple of months. She become pregnant right away and had three children in three consecutive years. During a fourth pregnancy the patient miscarried. Following this she developed an ovarian tumor and had a bilateral ovariectomy. "When I returned home from the hospital my husband announced that since I could not have babies anymore he saw no use sleeping with me. He called me an empty box. He started visiting my girl friend and she became his mistress." For the last eighteen years the patient has had no sexual relations with her husband. During these years she has been free of somatic symptoms for only very short periods of time. The skin disorder first appeared eight years ago at a time when the husband's business was going poorly and the patient and her children were materially deprived. The psoriasis started as a diffuse maculo-papular itchy rash over the whole body. The patient was admitted to the hospital for one month and was discharged improved. Shortly after discharge the rash reappeared. The recent exacerbation, for which the patient was referred to the psychosomatic skin clinic, was related to the approaching wedding of the patient's oldest daughter. "I know I have no reason to be unhappy now, but I will miss my daughter." At the time of the examination the rash was so itchy that the patient could rest and sleep only under heavy sedation. In addition to the skin condition she complained of frequent vomiting and diarrhea. "If I am nervous when I eat I throw up all my food. I can't keep it. If I don't throw up I have diarrhea."

Thus, in this woman, we see reactivation of psychosomatic illnesses that had existed in early life (bronchial asthma, obesity, G.I. symptoms), as well as development of new ones related predominantly to the lack of gratification of dependency needs in the marital relationship.

Although both these patients had a rather unusual early life, they are presented here to highlight the significance of mutual satisfaction of needs in the maintenance of marital homeostasis and the relevance of frustration of basic needs to the development, recurrence, and exacerbation of psychosomatic illness in one of the partners. Both of these women were looking for a parent substitute in their husbands, seeking the loving parent who was so sorely missing in their early childhood. The relationship with the husband was modelled on the parent-child prototype. The fact that both were unable to make a more appropriate parent-husband choice reveals the inadequacy of their reality testing.

However, it is not only the failure to gratify dependency needs that causes marital disharmony and reactivation of psychosomatic illness. In our study we observed that unresolved neurotic conflicts in psychosomatic patients may become reactivated in the course of marital disequilibrium and thus precipitate "psychosomatic" illness in the predisposed individual. It was observed that some of these neurotic patients presented a higher organization of psychic systems than the previously described group. Nonetheless, marital disharmony in these cases could also reach peaks of disorganization of the relationship and consequently provoke affective disturbances and psychosomatic conditions. In other words, although these patients had achieved a certain level of psychological maturity, when exposed to the vicissitudes of their marital relationship, their latent conflicts were reactivated and disintegrating situations emerged. The following two cases illustrated this point.

3. Mrs. E. C., age fifty-six, housewife, suffering from seborrheic dermatitis with pronounced itching. The rash was localized on her scalp, under her breasts, in the axillae, and in the pubic area. Despite local treatment no relief had been effected so the patient was referred for psychiatric evaluation. She was described as a short, obese, grey-haired, middle-aged woman, neat in appearance and pleasant in manner but tense and depressed.

This patient had been having seborrhea of the scalp for a number of years. The onset was insidious and the patient could not associate the beginning of the illness with important experiential-emotional happenings. However, she stated, over the last three or four months there had been a sudden exacerbation and spreading of the seborrhea, and this she was able to associate to her "bad nerves" over the past several months. During this time the patient was taking care of an eighty-four-year-old friend following the death of his wife. "I couldn't leave the poor old thing alone. I had to take him home and care for him the best I could." The old man was senile, had marked loss of memory, was often disoriented, unclean, and childish. He used to wander aimlessly in the streets, to forget his belongings here and there, and to take things from the stores. On a few occasions he defecated on the floor of the patient's living room and in the bathroom sink. Once he threw his feces out of the window onto the street. "I was trying so hard to hide this from my husband. He didn't approve of my doing so much for the old gentleman, but what else could I do? He said I should let his relatives take care of him but they were not interested." Finally the husband prevailed on the patient, and the old man was admitted to a Veterans Hospital. The patient's charitable activities, however, did not end. She belonged to a church organization that visited invalid old people in their homes. "I make my calls between meals. I visit four or five people a day." Besides her "old people" the patient was taking care of a young couple. "They are both very young and they cannot take care of themselves. They were kicked out of their room because they didn't pay their rent. I give them a good meal a day and try to get some clothes for them. I can't take them home because of my husband but I see to it that they don't starve." The husband objected vigorously to the activities of his wife and had tried to restrict her either by appealing to her reason or reducing her allowance. Neither measure however had any result. Lately they have had many arguments and fights on the subject. It is these arguments, she claimed, that made her "nervous" and have a bad effect on her skin. She stated that under normal circumstances she is not a nervous person and had never considered herself as such.

The patient was born in England, the youngest of five in the family of a low-income farmer. She stated that her early life on the farm was a happy and free one and that she has warm memories up to the age of eight when her mother died. She was then sent to a maternal uncle living in the city to study music. Living with the uncle's family was an ordeal for the patient, mainly because of the fierce competition with the uncle's daughter who had everything the patient thought she was deprived of, such as nice clothes, toys, more opportunities to go out, adulation from her parents, etc. The patient stayed with the uncle for about four years and eventually returned to the farm. Upon completion of her school she worked as a nurse's aid. "I wanted so much to become a nurse. I always liked to take care of sick people." At twenty she married a local boy and soon after marriage they emigrated to Canada. The patient brought up five children through hardships, poverty, deprivations, and sickness, with strength and competence. Her evaluation of the husband was fraught with marked ambivalence. First she said he is a wonderful man. Then she recalled how he used to drink and have a good time while she had to cope with five small children. Despite the patient's ambivalence, however, the marital relationship was not in jeopardy as long as the patient was able to channel her boundless, aggressive energy within the family and to exercise her numerous reaction formations in the service of her husband and children. When the time came for the children to marry and leave the family home, and for the husband to attain some maturity and achieve independence from his wife, the patient turned her energy and attentions to her church's old and needy. Her husband and children did not reject her as had happened to the previous patient. They simply ceased to demand as much care, attention, and sacrifice as they did during the early years of the marriage. The patient was thus compelled to turn to other love objects. The husband, either from jealousy or because of simple common sense, objected to this unending martyrdom of his wife which kept her away from her house in a whirl of charitable activities. The patient's angry feeling at the husband's objections stirred hostility and aggressive impulses that made the patient "nervous." Reinforcement of her reaction formations and greater sacrifices brought up more antagonism and resistance from the husband. A conflict situation was created that acted as a stressful stimulus for the patient. The development of the skin condition indicated the inappropriate adaptation of the patient to this inordinate life situation.

4. The case of a thirty-eight-year-old man with ulcerative colitis illustrates a similar situation. Mr. H. L. was referred for psychiatric investigation because of attacks of colitis that recurred each time his wife gave birth to a child.

This man had been born on a farm in central Europe. He gave little information about his early life but it appeared to have been sheltered and restricted. At the war's end the family was dislocated and the patient's adolescent years were marked by external instability and turmoil. In his early twenties the patient escaped to West Germany alone and spent several years as a farm worker, moving from one place to another. Eventually he emigrated to Canada and for some time he continued this type of "carefree" existence. His subsequent marriage did not create problems at first, as the wife allowed or rather encouraged the patient in his adolescent fantasies and narcissistic pursuits. However, when she became pregnant things changed. The wife developed some "kidney problems" and with the arrival of the baby and "nobody but me to help" he developed Asian flu and subsequent bowel symptoms. This was the onset of the ulcerative colitis. The patient attributed his illness to the "heavy responsibility" he felt at work and the feeling he was the only one his wife and baby could depend on. Besides, he disliked children as "they got in the way—everything is always in a mess when they are around." As soon as the wife regained strength and the patient was "advised" to change to an easier job, his situation improved and the symptoms subsided. The birth of the second and third child, however, produced a predictable relapse.

This man showed a clear-cut picture of onset and exacerbation of ulcerative colitis in response to the arrival of children who serve initially to interfere with the care and attention he requires from his wife and later to interfere with his anal need for orderliness and systematization. The marriage, for him, represents only a step further from his carefree adolescent existence. The presence of the wife is tolerated only as long as she is a companion and a helpful partner for the patient's realization of his own yearnings. When the marriage, through the arrival of children, put demands on the patient, the situation became different. The patient was faced with the responsibility of being not the companion of a young woman but the husband and father of a mother and children. He was faced with the end of his self-centered existence. His illness, in a way, represents a maladaptive compromise in a conflict situation that the patient and his wife were not able to resolve more successfully. The meaning of the diarrhea is a regression to a pre-responsible stage. This man conveys by his symptoms that he identifies himself with the incontinent babies and envies them for the maternal care which they receive.

The four cases presented above demonstrate *that, why,* and *how* marital discord, in predisposed individuals, precipitates and/or aggravates psychosomatic illness. In the majority of cases, of course, more than one factor (neurotic conflict, unconscious expectations, ungratified dependency needs, failure of complementarity, role reversal, cultural clashes, etc.) may be involved in the clash of marital partners. A corollary of what has been presented is that, in the treatment of patients suffering from psychosomatic illness, treatment of the disease without due regard to the patient who suffers from it is of little avail and that, in particular, problems of interaction in marriage deserve special attention.

Not infrequently patients are unaware of the causal relationship between their stressful experiences and their somatic manifestations. In these cases demonstration of such a connection by and ventilation of problems to an understanding physician may have a beneficial effect on the patient's marital and physical condition. In others, the physician may have to spend considerable time interviewing the spouses separately, or together in joint sessions, in order to develop insight into their marital problems. In still others, expert advice may be required and psychiatric treatment, not necessarily only of the marital partner suffering from the psychosomatic illness, may be indicated. Should psychiatric treatment of the sufferer from the psychosomatic illness be decided upon, close cooperation between psychiatrist and physician is essential.

Finally, brief mention may be made of the secondary disturbing effects of psychosomatic illness, and for that matter of any illness, on marital relationships. In other words, a circular reaction may develop within which marital stress creates somatic illness and this, in turn, creates marital stress or at least feeds it. Our first patient mentioned how her disfiguring and itchy rash interfered with her sexual contact with her husband. Disfiguring symptoms or symptoms interfering greatly with the healthy partner's privacy or offending his or her sensitivity could create a great deal of marital stress. These self-perpetuating situations, if neglected for long may lead to the dissolution of the marriage and need, obviously, attention by the treating physician.

References

1. Ackerman, N. W. 1958. *The Psychodynamics of Family Life.* New York: Basic Books, Inc.
2. Alexander, F. 1950. *Psychosomatic Medicine.* New York: W. W. Norton & Co.
3. Chapman, L. F., L. E. Hinkle, and H. G. Wolff. Sept., 1960. "Human Ecology: Disease and Schizophrenia," *Amer. J. Psychiat.,* 117:193-204.
4. Cormia, F. E. July, 1952, "Experimental Histamine Pruritus: 1. Influence of Physical and Psychological Factors on Threshold Reactivity," *J. Invest. Derm.,* 19:21-34.
5. Dicks, H. V. Sept., 1953. "Clinical Studies in Marriage and the Family: A Symposium on Methods," *Brit. J. Med. Psychol.,* 26:181-221.
6. Dunbar, F. 1953. *Emotions and Bodily Changes.* Rev. ed. New York: Columbia University Press.
7. Engel, G. L. Summer, 1960. "A Unified Concept of Health and Disease," *Perspect. Biol. Med.,* 3:459-85.
8. Fry, W. F. 1962. "The Marital Context of an Anxiety Syndrome," *Family Process,* 1(2):245-52.
9. Goldberg, E. M. 1958. *Family Influences and Psychosomatic Illness.* London: Tavistock Publications.
10. Halliday, J. L. 1948. *Psychosocial Medicine.* New York: W. W. Norton & Co.
11. Ham, G. C. Jan.-Feb., 1962. "Psychosomatic Perspectives: The Cardiovascular System," *Psychosom. Med.,* 24:31-36.
12. Mirsky, I. A. Feb., 1960. *Physiologic, Psychologic and Social Determinants of Psychosomatic Disorders,* Dis. Nerv. Syst. Monograph Supplement, pp. 50-56.
13. Parsons, T., and R. F. Bales. 1955. *Family, Socialization and Interaction Process.* Glencoe, Ill.: The Free Press.
14. Ruesch, J. May-June, 1948. "The Infantile Personality," *Psychosom. Med.,* 10:134-44.
15. Weiss, E., and O. S. English. 1957. *Psychosomatic Medicine.* Philadelphia: W. B. Saunders Co.
16. Wittkower, E. D., and B. Russell. 1953. *Emotional Factors in Skin Disease.* New York: Paul B. Hoeber.

17. ———, and E. P. Lester. 1963. "Emotions and Skin Disease," in H. Lief, V. Lief, and N. Lief (eds.), *The Psychological Basis of Medical Practice.* New York: Paul B. Hoeber.
18. Wolff, H. G. Jan.-Feb., 1962. "A Concept of Disease in Man," *Psychosom. Med.,* 24:25-30.

5

Counseling Help for the
Alcoholic Marriage

John A. Ewing, M.D.

The alcoholic marriage can be fairly easily defined as any marriage in which one or both partners suffer from alcoholism. Alcoholism itself is more difficult to define [10] and thus sometimes difficult to diagnose. Probably the best operational definition is that the alcoholic is someone whose uncontrolled excessive drinking harms himself, his family, and his work and who either cannot realize this fact or can recognize it but cannot do anything about it. This is similar to the definition given by Diethelm [3] and is as satisfactory as any.

This is not the time to venture into a long discussion of alcoholism, its nature, the typical course of the illness, and the various forms of treatment in general. There are excellent textbooks, both technical and popular, on the subject and the interested reader is referred to them. [2, 6, 9, 18]

It is obvious that alcoholism has severe effects upon a marriage in many ways. The relationship between husband and wife may be severely strained and the environment for the children is likely to be a disturbed one. Indeed, psychiatrists see many examples of adults whose present illness seems to be the result of emotional trauma at the hands of an alcoholic father or mother in childhood. Such injury need not only be abuse during drinking spells but may be more subtle things such as the overwhelming fantasy life within the child who sees or hears one or both parents acting in a very uncontrolled way. This may have serious effects on the personality development of the child. Sons of alcoholic fathers often have extreme attitudes about alcohol, either leaning toward teetotalism or toward alcoholism. The daughters of alcoholic men tend to have severe psychoneurotic problems including conversion reactions.

Other marital strains include the financial consequences of the excessive drinking, the loss of work, and the failure to achieve promotions. Sometimes the family may show a consistent downward social sliding. Broken homes and broken marriages are a frequent result of alcoholism and for this reason alone the alcoholic marriage must be the concern of anyone who is interested in marriage counseling and family life.

A Symptom

The days are gone when alcoholism was seen as a moral issue or simply as a form of sin. In the last decade or two it has been presented to lay people and professionals alike as "an illness." Rather than get into this debatable area, I would simply say that for our present purposes it will be sufficient for us to conceive of alcoholism as a *symptom of underlying disabilities* of various sorts.

This leads to the conclusion that behind alcoholism must lie various causes in various combinations. It is possible that there are physical predispositions to alcoholism in the sense of hereditary or acquired constitutional factors. Theories about hormonal, dietary, endocrinological, biochemical, and other disturbances are quite frequently propounded. For the present it is sufficient to say that no such theory has yet been proved. If it is a fact that alcoholic people metabolize alcohol in a different way from those who do not develop alcoholism, this will eventually be demonstrated. I think we should take all such claims in this direction with appropriate scientific caution. The existence of some therapeutic success by no means proves the theory that lies behind a therapeutic plan. For example, some physicians use combinations of vitamins in the belief that there is some, as yet unknown, metabolic alteration. The fact that some success occurs with this treatment should not surprise us when we study the effect of the "powerful placebo"[1] and when we recognize that the enthusiasm of the theorist is often communicated to the patient. Frankly, it seems to me that any form of treatment in which one really believes is going to get *some* good results with *some* cases of alcoholism.

Cultural Factors

A great deal has been said and written about culture in relationship to alcoholism and there is no question that this is important. For example, there are societies in which alcoholism is virtually unknown although the intake of alcoholic beverages may be quite frequent. The traditional Jewish family sees the use of alcoholic beverages as a religious and eating phenomenon.[7] As long as such attitudes are maintained there seems to be a very low tendency to become dependent upon alcohol as an escape from tension. There are many other examples, such as the change in attitudes about and toward alcohol that develops among Italian immigrants. In the United States some gradually move away from Italian patterns of drinking and within a few generations have as much insobriety as those around them.[12]

I have already indicated that the attitudes within the family may be very important in determining the attitudes of the developing child. Certainly, if alcohol is a bogey to be feared and to be talked about in frightening terms this may very well promote later use of alcohol by an anxious and rebellious adolescent or young adult. In a similar way excessive drinking in the family will tend to produce extreme attitudes in those exposed to this. The clinician working with alcoholics often notices that many patients come from homes that included an alcoholic parent or near relative, or in which the attitudes toward alcohol were extremely prohibitive. To me this suggests the importance of exposing our children to attitudes of moderation and of tolerance rather than showing an extreme viewpoint in regard to alcohol.

Personality

There is no "typical alcoholic personality" but psychiatric study tends to show some recurrent pictures. The existence of "oral" tendencies has frequently been corroborated by psychoanalytic investigations.[8, 11] To the physician's even casual scrutiny, some aspects of this may be quite obvious. The alcoholic may display at times an extreme attitude of dependence upon others. However, it is not uncommon for him to have developed quite strong defenses against such dependent, infantile needs so that he may present himself as a very successful, self-made, independent, aggressively-striving individual. Often we may see the deeper layers of his personality only when the defensive layers have been torn away in states of drunkenness and in the initial days of hospitalization for alcoholism.

Historically these male alcoholics have often been the only boy or the youngest child.[16] Frequently, the childhood pattern consisted of being "mamma's boy." A typical history is one of either extreme deprivation or extreme overindulgence, with the latter predominating among the cases I have seen. One often gets the impression that he has not been allowed to face the normal problems of growing up and has not been given the opportunity to experience and master the normal frustrations and privations that line the road to maturity.[20] Certainly as an adult the typical alcoholic shows a very poor toleration of anxiety and has a low threshold for frustration. He tends to be a rather impulsive and self-centered individual but may also be quite self-punishing at times.

When a psychiatrist examines a large number of alcoholic patients he is likely to find certain characteristic personality groupings. These are by no means exclusive each of the other nor are they always outstandingly obvious. However, predominance of such patterns is usually fairly apparent in a majority of alcoholic patients.

Of course, it might be argued that the personality now seen in the alcoholic is the result of his drinking and not the forerunner. There could be some truth in this, for certainly the social degradation in some cases of alcoholism might be expected to produce personality changes that parallel the loss of self-esteem. Such a picture is seen in narcotics addicts who stoop to stealing and prostitution in order to earn the vast sums of money required for their drug supplies.

However, the majority of alcoholic patients are still working and married and may present a fairly stable picture to the outside world between alcoholic bouts. They are not to be confused with the relatively small number of people who congregate in the "Skid Row" districts of major cities.

Psychiatric studies have tended to show that in general personality is relatively fixed after childhood. In other words, there is no very good reason to assume that the alcoholic should show major personality changes between his pre-drinking state and his present condition. In addition, the most careful and critical history-taking usually fails to reveal any clear-cut evidence that personality changes have occurred.

Sherfey,[19] in a study of 161 cases of alcoholism, describes the patients as "individuals with personalities that could not be considered within normal limits." She also states, "In none of these cases did alcoholism exist without previous personality defects antedating the drinking."

Of course, what is required is a careful prospective study of large numbers of people who are scrutinized psychologically and psychiatrically during childhood and adolescence and are then followed into adult life. Comparisons between those who later develop alchoholism and those who do not would reveal if there were any significant personality differences in earlier life. McCord, McCord, and Gudeman [13] have attempted a study that is similar to this plan. Unfortunately the personality study during adolescence was quite superficial. Therefore, at the present time there has not yet been reported a really reliable study of this sort.

A final point that tends to support my belief that the personality one finds in alcoholics is that of a life-long pattern is the continuation of such patterns long after drinking has been given up. In general I think the average alcoholic who gives up drinking simply learns better to accept himself as he really is and to replace the drinking with other types of defenses.

Returning, then, to the statement that certain characteristic personality groupings can be observed, I shall describe three main types centered around three kinds of conflict.

Conflicts

First of all are those whose main conflicts revolve around the struggle between dependent cravings and independent strivings (defenses). The underlying personality is one of extreme immaturity and the defense of the self-made, successful man has already been referred to.

Then there are the patients who have extreme difficulty with self control. Frequently they have a history of rebelliousness and they may show many episodes of rage, especially toward those who foster dependent feelings and attitudes within them. The defense under which such an alcoholic patient tends to hide the angry attitudes is one of being a very charming and pleasant person. Such a defense, of course, is only apparent when he is sober.

A third conflict area involves sexual matters. This man has a poor sexual identification and his concept of himself is unclear. There may be overt homosexual trends but more often than not these are unconscious and hidden. The defense against such conflicts is to be a "he-man," and this of course includes heterosexual promiscuity. It must not be forgotten that in our culture the ability to be a heavy drinker is associated with demonstrating virility and masculinity and this in itself may therefore foster the he-man defense.

Although I have outlined these three groups of conflicts as if they were separate, I must now emphasize that the sexual difficulties and aggressive problems are essentially secondary to the childhood fixations involved in the development of the dependent or "oral" personality. Normal maturation consists of a series of steps and if the personality falters on any one step the capacity to develop normally on the later steps will be impaired. In any alcoholic patient, aspects of all of these conflicts may be apparent as well as other evidences of neurotic and characterologic disturbances. Anyone who wishes to study this in more detail must be referred to appropriate references in psychiatric and psychoanalytic literature.[3, 8, 11]

Alternatives to Alcoholism

Of course all the above personality characteristics are going to affect a marriage if they exist in one or other partner, whether or not alcoholism exists. Alcoholism *can* accompany the above patterns

of personality maldevelopment but is by no means essential. For example, an alternative to fighting against cravings for infantile dependent relationships may be to accept these wishes. Some people do this by a lifetime of chronic illness. Certain psychophysiologic disturbances such as peptic ulcer and obesity are appropriate examples of illnesses associated with such cravings. Other people develop chronic personality disturbances that may, in a sense, protect them from the need to drink excessively.

It seems to me that the major factors determining whether or not alcoholism will develop are to be found in the environment. The first prerequisite is a person with hidden neurotic conflicts such as those just described. If such an individual obtains from alcohol a marked and overwhelming relief from inner tension, anxiety, self-critical feelings, inferiority feelings or self-doubt, there is bound to be a tendency to repeat the experience again and again. Obviously whether or not there is an attempt to use alcohol in such seeking for relief will depend partially upon the attitudes in the family as indicated already. In addition there is the cultural attitude. We live in a culture in which it is considered perfectly normal to "need a drink" after a hard day at the office. Here, alcohol is a panacea, a universal tranquilizer. In contrast, those cultures where drinking is a frequent part of everyday experience produce alcoholism in lesser amounts and in different patterns.

Drinking Behavior

Our patients give us some vital clues about the nature of their conflicts from their drinking behavior and I believe that it is essential for us to study this in every case. Whenever possible the patient's own account of his drinking problem should be taken in considerable detail. This report should be corroborated and enhanced by reports from family and friends as soon as available. Certainly, it is no surprise to find that many an alcoholic who is known as a hell-raiser thinks of himself as a very quiet and well-behaved drinker. The importance of knowing this history is that it tends to point toward the conflict areas. For example, the patient with major conflicts about expressing his extreme dependent infantile wishes may show quite infantile and dependent attitudes toward people when he

is drunk. It is not infrequent for a prior phase of aggression to appear in such people. Such expression of the underlying anger by fighting behavior, including attacking the spouse, is understandable if we realize that aggressive impulses have been kept in check during the preceding days, weeks, or months of sober behavior. The alcoholic who is reported to cry when he gets drunk should be thought of as probably suffering from a depression, and again this is a very useful clue for the management of the patient.

I recently saw an alcoholic man who was described by several observers as becoming much more friendly and pleasant when he was drinking. When sober he was rather critical of others, difficult to get along with, and generally seemed ill at ease. Even his wife admitted that she preferred him drunk to sober in terms of the personality change but she did not like having a drunk person in the home nor did she like the effect on the children or the neighbors. Psychiatric study of this individual revealed that here was a guilty man, beset with self-doubts and criticisms which, when he was sober, he readily attributed to other people. This is the defense mechanism called "projection." He used alcohol to feel less guilty and thus to feel free from pangs of conscience and self-criticism. Indeed, it has been said by several psychiatrists that the superego (an unconscious part of the personality, which can partly be equated with the conscience) is soluble in alcohol! This merely means that for conscience-ridden people the only relief may be when they are drinking.

Some schizophrenic patients or people with borderline psychotic states are reported by others to be "more like normal people" when they are drinking. Indeed, if you should come across a patient who is considered strange or odd or asocial when sober and who only seems to be a "regular fellow" when he is drinking, you should seek psychiatric consultation for him. If the patient basically is suffering from a psychosis, a psychiatrist's diagnosis and guidance are almost essential.

Dynamic Diagnosis

Understanding the drinking behavior leads to a more accurate diagnosis. Instead of simply calling it alcoholism we may now say that there is alcoholism that seems to be related to major conflicts in this area or that. Another very important reason for exploring

the drinking behavior is in the therapeutic work that is to be done with the patient. Alcoholic patients more than most other people tend to remain very isolated from their feelings. In a sense they remain relatively unaware (unconscious) of the everyday kinds of feelings they have in relation to people in their families, work situation, and elsewhere. This partly reflects the strong conscience of such people who act as if they preferred not to be aware of feelings of which they might be ashamed (at least while they are sober). Very frequently one finds in people with alcoholism the personality characteristics called the passive-aggressive personality by psychiatrists.

Typically, these patients will report a lack of appropriate feelings about situations and people that would be quite irritating for most people. For example, in either individual or group therapy it is not unusual to hear that the boss or the wife or the mother-in-law is doing or is expected to do certain things that would be quite irritating to the average individual. When confronted with this possibility, the alcoholic will say in all honesty that he has no feelings about this whatsoever. However, very often within minutes of a precipitating event, such as being confronted by an angry wife or criticized by the boss, the patient will suddenly feel the "I need a drink" sensation. Then, in the behavior which accompanies the bender that follows, out pour the angry feelings about the wife or the boss. Incidentally, a sobering thought for those of us who work with alcoholics is that frequently angry feelings about the physician appear at these times. This may indicate that we failed to recognize some hostility in our own attitudes toward the patient; nevertheless, he detected this although he was not conscious of his reaction at the time. It may also reflect the fact that he has entered into a state of emotional dependence upon the physician that frightens him.

The Marriage Partner

Where alcoholism has existed in one or other partner before the marriage, one must suspect the motives of the prospective spouse. Of course, for some women the marriage becomes a crusade in which she is determined to save this drunken man. While possibly this does occur on occasions, more frequently the attempts are a failure and we must wonder why women marry such people and what kind of

women do so. Those of us who have much experience with alcoholics have ceased being amazed to find women who have been married to a succession of alcoholic men—three, four, and even five times. This cannot be called coincidence!

Sometimes, of course, the alcoholism only becomes apparent after the marriage and here we must remember that the personality features that predisposed to the development of alcoholism were present before. However, it may be that this marriage itself constitutes the trauma that precipitates the use of alcohol as a relief measure. Although divorce and separation are more common in alcoholics than in non-alcoholics, the majority of alcoholic patients are still married. This at least has been my experience with patients who are still struggling to maintain themselves in the community and have not reached the level of "Skid Row."

At the present moment there must be about three million alcoholic marriages in the United States. It is important to realize that these people are not drunken bums but are successful men and women whose future life and happiness depend upon adequate help being given.

When we study the woman who has married the alcoholic, we find certain trends. Often she had an alcoholic father. Typically her mother was the dominating parent and often she had younger brothers to look after. She sees herself as most fulfilling her purpose in life when she is caring for others. In this regard she is not infrequently found in the health professions. (We must recognize that in our work as physicians we are using a socially acceptable defense against expressing more overtly our own hidden dependent cravings.) The alcoholic's wife sees herself as the strong member of the marriage. Often she has marked feelings of rivalry toward males and, this being so, it is no surprise to find that she may glory in his failures.

In our experience with the treatment of the wives of alcoholic males mostly in group psychotherapy, we have repeatedly seen examples of sabotage of the husband's sobriety. There has been consistent resistance to seeing her own part in the drinking episodes.[5]

In quite a significant percentage, the wives of successfully sober alcoholics become depressed.[5, 14] Sometimes this involves reactions of extreme jealousy toward the man's sobriety and one may hear angry remarks about Alcoholics Anonymous. Of course, for some alcoholics

AA does become an all-consuming cult and the wife's reaction is easily understood. We have even seen examples of wives who become more dependent themselves on drinking as their husbands give up alcohol.

An interpretation of the above reactions is that the alcoholic's wife is someone who has been keeping her own dependent wishes in check by taking the role of caring for her husband. For this reason I would say that the wife who remains married to a man for two or more years after her husband's alcoholism has become apparent is in need of treatment herself. The fact that she has stuck with him through these difficult experiences points strongly to the probability that she is obtaining from this relationship some psychological gain. A more "normal" woman would have given up the marriage even if there were children.

Alcoholic Marriages

It is for this reason that I feel that we must emphasize the fact that there are not just alcoholic men, there are alcoholic marriages, and the marriage itself may be the thing which is perpetuating the alcoholism.

From the above discussion several basic conclusions can be reached.

1. The alcoholic must be helped to know himself, to be as aware as possible of the trends, both infantile and adult, that he contains and to be able to accept their existence.

2. The alcoholic must be helped to find *acceptable* dependent relationships, that is, ones of which he need not be ashamed or required to fight against.

3. The alcoholic needs to find acceptable outlets for his anger.

4. The wife of the alcoholic needs to be helped toward the stage where she will have less "need" for her husband to continue as an alcoholic.

5. The wife of the alcoholic needs to learn to understand herself and to accept the existence of her own hidden dependent wishes.

6. The alcoholic's wife needs then herself to find an acceptable dependent relationship and to find new defenses against the more unacceptable aspects of these wishes. For example, instead of having to have a drunken husband who gets looked after periodically, some

of the wives of alcoholics in our experience have taken up nursing or practical nursing or looking after children.

How to achieve some or all of the above aims remains a major concern and will be the aim of our counseling.

The Need for Counseling

The seeking of counseling usually occurs because of financial, legal, or family difficulties. Of course you will come across some cases of "hidden" alcoholism in your everyday medical practice. Pearson [17] points out that such a patient "may complain of various symptoms that are a direct result of excessive drinking, or that are aggravated by it, yet in no way indicate to the physician the extent of his addiction."

The first step must be to make a full and adequate diagnosis. This can only be done by careful history-taking along the lines already outlined. If possible the patient himself should be seen. The spouse should be interviewed and preferably other members of the family including children if they are not mere infants.

In parentheses it might be added at this point that children are practically never unaware of and unaffected by parental drinking. For this reason alone the child needs to be given an opportunity to ventilate his feelings, his anxieties, his hostilities, and his fears about the situation that he has been exposed to. For teenagers the possibility of joining a local group of "Alateens" should be explored. The latter is an offshoot of Alcoholics Anonymous and consists of the teenage children of alcoholics. The support obtained from a group such as this can be very important.

When the parents of the alcoholism sufferer can be interviewed, very often the attitudes that they show openly or in a hidden manner may be quite revealing to the physician as he seeks to understand the background of the patient.

By the time a diagnosis is made the following questions should have been answered: Does alcoholism exist and if so in whom? Does the alcoholic recognize the existence of this and if so is he ready to seek help? Does the spouse also have an alcoholic problem? Does the spouse recognize his or her involvement in the drinking of the other partner? Is the spouse ready to do something about it other than simply giving up the marriage?

When the alcoholic himself is contacted in the initial counseling, it is most important to offer him specific help as soon as possible. This will include the possibilities of hospitalization and medications such as tranquilizers (although these should be given with circumspection and in limited amounts, otherwise they may merely replace the alcohol). For some patients disulfiram (Antabuse) may be a desirable drug but it is never a treatment in itself and should only be used if it is part of a total treatment plan that includes frequent contacts between physician and patient and general psychotherapeutic exploration of the patient's life. Alcoholics Anonymous is an excellent source of help for many alcoholics and an attempt should be made to suggest this. Some people reject it because it threatens some of their defenses of independence, but in the long run the capacity to accept belonging to a group such as AA can be crucial in the achievement of sobriety.

Talking to Patients

At this point I want to make some brief comments about talking to patients who seek marriage counseling with particular reference to the alcoholic. Of course a physical examination is essential and should be performed as soon after the first contact as possible, preferably at the time of the first visit. Even as the examination is conducted the relationship between you and the patient is being established for better or for worse. For this reason it is vital to watch one's own reactions to the patient, how one talks to him, reassures him, responds to his questions, and so on.[4] Of course, we would not be physicians if we did not tend to like people, but in the case of the alcoholic our own past experience and our own repugnance may provoke attitudes that we would rarely show toward patients with some other kind of illness. We must watch for this and carefully control it.

In talking with the alcoholic patient, it is most important to get out from behind the desk and to sit down comfortably with him in the same kind of way that one might chat with a friend. This is not to recommend an unnaturally "friendly" approach. It is not our purpose to get "buddy buddy" with the patient, however two people seated comfortably in arm chairs do talk on a more relaxed and confidential plane than is usually accomplished in the typical "medical interview" setting.

Even before sitting down to talk with him, it may be necessary to give him something. This is particularly true if he has recently been drinking and still is in a shaky condition. Even a small dose of some tranquilizer with which you are familiar, given with a smile and some orange juce, will work wonders. Practically all alcoholics smoke (perhaps a reflection of their "oral" personality) and you should put an ash tray handy for him and be prepared to help him with lights. Even if you feel strongly about smoking and its carcinogenic properties I doubt if you should ask an alcoholic patient to give that up as well as the bottle!

Even asking him to give up the bottle is not a request that we should make. He has been asked to quit drinking by many other people before he reached us and there is only one person who can ask him to quit legitimately. This is, of course, himself! Some statements to this effect can certainly be made to an alcoholic patient early in our contacts with him. Of course you are concerned about his physical condition but it is important to show him that you are not just worried about his liver but you are worried about his total situation in all its respects. Your task is to tell him that the drinking problem that he clearly has is a medical concern and you wish to make it your concern about him.

All alcoholics tend to use denial and you must avoid falling into the trap. Tell him that even if he cannot yet admit his powerlessness to handle alcohol you want him to know of your availability when he is ready. Your experience with other people has shown that this kind of illness does require a great deal of help from other people. The fact that the patient asserts, "I can lick it on my own, Doc," impresses you with his determination but does not prevent you from emphasizing your willingness to help, anyway.

If this particular patient is not going to require a visit to the hospital· you might well decide to invest a few minutes of your time each day for several days. This is especially true if he is to get tranquilizers, as you can then ask him to come in each day to have you vary the amount. Typically, you will be aiming at tapering off as soon as reasonably possible. On the other hand, you should freely prescribe dietary supplements, tasty vitamin preparations, and the like. It is unreasonable to expect a patient to promise to stay sober from one week until the next. However, if he says he really wants to try but does not know if he can make it, you may help by asking him if he thinks he can make it until tomorrow. If he agrees that this would be much less difficult, then you should offer to see him tomorrow even if only for a five-minute visit. Gradually the length of time between visits can be lengthened. Do not forget to charge a realistic fee for each visit. It will help his self-esteem to pay you an amount he can afford, and he knows it is cheaper than drinking!

Continued Treatment

Offering some kind of continued relationship will frequently be the most vital single thing that the physician can do. Whether this is called marriage counseling or psychotherapy makes little difference. For the physician who has several alcoholics in his practice, group psychotherapy is the treatment of choice. An hour and a half spent weekly with a group of several alcoholic patients can be very rewarding. The doctor must learn to listen more than he talks but he will learn much as he listens.

Many states have alcoholic treatment centers of one sort or another. These can be utilized either to help patients to get off alcohol or, more important, to make an initial inventory of their own lives and to get them away from the home situation so that a more objective self-examination can take place. As more and more mental health centers and clinics are opened throughout the nation, these will often be a suitable place for referral of alcoholics seeking help. However, it is crucial for the alcoholic to be referred in a meaningful and positive way and not simply in order to get him out of the way.

Nearly all physicians should be capable of dealing with alcoholic patients. Anyone who has been interested enough to read this chapter this far has the appropriate attitudes. However, for the physician who has very strong views about drinking and cannot see alcoholism as an illness, who has strong attitudes about abstinence, or who simply feels that he cannot be bothered with alcoholics, at the very least let me appeal to him—please refer the patient in a positive and meaningful way rather than simply as a means of getting rid of him! There never will be enough psychiatrists to take care of alcoholics and in any case I am not sure that they are the best people to do it. Do not threaten your patient with a psychiatrist. If you feel a consultation would be helpful, tell the patient you think so.

For the alcoholic what really is required is an attitude of acceptance. Anyone who is attempting to work with him must be non-critical and must be willing to lead him in an encouraging way to look at his drinking behavior. Regular meetings should be set up and these need not be very time-consuming. They should not take the form of a question-and-answer session or being exposed to a preachy kind of attitude. In the long run the physician who chooses to work with alcoholics will find that it is very gratifying to meet with such patients in a group. The group technique in itself tends to dilute the extreme dependent feelings that may come up in the individual patient-doctor relationship and may also prevent the appearance of sexual fantasies in the patient which might be difficult for him to handle.

Psychotherapeutic Principles

Whether in group treatment or individual sessions, there are some basic principles that should be kept in mind. We want the patient to recognize as far as possible the effects of his drinking and especially his drinking behavior upon himself and those around him. In particular, we want him to recognize that what he does when drinking can be seen as "a message." In other words, we want him to begin to be aware that he has used his drinking to express feelings that otherwise were bottled up inside of him. At the same time we must recognize the sequential occurrence of his drinking and help him to see the patterns, especially the repetitive ones. For example if he drinks at the weekends when he is around the home, perhaps he needs to recognize his reactions to his wife as being a crucial factor in his drinking. If he is a periodic drinker who gets along fine as long as he is busy and active but gradually becomes tense and irritable when he has less to do, finally getting drunk and violent, perhaps he needs to recognize the importance for him of work. Such a patient probably handles a great many angry feelings in his working relationships without too much trouble being caused. If, however, he is not able to use this defense of "sublimation" the tensions building up within him may become overwhelming.

Careful history-taking may reveal that another patient has always gotten drunk in relationship to things that stirred up rivalrous feelings. We may find that this is related to his feelings about a brother.

Some patients get drunk whenever things happen to remind them (unconsciously) of their infantile cravings. When the wife gets pregnant, a child is sick, or even if he simply sees a picture of a baby nursing at the breast, the overwhelming feelings may take control of him.

I cannot possibly give examples of all the kinds of things we are looking for. What we must do is to keep our eyes and ears open and help the patient to do the same. If we can help him to develop a truly investigative and scrutinizing attitude about himself, we shall enable him to recognize the fact that drinking does not come "out of the blue" but is a reaction to circumstances in his immediate life.

In both group and individual therapy, it is most important not to forget the current day-by-day life. The patient should not be directly questioned about these things but should be encouraged to talk about whatever is on his mind. Everyday things at home, at work, or even in the group discussions or with the individual doctor are important and should be considered. Particularly we should watch for evidence of his tendency to deny feelings. If we are late for our appointment, we should point out that many people would be angry and disappointed with us. If we are going on vacation and he denies any feelings about this, we should emphasize our expectation that he would be anxious and even feel deserted. Incidentally, at such a time we would probably want to arrange for someone else to be available in our stead.

The idea generally is to encourage the patient to expect to find emotions in himself which are typical of human beings and to encourage him to explore them, express them, and examine them freely in an atmosphere of mutual interest in which there are no penalties for expressing feelings and it is understood that the penalty for *not* exploring one's feelings may be the recurrence of the craving for "just one little drink."

When the Alcoholic Does Not Come

If the request for counseling comes only from the sober spouse and the alcoholic refuses to visit the physician, it still remains possible to do something useful. In the first place the spouse should be put in touch with a source of appropriate literature for her own reading and for leaving casually around the house. I can think of several cases where finding the correct pamphlet at the correct time has led an alcoholic to seek help which he had refused on the exhortation of his wife. It is most important that the spouse of the alcoholic or any other family member has reliable objective information about alcoholism. It is for these people in particular that the theme that alcoholism is an illness has done the most good.

Now I want to describe what I call the *indirect treatment of alcoholism*. Although this has been something we have experimented with for less than a decade, it has proven itself useful again and again. In this plan we persuade the non-alcoholic spouse to participate in a program which, we tell him or her, offers a real prospect of change in the alcoholic.

Regular appointments are set up for the spouse to talk with a physician, a psychiatrist, a social worker, or other professional person. Group meetings for several such spouses at one time are an excellent arrangement. What is called for is a careful and repeated scrutiny of the spouse herself in terms of her personality, what led to her being the kind of person she is, and so on. In particular she must be encouraged to see the kind of relationship she has with her husband and to recognize the ways in which she may be fostering his dependency. In many cases she can be persuaded to be more permissive about her husband's drinking. I know of several instances in which the wife has sufficiently changed her attitude about her husband's drinking so that she has no longer poured out liquor she has found but has left it in full view. In some cases this has sufficiently conveyed to the alcoholic the existence of real change in his spouse and he has joined Alcoholics Anonymous within days or even hours. As we work with the alcoholic's spouse, we encourage her to bring about more direct communication in the marriage of the feelings that occur in one or the other partner of any marriage. We also encourage her to be more accepting of his aggressive feelings when he is sober and more accepting of the sober periods themselves.

All of these things can be accomplished more rapidly when a group of women who have the common problem of the alcoholic's spouse are meeting together with a skilled counselor. The existence of common problems and the ability to exchange solutions can be very helpful and indeed the group membership itself is a way whereby the woman is helped to be more aware of her own dependent wishes.

Until such indirect treatment has been attempted the physician is making a serious mistake if he merely advises breakup of the alcoholic marriage. Repeatedly in our experience such unilateral "treatment" of the non-alcoholic spouse has been associated with real changes in the alcoholic. Not only may the drinking pattern itself be changed even to the extent of total sobriety in some cases, but the wife's scrutiny of herself has quite often led to a competitiveness in the alcoholic who has then started seeking a therapist or a group therapy situation for himself. Even if this does not happen, the spouse often learns to take a much more relaxed view of her husband's alcoholism and as she does this it loses its previous impact on the marriage. Obviously, if his drinking no longer seems to disturb her and if he drank as an aggressive maneuver, one of the reasons for continued drinking has gone.

Another group of activities comes under the heading of manipulation. In particular it is important to try to define the dependent relationships that exist and to try to interrupt these. This will be particularly so for the alcoholic who is involved with a woman who is protecting him from the consequences of his drinking. Not infrequently we will find that this is his mother, an aunt, or some other female relative. If she can be persuaded to remove herself from the situation for some months the alcoholic will see himself in a more naked and objective state. In one such case persuading the wealthy and protective mother of a very dependent alcoholic to go on a world cruise led to his presenting himself for therapy within a few months!

Therapeutic Separation

When all else fails I think the possibility of "therapeutic separation" should be brought up. Notice the emphasis on separation as a therapeutic and not a punitive measure. Here, the plan must be discussed by the physician with both partners present. The doctor must control the conditions of the separation and must point out from the beginning that in the long run divorce will be accepted if it is the only realistic solution. However, before this, separation for a reasonable length of time should be tried. During this time which usually should be initially for four to six months, the marriage partners must agree to have no contact each with the other. Often this will mean going into some detail with regard to such matters as visiting privileges of the children. It is important that if the husband is coming to visit his children he should not be allowed to talk to his wife at these times. In my experience the breakdown of such plans occurs when the alcoholic presents himself as sick and dependent (or contrite and sober) and the woman takes him back prematurely only to find of course that the old patterns resume almost at once. Full agreements must be obtained about such matters as financial support during the separation, who is to live where, and so on. There should be no conditions placed regarding sobriety on the part of the alcoholic person; however, it should be emphasized that only if some real change has occurred at the end of the six months' period is separation to be terminated. As a final point the physician should insist that the initial meeting of the separated partners at the end of the six months' period must take place in his office with him present.

My experience with the therapeutic separation, when it has been fully accepted by both partners and has been carried out in detail, has been very promising. Under these conditions the alcoholic patient finds himself unable to hide from himself as he has formerly done. Instead, he now becomes aware of cravings, impulses, and feelings which he formerly denied. At this point he frequently recognizes the need for help himself in the form of Alcoholics Anonymous, psychiatric treatment, group therapy, marriage counseling, and so on. However, if no real change has taken place in the sense of recognition of the alcoholic problem and the need for acceptance of help, at the end of such a period of separation it may be possible and even necessary to start discussing divorce. Please note, that in view of all that I have said regarding the spouse of the alcoholic it is by no means certain that she will accept the separation. For her, *not* having a drunken, inferior, dependent male to look after may be very difficult in itself. She too will probably need support and therapy during this period of time and she too should be helped toward insight.

Alcoholic Wives

Until now I have tended to discuss the alcoholic male but there are probably about one million alcoholic females in the United States at this time and many of these are married. The alcoholic wife tends to be a secret solitary drinker frequently taking sherry rather than hard liquor and imbibing all day long. She is often a lonely, dependent, and frustrated person whose husband typically is successful and very busy. From this point of view alone, it has usually been much less possible to involve him in any therapeutic planning such as concurrent group psychotherapy in our experience. When I first studied alcoholic marriages in which the wife was the alcoholic, it was my impression that the husbands of alcoholic women were less prone to sabotage their wives' sobriety than were the wives of alcoholic men. However, examples of this have been seen with increasing frequency and do lead to the conclusion that the successful, go-getting men who are married to these alcoholic women may have personality problems similar to the wives of alcoholic men. In their case the success represents the defense formation under which hide dependent cravings. Again, typically, the dependent feelings of the wife may be a way whereby the husband keeps his own hidden infantile wishes at bay. So far, however, I have not had the opportunity to study the husbands of alcoholic women in the same detail that we have studied the wives.

For the alcoholic woman a general medical counseling and psychotherapeutic program is again required. In particular, she needs to be encouraged to find new dependent relationships and new defenses against the more overwhelming infantile components of her personality. If she can be encouraged to find interests outside of herself and her home, this will be helpful. Many of these women tend to have a depressive component and this is particularly so of those in whom the alcoholism has become apparent around the time of the menopause. In this respect they may be similar to certain middle-aged males whose alcoholism appears in a field of general over-all depression. Under these circumstances it is vital to treat the depression and to recognize the potential for suicide. Indeed, it has been pointed out by Menninger [15] that alcoholism itself is a chronic form of suicide.

Arrest—Not Cure

As a general comment regarding the management of anyone suffering from alcoholism, let me emphasize the great need for patience and tolerance. A realistic goal is arrest of the alcoholism—not "cure." We should never demand sobriety of the patient but should wait until he can demand it of himself. We must be willing to accept his relapses and to use these as a stepping stone toward greater insight. I recommend here the "every cloud has a silver lining" approach—the fact that drinking occurred was a pity but can now be turned to advantage. The question is why did the drinking occur at the particular time that it did, rather than an hour earlier or a day later? Promoting such a search for understanding in terms of environmental impingements upon the patient helps him to recognize the importance of his feelings about what is going on in his relationship with others.

The physician working with alcoholic patients must be willing to accept the development of irrational feelings on the part of the alcoholic toward him. In psychoanalytic terms these are called "transference" and essentially represent the recurrence of feelings that existed earlier toward some important figure in the patient's life. Typically, these will involve hostile and dependent feelings as if toward a mother or father. We must recognize that these do not represent something personal and we must be willing to accept them and gradually to turn them toward insight in the patient. If we take them personally, we will be much more tempted to act irrationally toward the patient in return.

Our Feelings

Finally, all of us who work in the health professions must watch for our own irrational reactions to sick people.[4] In particular with alcoholics, we may find ourselves reacting in one of two extremes. On the one hand we may be hostile and rejecting because of resentment over his ability to get away with being so infantile, so regressed, and so dependent. On the other hand we may find ourselves being over-indulgent toward him when he is in this condition as if to say: "I, the physician, am strong and independent and do not need to be weak and infantile like you." Of course, this is merely our own defense against similar impulses that we find unacceptable in ourselves (and therefore keep out of consciousness).

Such reactions are identical with those found in the wife of the alcoholic man and the husband of the alcoholic woman. In this sense, there is a considerable psychological similarity between people who choose the health professions and those who are married to alcoholics.

In dealing with alcoholics, their spouses, and their marriages, it is helpful for us to utilize all available services. Sometimes this will be the public health nurse, the minister, the marriage counselor, the social worker, or community mental health programs. The psychiatrist should also be called upon by the physician whenever necessary but not, preferably, for referral purposes but rather for consultation purposes. At the present time there are three hundred alcoholics for every psychiatrist and only twenty alcoholics for every physician. General physicians can and should treat alcoholics. If they get into difficulty or if they find a particularly knotty problem confronting them, they should feel free to call upon a psychiatrist for discussion of the case. It is clear that alcoholics, and therefore alcoholic marriages, will be around for a long time to come. We cannot ignore this desperate health problem in our midst. It is vital for future generations that we do all we can to treat this problem and prevent its occurrence whenever possible. From this point of view, the active treatment of the alcoholic marriage is preventive medicine. It is also good medicine because it is good for our alcoholic patients, their spouses, and their children.

References

1. Beecher, H. K. Dec., 1955. "The Powerful Placebo," *J.A.M.A.*, 159: 1602.
2. Chafetz, M. E., and H. W. Demone. 1962. *Alcoholism and Society.* New York: Oxford University Press.
3. Diethelm, O. 1955. *Etiology of Chronic Alcoholism.* Springfield, Ill.: Charles C. Thomas.

4. Ewing, J. A. Jan., 1960. "Having Feelings about Patients," *Practitioner*, 184:70-79.

5. ———, V. Long., and G. C. Wenzel. July, 1961. "Concurrent Group Psychotherapy of Alcoholic Patients and Their Wives," *Int. J. Group Psychother.*, 11:329-38.

6. Fox, R., and P. Lyon. 1955. *Alcoholism—Its Scope, Cause and Treatment*. New York: Random House.

7. Glad, D. D. Dec., 1947. "Attitudes and Experiences of American-Jewish and American-Irish Male Youth as Related to Differences in Adult Rates of Inebriety," *Q. J. Stud. Alcohol*, 8:406-72.

8. Higgins, J. W. June, 1953. "Psychodynamics in the Excessive Drinking of Alcohol," *A.M.A. Arch. Neurol. and Psychiat.*, 69:713-26.

9. Jellinek, E. M. 1960. *The Disease Concept of Alcoholism*. New Haven: Hillhouse Press.

10. Keller, M. March, 1960. "Definition of Alcoholism," *Q. J. Stud. Alcohol*, 21:125-33.

11. Knight, R. P. Nov., 1937. "The Psychodynamics of Chronic Alcoholism," *J. Nerv. Ment. Dis.*, 86:538-48.

12. Lolli, G., E. Serianni, G. M. Golder, and P. Luzzatto-Fegiz. 1958. *Alcohol in Italian Culture: Food and Wine in Relation to Sobriety among Italians and Italian Americans*. Glencoe, Ill.: The Free Press.

13. McCord, W., J. McCord, and J. Gudeman. Dec., 1959. "Some Current Theories of Alcoholism: A Longitudinal Evaluation," *Q. J. Stud. Alcohol*, 20:727-49.

14. Macdonald, D. E. June, 1956. "Mental Disorders in Wives of Alcoholics," *Q. J. Stud. Alcohol*, 17:282-87.

15. Menninger, K. A. 1938. *Man Against Himself*. New York: Harcourt, Brace and Company.

16. Navratil, L. March, 1956. "Alkoholismus und Geburtennummer; zur Frage der Konstitution des letzten Kindes," *Wien. Klin. Wschr.*, 68:158-60.

17. Pearson, W. S. Jan., 1962. "The 'Hidden' Alcoholic in the General Hospital," *N. Carolina Med. J.*, 23:6-10.

18. Pfeffer, A. Z. 1958. *Alcoholism*. New York: Grune and Stratton.

19. Sherfey, M. J. 1955. "Psychopathology and Character Structure in Chronic Alcoholism," in O. Diethelm (ed.), *Etiology of Chronic Alcoholism*. Springfield, Ill.: Charles C. Thomas.

20. Strecker, E. A. 1951. *Their Mothers' Sons*. Philadelphia and New York: J. B. Lippincott Company.

Bibliography

There are many sources of appropriate literature, mostly in pamphlet form, which is suitable for giving to alcoholic patients and others. Often, you will find it useful to investigate available publications from your state or city alcoholism information or rehabilitation program.

The American Medical Association publishes a useful "Manual on Alcoholism" which is directed to physicians. It is obtainable from the association at 535 North Dearborn Street, Chicago 10, Illinois.

Alcoholics Anonymous World Services, Inc., Box 459, Grand Central Station, New York 17, New York, publishes many useful brochures. Pertinent to the present chaper are three directed to lay people entitled, "Alcoholism the Illness," "The Alcoholic Wife—A Message to Husbands," and "The Alcoholic Husband—A Message to Wives."

In North Carolina the Alcoholic Rehabilitation Program supplies literature to doctors and lay people. A useful publication for alcoholics and their relatives is, "The New Cornerstones." Also the program reprints various articles, such as "Thirteen Steps to Alcoholism," and distributes them on request. Their address is P.O. Box 9494, Raleigh, North Carolina.

For teenagers a most useful publication is a "Life Adjustment Booklet," price $0.40, available from Science Research Associates, Inc., 57 West Grand Avenue, Chicago 10, Illinois. The booklet itself is entitled "Facts About Alcohol" and is by Raymond G. McCarthy.

Two books should also be mentioned here. First is, "New Primer on Alcoholism," by Marty Mann, published by Rinehart and Co., New York, 1959. The Alcoholics Anonymous Publishing Company, New York, prints "Twelve Steps and Twelve Traditions" about the organization.

6

Marriage Problems
and Gynecologic Illness

Eleanor B. Easley, M.D.

During twenty years of practicing obstetrics and gynecology, I have found marriage problems contributing often to gynecologic illness. If marriage problems make my patients sick, I have no choice but to try to deal with them. I wish the situation were otherwise. For a doctor—and especially for a gynecologist—dealing with marriage problems is an unsatisfactory business. Success for a doctor is to cure patients. Amelioration is about the best one hopes for in cases involving marriage problems, and this partial result is to be achieved only by the use of much time. Causes are in the past or beyond the reach of a doctor; in our specialty, as a rule, we do not even have an opportunity to see the husband and are left with the thankless task of trying to modify the wife's reaction to the situation. The old expression comes to mind: There are many different ways to skin a cat, but no way to make the cat like it! Folks want a quick, easy cure for every ailment. The last thing they want is to help cure themselves. And finally, but important, they do not want to pay the doctor for his time, but for results. A doctor who deals with marriage problems is in a bad tactical position. I wish I could figure a way to let them alone; but every year I become more impressed with the fact that they are part of the very warp and woof of obstetric and gynecologic practice.

From long frustration, my mind keeps turning to seek prophylaxis. To deal with fully developed marriage problems is uneconomic for everyone. As I work at the job, inefficiently and ineffectively, I feel my predicament to be like that of the doctor of a hundred years ago who went about dosing malaria patients with quinine. I have come to believe that there are in our culture swamp-and-mosquito equivalents mass-producing problem people, especially problem women. These troubled individuals are the drops of water and grains of sand that go into the making of all social problems, including marriage problems. Recently I have turned to the writings of psychiatrists and have found constructive, unheeded advice that could be used for an effective attack on the problems we are considering. Before I come to this advice, however, let me discuss some of the problems as I encounter them in my practice.

Common Marital Problems and Their Relation to Gynecologic Disturbances

In the books on marriage, problems are neatly divided into categories: religion, money, in-laws, work, sex relations, children. In patients, categories tend to get mixed up—and so do the symptoms that result. Women with emotional turmoil complain of all sorts of menstrual disturbances: periods that are early, late, irregular, excessive, or scanty. They come with pelvic pain, pressure, backache, itching, discharges, and disturbed sex relations. Let me present a few examples.

CASE 1—*In-law troubles because of religious differences*
The first is a patient with temporary amenorrhea because of in-law trouble. Mrs. A. B., still beautiful at thirty-eight, had been two years married to her second husband, aged thirty-seven. She was brought by her husband, who was obviously devoted. He succeeded in pressuring his way past my receptionist to have her seen as an emergency. She was nauseated, nervous, did not sleep well, and had missed two menstrual periods. They wanted to know whether she was pregnant. She was not, and her general physical condition appeared to be ex-

cellent. A week after her visit, and with no treatment except reassurance, she menstruated normally. When she returned, at my request, for a less hurried evaluation, I got the following story:

"I might as well admit that I have trouble with his family. One sister will speak to me in a crowd, but I've never seen his mother. I think his daddy and his brothers would be fairly nice if they dared. They're Catholic, and I've been married before. My husband's the pick of the family. Whenever they get into any kind of trouble, they call on him. When they call him to come home, he's not allowed to bring me with him. When he gets there, his mother cries and carries on and tries to get him to leave me. I give him permission to go to them, but I've asked him not to spend the night away from me." The episode of amenorrhea followed the husband-wife discussion in which she made the request that her husband not spend nights at his family home.

This case was easy. The lady went away satisfied, and has not been back in several months. In addition to listening to her story, I discussed briefly the natural strength of a mother's ties with her son and the bolstering by religious conviction of this mother's natural wish to hold her son. I pointed out the near certainty that this elderly mother would not be able to forgive the wife, particularly since the wife had won the battle and was in possession of the prized husband-son. Finally, I emphasized the need for the wife to be understanding and kind to her husband, since he, torn between wife and mother, was the one who was really on the spot.

CASE 2—*In-law trouble and sex relations*
The next case illustrates a more common pattern of in-law trouble, combined with a common husband-wife problem—namely, the frequency of sex relations. Mrs. C.D., aged thirty-seven, had been married eighteen years to a husband five years her senior. She wanted a "complete female examination" because she had had "so much trouble over the years." As a young girl, she had started off with dysmenorrhea and an appendectomy. She described a badly managed first delivery at home, followed by a uterine prolapse and dyspareunia. After two more babies, a hysterectomy and vaginal repair were performed.

She and her husband got along very well in general, but all their married life there had been "a little trouble about sex relations." She did not feel like having relations as often as they had them (three times a week), and the experience was satisfactory for her only about one time in three. At the time of her visit she was concerned because she often felt "sort of raw and sore" during relations, and the next day had lower abdominal discomfort. Also she was nervous. When I asked what made her nervous, she knew exactly. Her mother-in-law, aged sixty-seven, lived with them. In addition to having hypertension and an enlarged heart, she had had a stroke and had to be humored. She had never forgiven the patient for marrying her only son. She interfered with the patient's management of her youngest child, who was supposed to be on a special diet, but to whom the grandmother gave anything he wanted. The patient had thought of getting an outside job now that the youngest child was six, but Grandma insisted that a wife belonged at home, and would not allow an outsider to take care of her.

A brief explanation of the biologic reasonableness of discrepant male-female libidos gave some comfort to this woman, by reassuring her that there was not necessarily anything further wrong with her female organs. She recognized the effect that her mother-in-law had on her feelings, because all her symptoms improved on the rare occasions when she was able to get away. I have long since rejected the medical rule that one should never give advice. I advised this patient to try a job if she wanted to, and tell Grandma kindly but firmly that she would have to get along as best she could with outside help.

Factors affecting libido in women: Many wives ask why they do not feel like having sex relations as often as their husbands, and why the libido gap is increased during pregnancy and lactation. Rutherford [7] of Seattle says that sex relations every forty-eight hours would be an average and reasonable frequency for a normal, vigorous male. Individual variations are so great that I would not hazard an opinion as to a comparable figure for the human female, but I think it safe to say that her natural pattern is episodic and that in general she desires relations less often. Psychologic considerations have been for a long time the predominating determinants of her behavior and so tremendously important as to obscure her intrinsic natural pattern. Throughout the animal kingdom, the correlation of mating behavior with hormones and fertility is too obvious to be doubted. I think these same biologic considerations affect the human female and modify her responsiveness. No matter how much she wishes to be responsive, there are times when, sexually, she can't get off the ground.

Many of the very young girls whom we see because of illegitimate pregnancies claim to have conceived from a single exposure. Many of their stories ring true, and it is impressive how often this single episode has occurred near the time of ovulation. I think these young girls were "in heat" and were simply overcome by their normal female impulses. Our society's requirement that a girl police her own virginity seems to me indefensible. If she is to stand a chance of success during the long, awkward interval between biologic and economic maturity, her training must be such that it will severely handicap her later responsiveness. Psychosexual inhibitions must be built into her personality; she must be schooled to repress her sex urges; she builds up bad habit patterns of response to male advances. In addition, she often resents intuitively the fact that she bears the major share of responsibility for keeping the situation under control. The nearly extinct chaperone had a much better influence on women's sexuality. The chaperone's existence gave status and recognition to it. A change in this social pattern would surely have a favorable effect on the sex responsiveness of wives.

The following phenomena are relevant also. When estrogenic hormone is in low supply, visible atrophy of the vulva and vagina occur, and women complain of actual dyspareunia. Both the visible changes and the dyspareunia are corrected when estrogenic hormone is supplied locally. To affect libido, however, the hormone must be given systemically. Symptomatic atrophy of the genital mucosa occurs following delivery (especially with lactation), postmenopausally, and after uncompensated castration in young women—for example, as a result of the treatment for breast or cervical cancer. Many eminent gynecologists now believe that we are not justified in withholding modest doses of hormone even from the women in this last group, who are at times utterly miserable.

Postmenopausal women vary greatly, both in their feelings and in the thickness of the vaginal mucosa. The naïve questions asked me by a significant number of such patients do not support Kinsey's [3] (p. 353) contention that adequate or even improved sexual performance is the rule after the menopause. I have come to breathe a sigh of relief if a woman seeking help with menopausal symptoms has had a hysterectomy. If she has, I can give her some estrogens without the risk of troublesome bleeding. Whenever I find that a patient for whom I am prescribing estrogens has a knowledge of Latin, I point out the derivation of the word *estrogenic*.

In most marriages the compromise on frequency of sex relations is in favor of the man. Margaret Mead [5] (p. 323) has defined success for a woman in our culture as getting and keeping a husband. Young women are aware of this fact without being told. With or without the benefit of education or advice, young women learn the importance of sex satisfaction to their husbands. However they feel, considerations of enlightened self-interest dictate their compliance. If they have small children, they are really under pressure to get along with their husbands. No medical audience needs to be bored with case reports illustrating what happens when any situation blocks a husband's sex fulfillment at home. Even in this era of antibiotics and chemotherapy, I average seeing one case a week of gynecologic damage from pelvic infection. The stories are monotonously similar. Because of some disturbance in sex relations with his wife, the husband, often bolstered by alcohol, starts "running around with women"—especially if he has a good chance to do so.

CASE 3—*Money*

Another marriage problem—illustrated by the case of Mrs. E. F.— is related to money. Her husband is a good companion and a satisfactory mate, and they have no trouble with sex relations. He is contented with his work but does not earn enough money for the family's needs. The wife was raised in an affluent home, and I suspect she is extravagant. It has never occurred to her to get a job, and she probably could not get one; but she is an excellent mother. Mrs. E. F. is greatly disturbed because there is no money to send the sixteen-year-old son away to school and because the eight-year-old daughter has to share quarters with her two younger brothers (ages six and seven). Mrs. E. F.'s reactions have been functional menorrhagia, pregnophobia, and premenstrual tension. In addition, at her last visit she confessed her dependence on sleeping pills and on two drinks every afternoon. She looked as though it were more than two drinks.

CASE 4—*A husband's dissatisfaction with his job*

The problem of Mrs. G. H., aged thirty-nine, is her husband's unsatisfactory work situation. After fifteen years in the army, he gave up a military career to take a civilian job. The job has an impressive title, but he discovered too late that he is little more than a clerk, hopelessly squeezed between superiors and those whom he is supposed to manage. No matter how hard he works, he gets nowhere. The pay is not very good and there is no hope of improvement. Mrs. G. H. is afraid he is going to "crack up." He comes home dazed and depressed; his gloom has spread to involve his wife and, to a lesser degree, their one daughter, aged nine. The wife stays tired and feels like crying over nothing. She has episodes of vulvovaginal irritation. She has irregular, sometimes excessive, and increasingly painful menstruation. Her menstrual disturbances, plus minimal cul-de-sac inelasticity, are consistent with early endometriosis. I have long suspected that psychophysiologic mechanisms are involved in the production of retrograde menstruation and its sequel, endometriosis. I hope to live long enough to see someone study this relationship.

CASES 5 AND 6—*Oversuccessful husbands*

Successful husbands contribute to marriage problems, also. I see a surprising number of women seriously bothered by husbands who have been ruthless in sacrificing family interests to their own advancement. As a rule, these men work nearly all the time, often very productively. Although notably more successful than their confreres, they never get to the point of satisfying their own ambitions. They are endlessly demanding, both of themselves and of their families. Indeed, they often regard their families as projections of themselves. One woman brought me this direct quotation from her husband: "I used to think my family was to help me do what I had to do, but now I realize they are people who have to be considered, too."

The menopause seems frequently to trigger the social decompensation of women married to such men. When they go to pieces, they do a thorough job of it. Deep, dark depressions, often complicated by alcoholism, seem to be their special predilections. Usually these women are intelligent, superior people.

Recently I have observed an interesting therapeutic development in two such cases. Each of the women, before I saw her, had spent several unproductive years in psychiatric therapy. One of them had moved and as a result had changed psychiatrists. The new psychiatrist had recognized the marriage problem as a factor critically important to her individual problem. Relieved of the complete burden of responsibility, she had made tremendous progress. She stated the purpose of her visit to me as follows: "I thought a doctor in good standing in this community should know how badly my case had been handled by Dr. X." The second woman's predicament was similar. With the first case in mind, I advised her to consider changing psychiatrists. She did so, and the maneuver was successful. Psychiatrists are human —and mostly male. It's natural and inevitable for males to have a masculine bias. Many women come to me because they want a bias in their favor for a change.

All the cases I have presented have several features in common. The emotional turmoil of each woman is related in some way to her marriage. In each case she has been essentially helpless to correct the situation that bothered her and has had to adjust to it as best she could. Partial failure of adjustment and continued emotional turmoil have in each case upset the woman's physiologic or psychosociologic functioning. Except for the last two cases, which were not presented in detail, these women were able to carry on. Probably their friends and neighbors consider them normal. Even the two women with postmenopausal depressions had carried on until they had finished the work of raising their children and had started on grandchildren.

I am sympathetic toward these women and willing to do anything I can to make things easier for them, but their plight is not my main concern, except as it affects a whole new generation of girls and young women. It is not good for a young girl to perceive the role of her mother as so unpalatable that she rejects it for herself. Such a reaction to the mother is one feature of the "rejection of femininity" syndrome, which I want to discuss in some detail. The next case is that of a younger woman who is a rather good example of this syndrome.

"Rejection of Femininity" Syndrome

CASE 7. Physically, this patient is a normal and uncommonly attractive woman who has proved herself as a female by producing two children. Psychologically she has been castrated. Her psychologic handicap contributes greatly to her being a bad wife, a bad mother, and a nervous, tense, unhappy woman. She goes from symptom to symptom, and from doctor to doctor, and each doctor she quits is thankful to be rid of her. The ideal instruments for trying to salvage her and her marriage would be a psychiatrist and a marriage counselor. Neither the individuals nor society can afford to pay what the salvage would cost.

I present this case for two reasons which seem to me to have great importance. (1) I think the cultural factors that have produced in Mrs. J. K. a full-blown clinical syndrome have a lesser adverse effect on many females in our society. With her case, I hope to achieve an emphasis such as a cartoonist gets with a caricature and so direct attention to these cultural factors. (2) There can be seen in her case the continuity of trouble from generation to generation, through the mother as an instrument. I have seen Mrs. J. K. only once. My work-up of her case is barely started. It is already apparent, however, that factors from her mother's management have contributed to her trouble; it is also apparent that, as a result of her unhapy experiences as a female, she is neglecting and damaging her own two children.

In the spring of 1962, Mrs. J. K., then twenty-nine years old and six years married, left a doctor of excellent reputation and came twice to Dr. Stokes, my partner. Topping her list of symptoms on the first visit was vaginitis and on the second, indigestion. In the late summer, when she deserted Dr. Stokes and came to me, her symptom recital started with premenstrual tension. Other symptoms were chronic tiredness, "nerves shot," menstrual discomfort, fear of pregnancy, no desire for sex relations, and dyspareunia part of the time. Her perineum was badly scarred and she had a fungus infection, which came under control quickly. Other physical and laboratory findings were negative.

For dealing with cases of premenstrual tension, I have adopted the following procedure: first, I make the briefest possible statement about the normality of physiologic changes related to the menstrual cycle; second, I state that premenstrual tension always indicates serious difficulty in adjusting to some kind of problem; third, I invite the patient to tell me her problems. After that, it is usually hard to get a patient to stop talking. Unscrambled and summarized, Mrs. J. K.'s story was as follows:

She was the only daughter in a large farm family and often felt lonely during her childhood in the country. Her mother never spoke to her of menstruation or anything else pertaining to sex and reproduction. She had very severe dysmenorrhea until the birth of her first child. At the age of twenty-three, she married a farm-reared man two years her senior. She was happy during the first two and a half years of their marriage, when he was in military service and they were together most of the time. Regarding sex, her comment was: "I don't think I ever had as much desire or pleasure from it as a wife should, but I didn't mind then. I don't care a thing about it any more."

Ten months after her marriage a daughter was born after a thirty-two-hour labor. A laceration into the rectum occurred at delivery, and the patient spent an uncomfortable fifteen days in the hospital. Eighteen months later a son was born. Labor was short, but again the patient had a rectal laceration and a very unpleasant puerperium. The patient dates many of her symptoms from this second delivery, but it is noteworthy that her life situation changed greatly just three months later, when her husband finished military service and began working long hours on a dairy farm, in addition to two nights per week at a service station and two nights per week in night school. He bought the service station in 1961 and runs it himself, with the after-school help of one boy. The week before his wife's visit he worked seventy-nine hours.

The following are direct quotations from the patient:

"My husband's a good man. He never misses church. Before we were married, he couldn't have been nicer to me. When I ask for money, he gives me twice what I ask for. He wants to accomplish a lot in life, and I do too; but I want some family life and a happy place for the children. He's proud of our children now they're here, but he had absolutely no extra consideration for me during pregnancy or for my hard time having them. He never turns a hand to help me with them.

"I never know when he's going to eat a meal with us or what time he'll come in. We have no friends. We never go anywhere. He thinks I should be happy because he's working to buy a home. . . .

"We used to be able to talk; then it got so every time we had a discussion it ended in a fight, practically. Now he won't talk. We actually separated for ten days once, and my brother got us to go to a psychiatrist. That didn't help. We only went one time. I've read Norman Vincent Peale's rules for a happy marriage, and we don't follow a single one of them. He's so stubborn I don't think anything would change him. . . .

"As long as I do exactly what he wants, we get along fine. Then it builds up in me and I 'blow up.' When we're getting along all right, we have sex relations every night. When we're fighting, we don't have them at all. . . .

"I've tried to adjust because of the children, but I don't seem to be able to. I stay lonely like when I was growing up. I cried all last weekend."

In 1959, when the youngest child was a year old and the home situation had gotten Mrs. J. K. to the stage of crying all the time, she took a full-time job. Her first home helper was fine with the children but left all the other work for the patient. Her next helper did the housework, but neglected the children, so that they would come "crying and pulling" at their mother when she came home tired from work. Very recently Mrs. J. K. has changed to a part-time job.

Just listening to this patient's story is a slight service and will ease her tension a little, but not enough and not for long. She has read about marriage counselors and thinks she could persuade her husband to go with her to consult one if he could get away from the service station. Most likely the couple will come to see me, an ordinary doctor; how much I shall be able to help them directly or through referral, I do not know. If it were not for the two unhappy little children "crying and pulling" at their tired, unhappy mother, I would give up. These children have been damaged already, and in them we have a good start toward another generation of marriage problems. Our best hope of reversing the threat to them is to help the mother.

Symptoms

From past observation, I feel that three of Mrs. J. K.'s symptoms have ominous prognostic significance. These are:
1. Continued functional dysmenorrhea after two babies.
2. Increasing premenstrual tension.
3. Complete failure of coital adjustment.
The significance of the first two symptoms, not ordinarily recog-

nized, is elucidated in a small book recently published: *The Gynecologic Patient*, by Dr. Somers Sturgis [9] of Boston. This book, which I recommend to you, correlates gynecologic, endocrine, and psychiatric studies on a variety of syndromes. Included are functional dysmenorrhea and premenstrual tension. Dr. Sturgis presents evidence that an emotional factor is invariably present in both. He says of severe dysmenorrhea that: (1) total ignorance of the reproductive system at the time of the menarche is probably the most common prelude to its development (remember that Mrs. J. K.'s mother never spoke to her of menstruation or anything else pertaining to reproduction); (2) in a young girl it is a clear manifestation that she finds her role as a maturing female as yet unacceptable; (3) in a girl who has reached full physical maturity it may be the only presenting complaint of a complex and deeply involved personality maladjustment, best dealt with through long-term psychotherapy or psychoanalysis.

Dr. Sturgis found evidence of more profound psychopathologic disturbance in severe premenstrual tension than in severe dysmenorrhea. He deals with failure of heterosexual adjustment only in passing, but this problem is generally recognized, I believe, as a more serious sign than either dysmenorrhea or premenstrual tension.

Causes

The frequency of disturbances of sexual function among women who are considered essentially healthy, as well as in neurotic women, was discussed by Karen Horney in 1927.[2] The disturbances that she listed were dysmenorrhea, amenorrhea, depression or irritability associated with menstruation, and, most significant of all, frigidity. She noted further that comparable disturbances were continued in all phases of maternity: conception, pregnancy, delivery, and lactation.

I value as uncommonly convincing this author's writing on material obtained from women by psychoanalysis. Before I became familiar with her work, the concept of penis envy seemed to me unbelievable and prerogative envy a more likely cause of trouble. I still believe the latter factor is important. Dr. Horney calls it cultural reinforcement and implies that it is of lesser importance than repressed psychologic material. She believes that penis envy occurs commonly as a part of the normal development of most little girls and that unresolved penis envy plays an important part in the "rejection of femininity" syndrome.

It is a fact, strange and shocking for the non-analyst, that these fantasies described by women during psychoanalysis are not of a general nature but are concerned in the deeper subconscious layer with the possession of the male genitals.... These desires go back to the time of early childhood.... The thought process of this age is very concrete. The little girl sees that the boy has something more than she has and she wants to have it, too.... To prevent misunderstanding, I want to emphasize that these fantasies, as well as their connections with psychic and somatic symptoms, are deeply subconscious and can never be detected in the usual medical interview. As an analyst one is in the fatal position comparable to a histologist who would have to tell what microscopic changes he sees in the organ without having a microscope available [with which to demonstrate them].... the further effect of such a secret attitude of envy is not different from any other kind of envy.... we observe clear-cut attitudes of resentment toward the man as the more privileged. These are comparable to the inner exasperation and secret hostility felt, for example, by a laborer toward his employer causing him to be on the look-out for an opportunity to paralyze the employer by the thousand different devices of everyday cold war. In short, we see a picture very much like that which we see right away in innumerable marriages. Through such a basic attitude, the question of influence, power, and superiority gains a specific importance.

This last sentence brings to my mind Saul's [8] concept of "specific emotional vulnerability" (p. 175).

If all women carry around inside this "rather tough worm," or its partly digested residue, it follows that husbands should be schooled in the fine art of skillful persuasion and taught to avoid coercion under any circumstances. If penis envy occurs in most little girls, it is to be presumed that most women resent being pushed around by men. Mrs. J. K., as the only daughter in a large family, certainly had an ideal set-up for developing penis envy. The postulated effect of an unresolved residue of penis envy is prominent in her personality. She tends to resent her husband's authority and to be sensitive about fair consideration for her own wishes.

The normal identification of a girl with her mother is supposed to bring about the resolution of penis envy, with no significant traces, into the wish for sexual union and a child. I cannot quote figures, but I am sure that many girls have great difficulty in identifying with their mothers, and many never succeed. The favorable resolution of maternity envy in little boys is far more dependable.

Dr. Horney believes that the actual *pathogenic agent* of the masculinity complex in women is fear of female experience. If we realize that fact, she says, "we easily understand why in such women symptoms of disease appear just at the moment when they are reminded of their female role. This happens with each menstruation, in the sex act, especially with defloration, in pregnancy and delivery. Frigidity is the most frequent and . . . important consequence of this disturbance in development." She mentions briefly that a little girl may be frightened by her misinterpretation of early observations regarding sex, where a milieu of secrecy prevails; but she develops with emphasis the concept that the little girl's vulnerability to *real* danger from eventual sexual aggression could be a reasonable cause for anxiety. "We see everywhere in nature that the fact of being endangered is reflected in the psyche as instinctual anxiety."

It is hardly necessary to enumerate the hazards intrinsic to being a female which make some reality fear reasonable. Rape and incest cases are not uncommon in our hospital emergency room. Unhappy high school girls illegitimately pregnant are seen almost weekly in our office. Pregnancy, labor, and delivery do usually entail some discomfort and leave a residue of physical damage. Finally, a woman encumbered with small children *is* "tied down." I have pointed out already that our social pattern trains girls to be fearful of sex experience by requiring them to police their own virginity.

The over-all behavior of young women with relation to the marriage-pregnancy-motherhood complex has many features in common with the behavior of young men toward wartime military duty. In each case the young people are fascinated by the prospect of the experience, and the majority can be depended on to try it out. Young men will go to war, be afraid, and gripe about their hard times; young women will get pregnant, be afraid, and similarly gripe.

In the case of Mrs. J. K., her lonely childhood and unhappy marriage experiences were reinforced by her bad obstetric experiences. Standard obstetric practice is under attack for having neglected humane considerations in its zeal to reduce mortality and morbidity. I think we are guilty, all right, but I have not yet been able to figure out a satisfactory, reasonable compromise course. The economic cost of pregnancy and delivery is already high, and young married couples are not usually affluent. Complications do occur, and some are dangerous. Our whole system is geared to the fact that, at any moment, the most normal obstetric case can become an emergency. Mostly, we have ignored the fact that the vast majority of cases remain normal, and that with different management they could be richly rewarding human experiences.

Nearly all women starting labor are a little afraid, and a few are so purely terrified that their only interest is in oblivion. They have recognized the kernel of truth in old wives' horror stories (and, more recently, television programs). There is no avoiding the fact that the human female can remember, think, and imagine. Some anxiety, especially for a primigravida, seems reasonable and realistic. Truly her situation is not unlike that of a soldier about to face real fighting.

Why Women Fail to Achieve Sexual Fulfillment

One hundred years ago, if men were to be satisfied sexually, women had babies; the responsibility for the babies belonged to both husband and wife. Nowadays birth control, albeit troublesome, is practical. Men can be sexually satisfied without producing babies—and to do so is precisely the wish of many men. Women are coming to realize, not without chagrin, that their built-in specialism for baby production is both physiologic and psychologic. For women, sex satisfaction is more than just coitus; the whole complex biologic function of reproduction is involved. Said one patient recently after delivery: "That wasn't easy, but I sure got a primitive satisfaction out of it." In the feminist movement, a portion of womankind, figuratively, "crawled out on a limb" in the matter of having babies; now, aware of their mistake, many of them are trying to crawl back. Instead of giving them a hand, many husbands are chopping away at the limb.

The female urge toward all-out baby production is dampened by many pressures: the population explosion; the fact that our complicated civilization makes children an economic liability; and discouragement by the husband, who has to pay for the babies, and who soon finds out that pregnancy and lactation make his wife a less satisfactory mate. One wife reported that at the onset of her labor her husband tossed her the car keys and said. "Having this baby was your idea. Go on to the hospital and have it." (Incidental information: some five years later, I did a hysterectomy on that woman for endometriosis with dyspareunia; Enovid made her sick.)

The behavior of such husbands brings to mind business tactics whereby consumer pressure is often used successfully to break up a "package deal." Most husbands do not succeed in obtaining an optimal sex relationship without other encumbrances. Most women cannot continue enthusiastic participation in sex relations with a man who fails to provide also considerate general treatment and support of maternity. In women these three factors—considerate general treatment, support of maternity, and sex responsiveness—are as inextricably interrelated as the roots, trunk, and branches of a tree. Completely destroy any one, and the whole is lost; starve the roots, let insects damage the bark, or shade the branches, and you get a damaged specimen.

The Importance of Education for Marriage and Parenthood

Most women having their first baby face the situation with inadequate preparation and with less than optimal help. Specifically they need more emotional support in labor and less interference with natural delivery, as long as the case remains normal. Even more important than these obstetric considerations, however, is the new mother's need for actual supervised experience with child care at some time before she takes her first baby home. (The mother-daughter apprentice system in large families formerly helped greatly to fill this important need; but the really large family is going or gone.) The plight of the unprepared mother is often made worse by the lack of adequate help during her first few weeks at home with the new baby.

Most of the young primigravidas who come to us at this time for obstetric care have a vacuum where their education about pregnancy, childbirth, and parenthood should be. The same is true of their husbands. A few missionary-spirited obstetricians have organized classes for parents and provide some instruction along with medical care. The average doctor, however, has no taste, time, or talent for undertaking this extra burden. In a few cities parents' classes are taught by such organizations as the Maternity Center Association of New York. Other cities have adult education programs.

The recommendations of Anna Freud [1] (p. 259) after her experience with children removed from London during World War II could be adapted to meet this need for parent education. She believes that parents can and should be taught by direct experience how to raise their children. Her war experience convinced her "that dynamic child psychology can be taught by demonstration on the living object ... to those who are actually engaged in the task of upbringing, nursing, teaching, or otherwise caring for young children." (p. 277)

Other excerpts from her writings are as follows: "The success or failure of an adult ... depends on his childhood experiences ... specific childhood events and psychologic mechanisms lead to the formation of either positive or negative attitudes to fellow beings. ... The early relationship with the parents determines the character of all later attachments, affections or enmities. ... Since the attitudes are established in childhood, they can be influenced most efficiently in childhood."

Dr. Freud believes that parents and other workers in education who would not ordinarily have access to psychoanalytic or other scientific investigations should be enlightened. "Without such enlightenment," she writes, "the majority ... will continue to handle the next generation in a manner which will produce the very attitudes they are attempting to eliminate from the nature of the child."

The cases and conditions I have described are commonplace. My reason for trying at this late date in my career to focus attention on them is the observation of signs of distress in a whole new generation of girls and young women. I have lived long enough now to see the whole vicious cycle: troubled woman, bad mother, bad child, troubled person. In all the busy work about mental hygiene, juvenile delinquency, crime, and divorce, bad mothers are censured unmercifully. But everybody "leapfrogs" over the critically important pathogenesis of bad mothers. Some wise person has said there is no such thing as a bad boy. Surely the same is true for girls. Nature built into little girls the predilection for becoming good mothers.

The Predicament of Women in Modern Society

"What is honored in a country is cultivated there." So said Plato. In our culture motherhood is not it—nor is the work that women can combine successfully with raising even small families. Child-bearing women are part of the unskilled labor unemployment problem. We have noted already that at this time the law of supply and demand is against them in all-out child production. Yet they still have, in limited child production, their time-honored work handicaps: less skill, less time, less mobility.

Dr. Weston LaBarre, professor of anthropology at Duke University, has written lucidly of the American woman: "She seeks to retain her status through an artificial scarcity, a competitive, cultivated invidiousness of sexual appeal. This is so evident that prestige now accrues to woman as *consumer,* rather than as producer: it is as a suitable vehicle for the display of male buying power that a woman is now valued. Her socially useful contributions as a producer or worker carry no prestige at all, save in competitive-masculine terms. . . . In our society it is the nubile young female who achieves the most attention, who is the cynosure of all eyes." [4] She is displaced, says Dr. LaBarre, only by the soldier in wartime.

Although Karl Menninger was talking of contraception when he said, "Nothing is more tragic, more fateful in its ultimate consequence than the realization by a child that he was unwanted," [6] his words are equally applicable to the realization by a little girl that she has disappointed her parents by not being a boy. At least half the time when I assist a mother with giving birth to a baby girl I am aware that she is disappointed—and the father more so—that the child is not a boy. I have always known that my parents were hoping for a boy instead of a girl when I was born. As a result, all my life I have been studying two problems: (1) What is wrong with being a human female instead of a human male? (2) What is the best course to follow if you are a female? In the practice of obstetrics and gynecology I have continued to study, on behalf of my patients, these problems which I studied for myself when I was young, plus a few more.

The human female fits this time in history like a round peg in a square hole. Her biologic fulfillment, the need to produce babies, is unsuited to a world in the midst of a population explosion. She is caught between a biologic irresistible force and a sociologic immovable object. Society, not needing babies very much at the moment, is not in a mood to help women generously with the troublesome business of getting them born and raised. She has come to be sort of a scapegoat for the bothersomeness of reproduction. To this really staggering primary problem, social embellishments have been added from the cradle up. Consider this nursery rhyme:

> Grandma Grunts said a curious thing:
> "Boys may whistle, but girls must sing."

Women need help, not unenlightened censure and further handicaps. For their children—and quite possibly for the whole culture—such help is a necessity. Realistic, honest education for young people seems the best hope.

References

1. Freud, A. 1953. "The Bearing of the Psychoanalytic Theory of Instinctual Drives on Certain Aspects of Human Behavior," in R. Lowenstein (ed.), *Drives, Affects, and Behavior*. New York: International Universities Press.
2. Horney, K. March, 1927. "Der Männlichkeitskomplex der Frau," *Arch. f. Frauenk.*, 13:141-54.
3. Kinsey, A. C., W. B. Pomeroy, C. E. Martin, and P. H. Gebhart. 1953. *Sexual Behavior in the Human Female*. Philadelphia: W. B. Saunders Co.
4. LaBarre, W. March, 1946. "Social Cynosure and Social Structure," *J. Personality*, 14:169-83.
5. Mead, M. 1949. *Male and Female*. New York: William Morrow and Company, Inc.
6. Menninger, K. A. Jan., 1943. "Psychiatric Aspects of Contraception," *Bull. Menninger Clin.*, 7:36-40.
7. Rutherford, R. N., A. Laurence Banks, and W. A. Coburn, Jan.-Feb., 1962. "Psychodynamic Conflicts in Pregnancy and Parenthood," *Psychosom. Med.*, 3:28-32.
8. Saul, L. J. 1947. *Emotional Maturity*. Philadelphia: J. B. Lippincott Co.
9. Sturgis, S. H., *et al.* 1962. *The Gynecologic Patient*, Chapters 2 and 3. New York: Grune & Stratton, Inc.

7

Pregnancy as a Stress in Marriage

Lucie Jessner, M.D.

Marriage, as we know it in the Western World, is not a static condition but has a life history of its own, with the potential for growth and development or for pathology and decline. In our middle-class society, to which my experience is limited, marriages usually are the sequence to love. There is, as Kierkegaard [5] (p. 90) expresses it, a "schism"—an essential difference—"between first love and marriage." Great passion loves to be on an island, excluding the world; marital life becomes a part of a community and a link from one generation to the next, imposing the weight of responsibility.

This difference becomes most obvious at the time of first pregnancy when a transition from romantic to marital love seems imperative. It is a new step on the ladder of maturity of the future parents and of marriage as a focus in life. But it also may be a challenge that is not met or only partially solved. This change is for many people more difficult because of the misconception that love should remain what it had been on first sight and eternal not in a transcendental sense but remaining the same once and for all. It is fostered by movies and T.V.'s glorification of infatuation as it was in the fairy tale ending of "they lived happily ever after." But this problem is indeed basic to human nature, the wish to tell, as Goethe's Faust says, the moment to stand still. To quote Bernard Shaw [9] (p. 157): "Marriage as a fact is not in the least like marriage as an ideal." To give some examples: the mother of a schizophrenic girl came to see me because of her child's condition, but mainly because of her feeling that she had caused it. She recalled that on the way to the hospital for delivery, she had clung to her husband crying, "We will never be alone again" and that although she gave her child the best physical care, she always regarded her as an intruder in the marriage. She tried as much as possible to maintain the status quo of her former happiness *à deux*. It later turned out that she as a child had done her best to alienate her parents from each other, playing one out against the other; she indeed felt responsible for her parents' divorce later on. She, unconsciously, expected her daughter to do the same to her. We may speculate that in her case the family physician, the obstetrician, or the pediatrician might have sensed this lady's problem early enough to prevent the later distress.

Another young woman, though happy to be pregnant, recalled a number of friends and relatives whose husbands had either died or deserted during pregnancy. She figured out what she would do in case it might happen to her. This concern, usually not a serious one, occurs not infrequently. The fear that pregnancy might destroy the marriage may stem mainly from the woman's own problems, e.g., the expectation of being punished for hostile wishes against her husband or against her father in the past or for premarital sexual experiences, in actuality or in fantasy, which could have led to a pregnancy without being married.

But she also may sense an actual danger: while most husbands probably feel closer to their wives when they are pregnant, some indeed have the wish to get away. One young man, who was in psychotherapy for problems of his own, had been looking forward to having a child. But during the last months of his wife's pregnancy he became acutely disturbed, was disgusted by the sight of her protruding belly, and felt alarmingly attracted to slim young girls. His wife's appearance brought back to him the feelings of rage and contempt he had experienced when his mother was pregnant when he was ten years old. In working through his earlier resentments, the rejection of his wife subsided and marriage took on a deeper meaning.

Looking pregnant, of course, can also evoke feelings of awe and admiration. Some of the most beautiful pictures and statues of the

Middle Age and the Renaissance show the Madonna in a pregnant state. But the physical changes, welcomed and proudly displayed by some, arouse conflicts in some marriages. Freud speaks of two aspects of femininity: one her desirability as a woman and secondly her qualities as a mother (reproduction, protection, caring for and molding of a child). Here is indeed a transition, relevant for the future of the marriage, including the children; the first quality, the sex appeal in general, declines during pregnancy and it matters for both the future parents that the second quality, the motherliness, can be accepted.

There are changes not only in appearance but in the personality of the pregnant woman which call for a new adaptation in marriage. Irritability, overt or hidden fears, fatigue, a decrease in outside interests and in love making, and the need to be taken care of by and to depend on the husband are among the most frequent emotional concomitants. It often is crucial for the destiny of the marriage and the infant that the husband be able to respond to these changes. It is perhaps most obvious in the situation of students, who courageously married with the prospect that the wife would work to put her husband through school. The function of being the breadwinner and the support of the household, carried graciously, sometimes becomes a problem during pregnancy, when the need for dependency and quiet introspection is strong. And it matters even more that the husband gives psychological support—to which his wife's obstetrician might alert him. To give an example: a young couple married while they both were sophomores in two different colleges in Boston. They postponed pregnancy because the husband's career came first and the wife's earnings were just enough for the two of them. Their marriage was cold and distant, except for heated arguments when the young woman berated her mate for not being as brilliant a scholar as her father and brother. She considered herself a failure because she neither had finished college nor produced a child as had her sister. She decided to become pregnant, mainly to live up to her parents' expectations. She hoped the baby would be a girl because she was afraid a boy would be just like her husband whom she considered a child, making demands without giving her anything in return. In the last trimester of her pregnancy, while having a serious complication, she could not fail to realize that her husband did care for her and indeed took over household chores and the preparations for the baby. She then, for the first time in her marriage, turned to him for help instead of seeking support and consolation from her family. She finally could loosen her ties with the past and actually be a happy wife, oriented now mainly towards the future of a family of her own. By the time she delivered, she was happy that it was a boy who looked like her husband.

Sometimes pregnancy is planned in the hope that having a child will improve a marriage that has become meaningless and a source of frustration. This seldom works out and it easily creates problems for the child, who is supposed to bring his parents together. The most opportune time to revive the marital relationship is during pregnancy when the wife, out of her increasing passivity and need for care, turns either to her mother or to her husband. The physician may under these circumstances play a decisive role in alerting the husband's resources for sympathy and support.

There are other personality changes that may lead to estrangement or greater closeness in marriage, e.g., a more decisive shift to femininity in the expectant mother. This transition is vividly described in *An Interesting Condition* by Abigail Lewis,[6] the diary of the author's first pregnancy. One day she realizes: "The defiant tomboy that was me will be finally and irrevocably lost, but someone else will be born, though not so apparently as the baby is born." For some time she was furious at her husband for being insensitive to the changes in her. But her realization that he was under the stress of sexual abstinence and that they both missed reconciliation through sexual intimacy made her tolerant with him.

Other young women fight against such changes. Conflicts between the former ego ideal of having a career versus the demands of motherhood sometimes lead to neurotic complication [2] and envious resentment against the husband, who can go on developing his talents.

But can he? Certainly not in the same way his father or grandfather could under the same circumstances. Because we do see a very definite change in our culture, in which the father takes much more part in the upbringing of the child, as we all note and anthropologists, e.g., Margaret Mead,[7] have documented. The older concept of masculinity kept the father out of the nursery and playpen and had the child relegated to the mother. In the newer concept the father is expected to take part in the care and upbringing of the child and nobody can completely ignore the role expectations and values of his culture. Spock,[11] in his *Baby and Child Care* says: "A man can be a warm father and a real man at the same time." Spock suggests that fathers should share some of the routines of baby care—a proposition that does not appeal to all expectant fathers. Therese Benedek,[1] in "Parenthood as Developmental Phase" states: "The emotional attitude of the father in the family triad is significant from conception on. He responds to the receptive-dependent needs of his wife which are increased by her pregnancy, by her anxieties about parturition and the care of the child. . . . Independent of hormonal stimulation (in contrast to the pregnant wife), the father's relationship to the child is directed more by hope than by drive." The function as father is accentuated in the present generation through a change in the social structure of today: [8] formerly young couples often lived with or near their relatives, their parents, aunts, uncles, grandparents. But, as sociologists point out, the prevailing middle-class pattern now is "residential isolation" of the nuclear family from relatives, collateral or generational. Also, nannies are being displaced by the baby sitter. While the foolproof jars of baby food and the diaper service decrease much of the drudgery, the whole responsibility for the care of the child usually falls on the four shoulders of the parents. Anticipating this new role of life as father does in some cases arouse in the young man the fear of losing his identity and his chance for self-realization. Marriage may suddenly appear as a trap.

It is relevant for the harmony in marriage that such feelings can be mastered and that the child becomes for the father a part of his self-realization. This sometimes calls for working through childhood experiences, especially some unresolved early conflict with his own father.

Especially in the last trimester, feelings of estrangement and exclusion are sometimes aroused in the husband. Although most modern obstetricians do not prohibit sexual intercourse, love-making usually declines out of irrational fears that it might harm the baby or lack of enthusiasm in one or both partners. A state of frustration and feelings of rejection sometimes lead to impulsive infidelity of the husband with an aftermath of guilt and apprehension. Some prospective fathers feel much at one with their wives, even to the degree of similar physical discomfort and anxieties reminiscent of couvade. For other young people a spurt of maturing together and a common orientation towards the future occurs. It is sometimes surprising to see couples who appeared to be irresponsible adolescents transformed into thoughtful, planning, and self-sacrificing adults; as soon as the future baby has taken on the aspect of a reality, they anticipate and begin to mature. The relationship between husband and wife has a relevant bearing on the emotional climate which will receive the newborn, strengthening or inhibiting the wish for and the devotion to the child.

The last stage of pregnancy, the closeness to delivery, brings with it heightened discomfort and anxiety. Fears of death and of mutilation, justified in former centuries, are not extinct, in spite of the reassuring statistics. In this atmosphere of apprehension marital relationships are tested again.

At the time of actual delivery, the husband of the cartoon, pacing the floor and hoping he can distribute cigars, is replaced in modern hospitals by one who can stay with his wife. This is great comfort for many, giving support to both future parents and allowing them to share a major experience. But I feel that individual differences have to be taken into account. For example these situations might make the presence of the husband undesirable: the expectant mother wants him there in the spirit of "Look what you have done to me"; or she wants privacy; or the husband increases her anxiety by adding his own; or the husband has to deny any concern and be tough. In such circumstances the obstetrician's attitude of respect, empathy, and calm might come to the rescue.

In summary, I have described some of the stresses that pregnancy may impose on marriage. Marriage is not a state but a process that forever has to be revised. There are certain situations, and pregnancy is one of them, where a former equilibrium is challenged and where disequilibrium or a re-equilibrium on a new plane may be the outcome of this crisis.[3] *

* See also John Spiegel's [10] discussion of "failure of complementarity" in the family, especially when new situations require learning of new roles.

References

1. Benedek, T. July, 1959. "Parenthood as Developmental Phase," *J. Amer. Psychoanal. Ass.*, 7:389-417.
2. Greenacre, P. April, 1960. "Woman as Artist," *Psychoanal. Quart.*, 29: 208-27.
3. "Integration and Conflict in Family Behavior," Group for the Advancement of Psychiatry Report 27, 1954.
4. Jessner, L. 1959. "The Role of the Mother in the Family," in S. Liebman (ed.), *Emotional Forces in the Family*. Philadelphia: J. B. Lippincott Co.
5. Kierkegaard, S. 1959. *Either/Or*, Vol. II. New York: Doubleday, Anchor Books.
6. Lewis, A. 1950. *An Interesting Condition: The Diary of a Pregnant Woman*. Garden City, New York: Doubleday & Company, Inc.
7. Mead, M. Nov.-Dec., 1957. "Changing Pattern of Parent-Child Relations in an Urban Culture," *Int. J. Psychoanal.*, 38:369-78.
8. Ness, C. M. 1959. "The Role of the Father in the Family," in S. Liebman (ed.), *Emotional Forces in the Family*. Philadelphia: J. B. Lippincott Co.
9. Shaw, G. B. 1937. Preface to "Getting Married," in *The Doctor's Dilemma*. New York: Brentano.
10. Spiegel, J. P. Feb., 1957. "The Resolution of Role Conflict within the Family," *Psychiatry*, 20:1-6.
11. Spock, B. 1957. *Baby and Child Care*. Rev. Ed. New York: Pocket Books, Inc.

8

The Obstetrician's Responsibility
in Reducing Stress Due to Pregnancy

Charles E. Flowers, Jr., M.D.

Dr. Jessner's excellent and practical appraisal of the stressful aspects of pregnancy on marriage is approached from the viewpoint of the psychiatrist. It is appropriate that obstetricians become aware of the potential stress that pregnancy and the post-partum period may produce in marriage.

Maternal and fetal mortality have been reduced to an almost irreducible figure among the upper socio-economic groups. A similar reduction in the lower social groups must await improved educational facilities, increased motivation, and improved family planning. Today, the obstetrician's major responsibility is in prenatal care and the education of his patients in nutrition, physiology of pregnancy, preparation for labor and delivery, and giving assistance to the emotional needs of his patients. The appreciation of the emotional stress in pregnancy is the obstetrician's most important obligation; it is too often neglected.

A prenatal visit that consists of merely taking the blood pressure, palpating the abdomen, and making polite conversation does not meet the emotional needs of an expectant mother. Ideally, a prenatal visit must consist of an accurate appraisal of fetal growth and maternal adjustment to the physiological and psychological demands of pregnancy. Moreover, it must consist of a discussion period that will allow the obstetrician to carry out a preconceived program of preparation of the patient for labor and delivery and provide the patient with the opportunity of questioning and discussing with her obstetrician her physical complaints and physiological changes. Frequently, the expectant mother also needs assistance in meeting the emotional problems engendered by pregnancy.

This type of prenatal care can reduce obstetrical complications, assist the patient in making the emotional transition to motherhood, and provide valuable prophylaxis against major psychiatric disorders.

Obstetricians and gynecologists may help create stressful situations in marriage by failing to provide sufficient emotional support for their patients and by failing to assist them in adjusting to coitus and understanding psychic factors that lead to pelvic pain, dyspareunia, dysfunctional bleeding, and housewife fatigue.

The Unplanned Pregnancy

A particularly stressful situation in marriage arises when a young couple have an unplanned pregnancy because of an inadequate premarital examination. Virginity does not preclude the fitting of a diaphragm or the prescribing of oral contraceptives. When a young wife must work while her husband goes to school she deserves the best possible contraceptive advice. Moreover, the premarital examination must not merely prepare a couple for the physical intimacies of marriage, it must prepare them for the emotional stresses that are inevitable.

An unplanned pregnancy may lead to a chain reaction of unfortunate events. The financial difficulties engendered may be frightening, but the emotional problems may become volcanic. While the young bride is struggling to adjust to the sexual aspects of marriage, she suddenly finds the hormones of pregnancy reducing her sexual urge. She becomes fatigued, irritable, and nauseated. If the husband is too immature and fails to provide sufficient support, marital bliss may become a mirage. A more tragic long-range consequence may develop when an unplanned pregnancy necessitates the young wife assuming the role of mother, wife, and wage earner to the extent that she has little time to mature intellectually or to be with her husband. Mutual friends and interests are not developed and all too often she is finally outgrown and discarded.

Advice Concerning Coitus in Pregnancy

All normal women desire and need physical affection. It is unfortunate that many obstetricians advocate periods of abstinence during pregnancy. There is no evidence that coitus should be avoided during the early months of pregnancy or during the final six weeks. There is also no reason why coitus should not be resumed as soon as the episiotomy is healed and dyspareunia is not present. In the majority of patients this is within a two- to three-week period.

The gravid female is painfully aware of her blobby figure and the additional unclassical curves. She needs reassurance from her husband that his affection is unchanged. The mature expression of affection through coitus can alleviate many of the anxieties concerning the normality of her unborn child, the dangers and discomfort of labor and delivery, and the approaching responsibilities of motherhood.

This was illustrated recently by a patient who was becoming more irritable, anxious, hypochondriacal, and insomniac. She was eating excessively and gaining weight rapidly. A frank discussion of the problem in the privacy of the consultation room led the patient to say, "Doctor, I have always needed my husband's love and affection; please call him and tell him that it is all right to make love to me." The simple telephone call was more effective than the previously prescribed diuretics and tranquilizers.

Stresses of Pregnancy in Marriage Observed by the Obstetrician

The mature couple anticipates pregnancy and the birth of a child with great enthusiasm. However, hyperemesis and various psychosomatic complaints are frequent problems among immature wives who have never assumed a reasonable amount of responsibility as children in helping with the household chores, cleaning their rooms, and learning to cook. These women assume marriage to be merely a blissful continuation of their previous life. Thus the adjustment to marriage is difficult and the adjustment to a pregnancy seems formidable. If the husband is also immature, he often finds the physical and personality changes in his wife unbearable; he seeks the solace of his fraternity brothers or previous girl friend while the young bride may retreat to the seeming security of her home. It is important that the obstetrician anticipate these problems and discuss them in a forthright manner with his patient and her husband. Moreover, he must refer some of the more serious problems for psychiatric or marriage counseling.

The Jealous Husband

The majority of husbands are delighted when their wives become pregnant; they show greater affection and are more solicitous. There is an occasional husband, however, who becomes jealous of the increased attention paid to his wife by the two families and their friends. He also becomes unconsciously jealous of the newborn child.

This is unfortunate since this problem implies immaturity of the husband and possible future marital problems. The husband should be made to understand the reasons for his wife's greater attention from the families and friends—i.e., the approach of labor and delivery, the new heir, and the general awe concerning the birth process. Moreover, he should develop some insight into his personal problems that have caused this jealousy. It is important that the wife discuss these with her husband and when possible show increased affection toward him. Although this problem is rare, it is occasionally of such seriousness that marital counseling is necessary to assist the husband in adjusting to the pregnancy and to the marriage.

The Stress of Unsuccessful Pregnancies

Obstetricians must be sensitive to the stresses in marriage that may occur when a pregnancy terminates in an abortion, fetal death, or a severely damaged child. The unborn child may mean many things to different parents. It may represent the long-anticipated heir, the cement that will hold together a difficult marriage, or the assurance of adequate femininity or masculinity. The unborn child may represent a new being created in love and anticipated as a joy that will add greater motivation for working and living. But an abortion, a fetal death, or a damaged child may represent to the patient life's way of exacting payment for an illicit love affair, premarital sexual experiences, unhappiness with the unplanned pregnancy, a rebellious childhood, or even the failure to live up to parental expectation. The obstetrician must perceive these problems and explain the occurrence in such a manner that the patient does not have guilt feelings of omission or commission.

Labor and Delivery

Every expectant mother approaches labor and delivery with fears and uncertainty. Fear of childbirth is a natural inheritance of the generations that have preceded; they have been handed down by stories and innuendos. Unfortunately, it is the rare and exceptional woman who will tell an expectant mother that she looks well, is carrying the baby beautifully, and that the child looks just the correct size for her build and pelvis, and that she should anticipate having a simple and easy delivery. Most women are told horror stories about pregnancy and subjected to such trite remarks as "You will never go to term," "Are you sure the baby is in the correct position?" and "You know my aunt died in childbirth."

Thus the well-adjusted wife desires her husband to be with her during labor to add to her security as she approaches the unknowns of labor and delivery and is subjected to the embarrassing exposure in the labor area.

Although some expectant mothers want their husbands to be with them in order that they can watch them suffer in labor, the majority of women want their husbands' understanding and physical support and reassurance. They are disappointed if their husbands cannot provide this support and understanding.

A recent occurrence in the labor area was most revealing in this regard. The couple had been left by themselves in the labor room during the early first stages of labor. When the physician returned the husband was lying beside his wife reading a book, his shoes were off exposing his dirty white socks. His comment was, "Say Doc, can't you get this thing over?" The patient was embarrassed and apologetic; one could not help but wonder with her if any secure marriage could be achieved with such a husband. The obstetrician has no power to overcome the selection of an unfortunate husband, but the obstetrician should provide parent education for the husband and supervise a group of parents' classes that will allow the husband and wife to understand the physiology of childbirth, the nutritional and physical requirements of a normal pregnancy, and the appreciation of a properly conducted labor and delivery.

The Puerperium

The puerperium is generally associated with some episodes of depression. This depression is undoubtedly related to the rapid fall in the circulating hormones, the absorption of breakdown products of the uterus and the placental site, and the realization of the approaching responsibility of the new child. It is important that the patient and her husband appreciate the normal physiological causes of this mild depression and the particular personal problems that are involved. An understanding husband is a tremendous therapeutic adjunct; an immature husband can bring about the dissolution of a marriage. It is important that the obstetrician anticipate these problems and give the patient and her husband insight as to the causes of the mild depression and methods by which it may be remedied.

The immediate post-partum period is not the only stressful time in the puerperium. The change in the family life which the first child may cause and the added burden that additional children cause by increasing the physical fatigue of the mother and the financial burden of the father may be far-reaching. Wives often feel they are suffering from anemia or some chronic illness. The burdens of motherhood are often used as an excuse by the wife for not maintaining an attractive physical appearance, expressing her affection sexually, or finding time to appreciate her husband's anxieties and financial problems. The responsibility of motherhood is all too often not appreciated by husbands, and they fail to give the wife needed emotional support. A vicious circle develops without the husband or wife realizing or appreciating their mutual difficulties.

The obstetrician has a responsibility to explain the psychic and physical fatigue that does occur post-partum and help both marital partners realize that the solution of the problems will be found with improved communication between them, the setting aside of time for their own relaxation and recreation, and utilizing the valuable therapeutic effect of expressing mature affection with sexual love.

Summary

The obstetrician is intimately associated with two of the most important facets of life—reproduction and marriage. It is impossible for him to be all things to his patient and to her husband, but it is important for him to recognize his responsibility for the emotional and marital health of his patients.

Adequate prenatal care must consist of a preconceived program of preparation for childbirth and appreciating and understanding the emotional problems of pregnancy. Each trimester is usually associated with some physical and psychological complaints; adequate prenatal care can prevent these from becoming complications of pregnancy.

Obstetricians must develop the ability to anticipate marital problems, understand their causes, and appreciate their importance. He must develop the ability to listen to his patients and guide them to reasonable solutions. Finally, he must appreciate major problems that require particular skill and time in solving. These must be promptly referred for psychiatric or marital counseling.

The practice of obstetrics is the only specialty that allows the patient to achieve a real bonus from a hospital admission. In all other conditions, one must be happy to achieve the former state of health. It, therefore, behooves obstetricians to conduct a delivery in such a manner that the patient leaves the hospital with improved physical and emotional health.

9

Marital Problems in Pediatrics

Alanson Hinman, M.D.

Although absolute "proof" is not always possible, there can be little doubt that environmental tensions have direct and indirect physical and emotional sequelae in infants and children. The most effective treatment of the gastrointestinal hypermotility and spasm that is termed "colic" consists of relaxation of the parents and tranquilization of the environment. Sedatives and antispasmodics given to the infant are of help, but administration of them in actuality or verbally to the parents is more effective. There is good evidence that emotionally important stimuli underlie exacerbations of asthma, eczema, and urticaria. In mucous colitis, psychotherapy is an absolute therapeutic necessity. The list of illnesses in which emotional tensions have an etiologic or exacerbative effect is long and grows continuously. The interrelationships between environment and emotion, psyche and structure, functions and feelings, stress and sickness, insult and illness—these unproven but accepted continua of interaction—are best shown diagrammatically (see the accompanying figure).

Sources of Tension

With this as a structural substratum, a discussion is possible of the relationship of familial problems and the illnesses of infancy and

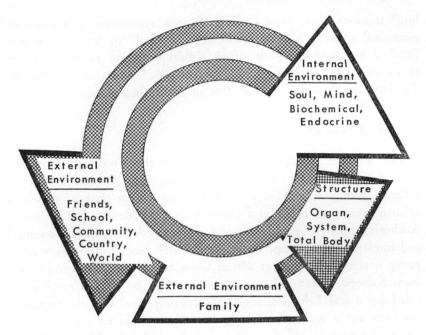

childhood seen in a pediatrician's office. For the single purpose of clarity the multiplicity of emotional stimuli, both positive and negative, occurring in any community-parent-child relationship and having direct or indirect effect on the totality of balances and adjustments known as "health" and "normality" will be called "tensions." It must be clearly stated at the outset that this emphasis on the reality of psychogenic factors in pediatric illnesses does not constitute a negation of any of the "organic" causes—endocrine, metabolic, bacterial, viral, traumatic, or degenerative. Neither is a value judgment implied nor an argument sought. These have been published before, and will be many times, before the "truth" or the "fact" can be established. On the contrary this emphatic restatement of the relationship between tension and illness has as its purpose the sincere hope that an increasing number of physicians seeing sick children will look beyond the physical examination and the laboratory studies to the patient's environment. Something more enduring than symptomatic therapeusis may then be possible.

Tensions can be acute or chronic; marked, moderate, or mild; active or passive. They are obvious or obscure. There are no "absolute" tensions, since some children express symptoms as a result of emotional stimuli that are considered "normal" or intrinsic in any family's interactions, while other children appear to respond not at all to "overwhelming" or "catastrophic" situational problems. Tensions can, however, be classified in a meaningful pattern.

Normal Tensions

The "normal" tensions of family life are those resulting from the mere combination of three or more distinctive personalities in an intimate group—the family. There are continuing changes to which adjustments must occur and about which decisions must be made. Authority must be established and maintained. Planning is essential and implementation must occur. Individual needs must give way to group needs. Group desires will at times be superseded by individual ones. Someone must tell and someone must be told. Compromise, aided by moral behavior, social structuring, and mutual respect is the basis for a successful family life. Some children are unable to accept the normal variations in parental moods, the demands for increasing amounts of self-control, or the recurrent need for self-denial and compromise. There may be biochemical, genetic, or other undemonstrable bases for such inabilities to handle "normal" variations in environmental tensions. Such children, happily enough relative medical rarities, need individualized help. Environmental manipulation is worth trying but it is not always successful. Sometimes placement, with a total environmental change, is helpful.

Abnormal, But Self-Limiting, Tensions

The next category of tensions might well be termed abnormal but self-limiting. The interruptions to smooth interpersonal relationships can be significant as a result of marked changes in economic status, acute illness, change of occupation, movement from one community to another, enforced absence of one parent because of business or professional demands, and so forth. Symptomatology in the infant or the child does not always have a direct temporal relationship to such increases in environmental tension. The symptoms may not be emotional or behavioral in type and obvious correlation with the causative occurrence may be difficult at times. Indeed, pre-existing sub-clinical maladjustments may be "triggered" into organic symptomatic expression by the added strain of one of these abnormal, yet self-limited, situations. Obviously, therapy must be based on direct knowledge of the environmental factors and it must be aimed at a practical and realistic readjustment of the child to his family and the family to its child.

Abnormal, But Seldom Self-Limiting, Tensions

The third group of tensions are also abnormal but seldom self-limiting. They are concomitants or sequelae of emotional pathology in the child's environment. Real marital pathology is a potent and persistent precursor in the production of psychogenic problems in pediatrics. The tensions resulting from emotional illness in either parent or in one of a child's siblings will frequently produce symptomatology in the child. One of the usual concomitants of emotional problems in any person is an increased concentration on self. This in turn prevents giving love or support to others. It is not difficult to see how emotionally "left out" the child may become if one parent is emotionally ill, the other upset and distracted by that illness, and the siblings disturbed by the lack of direction, interest, and emotional warmth from the parents.

A similar deprivation may result if one of a child's siblings is chronically ill, severely handicapped physically or intellectually, or has emotional problems. The concentration of maternal and paternal concern and the increased needs for daily care and nursing may leave the "normal" child with sub-minimal amounts of affection and attention. All too often parents feel compelled to "make it up" to the handicapped child and they overdo in matters of care and time and overemphasize their emotional involvement. The handicapped child is often infantilized and the normal siblings begin to show symptoms of deprivation.

The illnesses or symptoms seen in children of alcoholic fathers or mothers are legion. The eight-year-old daughter of a highly-successful advertising executive exemplifies the immediate or direct response. Every weekend her father drank himself into a boisterous, staggering state. Every Saturday night, the pediatrician would have to rush to the home and administer adrenalin for the child's severe, cyanosis-producing asthma. Such a direct cause and effect relationship does not require much diagnostic acumen on the part of the physician, yet there are other symptomatic responses in children to alcoholism in their parents that may not appear to be causally related when first seen. These may range from minor behavioral aberrations—fearfulness, evasiveness, lack of productivity, inability to concentrate—through socially-disrupting events, such as school phobia, to complete withdrawal and emotional breakdown.

It can be seen, then, that there exists a spectrum of tensions with an infinite variety of causes and effects. These ebb and flow in all normal life situations, but they may flood in some. Early recognition of the role of environmental tensions in the production and/or continuation of many different types of physical illness will frequently diminish the amount of damage done by any such flooding. Then the proper dikes and spillways of therapy can be designed and recurrences prevented.

Parental Attitudes Which May Affect Children's Adjustments

In addition to the environmental tensions just categorized, there are certain parental attitudes that have important and enduring effects on the developmental adjustments that infants and children must make if they are to remain in relative emotional and physical homeostasis. These attitudes are, for the most part, unconscious and hence all the more insidious. Many of them are secondary to similar attitudes towards the marital partner, to marriage itself, to childbirth, or to the role of female or male. A boy who is never allowed independence of thought or action may grow into a passive dependent adult. Reaction formation may produce a veneer of aggressivity but the unconscious strivings can, and often do, break through. A daughter with deeply rooted hostilities towards an overly-dominant mother may not be able to achieve sufficient feminine identification to allow her to accept marriage and motherhood as natural and real goals for her adulthood. Space does not permit a thorough evaluation of the many possible inhibitors of a successful marital adjustment and the pediatrician is not the person most likely to be consulted

about marital problems. However, he may be one of the first professionals to see some parental attitudes that may be, but are not always,
reflections of marital discord being expressed as feelings towards or
methods of management of children. Therefore, awareness of the
existence of such attitudes and some knowledge of the meaning and
importance of them is essential to the physician's ability to evaluate
more properly any parent-child relationship. For this reason, then,
re-emphasis at this juncture seems justifiable.

Unplanned Pregnancies and Unwanted Children

Not all pregnancies are planned and many children arrive at in-
opportune times, in too rapid succession, or too plentiful a supply.
In spite of assiduously applied human ingenuity, the ideal and error-
free contraceptive, with the exception of celibacy, has not been developed. In spite of the fact that not wanting children and being opposed
to motherhood are equivalents of overt anti-Americanism in the
expressed opinions of the majority of our citizens, there are many
unwanted children. Consider the case of the nearly blind and retarded
child whose hyperactivity was out of proportion to his handicaps.
Routine history revealed that he was "unplanned" by his young
parents. His father was in his third year in college and they lived in
a trailer park. Their finances were the mother's earnings and grandparental largesse, the latter accompanied by considerable demands for
continued dependency on the part of the young parents. These factors alone could account for the friction and emotional pressures that
seemed to underlie the boy's insecurity and hyperactivity. However,
further questioning revealed that because of fear of another unwanted
pregnancy and the even greater fear that they might produce another
handicapped child, the parents had practiced coitus interruptus since
the birth of the handicapped child. Their home life was little more
than an armed truce, since they were both sexually unsatisfied, even
though they had increased the frequency of their intercourse markedly. With this information it was not hard to see why the patient
was as he was, being but one more upsetting element in a grossly unsatisfactory marital situation. A frank discussion of the fear of pregnancy was held with both these young parents. It was kept at
superficial levels and centered on the fear of having a second child

with handicaps and the fear of adding to the already strained financial picture. No attempt was made to discuss attitudes towards motherhood or fatherhood and there was only indirect discussion of the grandparental influences. It was felt that intelligent contraceptive advice would decrease some of the intramarital tension and the wife was referred for gynecologic examination and fitting of a diaphragm. (As a side issue, this mother was so upset by physical examinations and, in particular, pelvic examination, that she had not returned to the obstetrician's for her six weeks' post-partum appointment. Time did not permit investigation of the basis for this apparently intense fear.) The advice and referral did appear to reduce tensions for a short while and the child did become somewhat less hyperkinetic. The "cure" was short-lived, however, because of an unwillingness to relax fully and trust the contraceptive device. Repeated counseling sessions occurred and some progress in quieting the environmental tensions occurred. In spite of the contraceptive device, however, the mother soon became pregnant. There was a short period of intense emotional turmoil; but with strong supportive help, the mother has been able to handle this new additional problem. She has had relatively little help from her husband, but she has shown considerable maturation in her own attitudes towards her handicapped son. He has responded by being less difficult behaviorally.

Methods of Handling Feelings of Rejection

Parents of unwanted children cannot flout public opinion. They must work out some method of dissembling their inner feelings. Most of them all but automatically repress any conscious feelings of rejection and attempt to fool themselves as well as the public. Unfortunately, the act is superficial and the disguise somewhat transparent. The underlying rejection, though seldom, if ever, overtly expressed, prevents the development of those strong and deep emotional necessities—affection, acceptance, and approval.

Overprotection

Overprotection is an easily defensible parental attitude. It is often impossible to distinguish between realistic and necessary protective acts and attitudes and overprotection. How can a parent be criticized for a constant, unceasing, and obviously unselfish effort to insure the child's health and safety? Yet such continuous hovering destroys the child's initiative and hampers the development of self-sufficiency. Why try? Mother or father is going to make the decision anyway. Such a child's frustrations can seldom be openly expressed. Often they are disguised as symptoms or illnesses.

There seems little value in selecting any given case to illustrate this, since all pediatricians see many examples. However, one mother who was just beginning to have conscious knowledge of her attitudes may help to clarify compensatory overprotection. Her child, born after her thirty-sixth birthday, was wanted and planned. She had ample help and his early infancy presented no great problems to her. However, at twenty to thirty months of age he showed increasing emotional instability and had temper tantrums when she left without him and when she came home. If she planned time with him, neither of them was relaxed and he continued to be infantile and irritable. Her chief complaint, after the initial standard history-taking was done, was that she became restless and unhappy at home with him. She would do her very best to be with him every minute, supervising his play, feeding, and rest periods, yet he would be irritable and difficult. She tried scheduling afternoons "off duty" because she wanted to be out playing golf (at which she was highly successful), but when she was out, she could not enjoy herself because she knew she should be home being a good mother. She had provided people and things and the best of care for her son, but she was not at all convinced that he was really being given the care he needed. Although she was quite aware that their relationship was unsatisfactory, she could not admit that he had become a serious interruption to her own pursuits and satisfactions. When she did realize this, with minimal professional help, she learned to share her time and the child's problems gradually diminished and normal growth and development ensued.

Perfectionism

Perfectionism is also defensible. Do not all thinking, feeling parents want their child to be unblemished, without handicaps, and as close to the "ideal" as possible? Who would dare to criticize a parent who watches for every early sign or symptom and wastes no time in seeking prompt professional help? Who can deny that unceasing efforts to teach and train are justified and that parents should not accept less than the right answers, the proper behavior, or the polished manner?

The paternal grandmother of the retarded boy with congenital cataracts had every minute of his daily care carefully scheduled. His diet was measured and balanced with precision; if he vomited he was re-fed almost immediately to prevent weight loss. She was convinced that no one could care for him as well as she. Further investigation showed she had raised her son in much the same way, objected to his early and "forced" marriage, was totally unaccepting of his "sloppy" wife. She had criticized her daughter-in-law from the outset for her inefficient and improper housekeeping. She harassed her throughout the pregnancy because she did not accept the advice of one who had "been through it once and knew what she was talking about." Needless to say, she began to usurp the mother's place just as soon as the boy was large enough to be brought home from the premature nursery. As soon as the diagnosis of congenital cataracts was established, the paternal grandmother felt her suspicions about the daughter-in-law's conduct in pregnancy had been confirmed and she fully usurped the role of mother to the baby. She kept him at her own home "because my son's wife would not follow the doctor's instructions," and it was not long until she refused to let the boy's mother have him even on weekends. Having achieved success at being the "mother" of her son's child, this grandmother gradually worked on until she had undermined any positive feelings her son still had for his young wife. When the little boy was about three months old, separation was "achieved" and divorce proceedings had been started. In the evaluation of this child, the clinic staff had to deal with the grandmother directly since the mother knew so little about the child's developmental and medical histories. The father's dependence on his mother was pathetically obvious and his own attitudes about his wife were essentially "parrotings" of his mother's. In the face of the outrageously perfectionistic handling to which this child had been subjected it seems needless to state that he was hyperkinetic, irritable, vomited his forced feedings frequently, and had a badly disturbed sleep pattern. Since the grandmother's routine was not subject to modification, the child was placed temporarily. Within a week in a warm structured environment, he was relaxed and responsive. The grandmother, however, could not relinquish her controls of her son and grandson and was apparently quite unable to be content with her own role of wife to her own husband. After the handicapped child had been placed, his father promptly remarried and moved away from his home town and his mother's direct influence. This, then, left the grandmother with no one to "mother." She promptly began a series of frequent visits to the child-caring facility in which her grandson had been placed and attempted to continue to control his care and environment. Some early allowances were made by the staff, feeling she needed a transitional period, but it soon became virtually impossible to absorb her constant harassments. Following a most direct and authoritative review of her many role-usurpations and the negative effects they had had on the child, she stopped visiting for a brief period. However, she found another resource for the child's care and prevailed on her son to come and remove the boy from the child-caring facility. Unfortunately, there has been no follow-up in this case. It is known, however, that the grandmother has reassumed control of her grandson and has him in her care again. His reaction to this is unknown.

Although this case has been cited to illustrate parental perfectionism, it emphasizes another area of marital disharmony that may often be first suspected in the pediatrician's office. This is the sometimes irritating, often destructive, effect of mothers- and fathers-in-law on parent-child relationships.

The reality of a prolonged adolescence in the present North American culture delays maturation in some individuals who may be parents themselves before they are independent of their own parents. Socio-economic factors being what they are, it is no longer unusual for individuals to be married and produce one or more children before they have completed their education or graduate professional training. Since the grandparents continue to pay the bills, they may continue to act *in loco parentis* and strive mightily to retain authority. Subsequent resentments are not infrequent. All involved have sufficient "right" on their sides to allow some reality to form the basis for the hurt feelings.

With such a power struggle going on at the top level, many infants are subjected to greater than normal tensions and may show symptoms of one sort or another. Very often questions concerning the "why's" of a mother's child-rearing practices and the "who-told-you-that's" will show the mother-in-law to be the power behind the throne and, as such, a source of conflict and tension.

Once having uncovered such a problem, the pediatrician may have a difficult time solving it. Frequently an open discussion, tempered with diplomacy, will serve to let the participants see the situation with greater clarity and some objectivity. Often, they are then able to make some compromises and reach a new balance of power.

Overt Rejection

The third parental attitude is overt rejection. This is rarely seen in "pure culture" but when it is present it presents a problem of great magnitude. Such parents do not try to dissemble their feelings but they do, as a rule, place their contact with the children on an appointment basis, infrequent, formalized, and emotionally cold. Their own needs continue to occupy first place and the emotional needs of their children are not often of any great importance to them.

The schoolteacher who wanted a husband and the social aspects of marriage, but felt children would only hamper her personal and professional freedom, could easily and openly express her conscious rejection. She was quite aware that she "shouldn't feel this way" but was intellectually and emotionally honest enough to discuss her true feelings. Insofar as could be determined, the pregnancy was "wanted" by both parents, but subsequent interviews revealed that the mother had considerable unexpressed reservation and it is doubtful that she had really desired either the first child, a normal female, or the second, a boy whom she brought in for evaluation because he had stopped saying words and begun to have nocturnal crying spells associated with head-banging at twenty-six months of age.

This mother's first pregnancy, when she was twenty-six years of age, was complicated by the development of a duodenal ulcer. The mother gained forty-three pounds while carrying the patient and was placed on a salt-poor, low-calorie diet. She reported some excessive nausea and vomiting but no signs or symptoms of toxemia. There was some uterine inertia before delivery, but the delivery itself was uncomplicated. The infant's neonatal course was normal except for colic and vomiting, which finally subsided after several changes of formula. Development and growth were quite normal throughout the first fourteen to sixteen months of life, but the child did not develop multiple word combinations nor continue to add to his vocabulary.

The mother cared for the boy and his older sister until he was five months old. She then returned to school teaching. There were no changes of any apparent emotional importance until the boy was twenty-five months of age, at which time the parents moved to a new state and new positions for both of them. The mother felt that her son's regression started just after this move. The symptoms, other than discontinuation of speech and the nocturnal crying spells, included a great increase in diurnal temper tantrums, marked hyper-kineticism, and the development of some unusual manneristic behavior including an apparently compulsive need to feel his mother's hair frequently, a perseverated opening and closing of doors, a habit of carrying a stick and beating on the floor or the ground at frequent intervals, a proclivity for hiding in closets, and an increasingly apparent look of being out of contact with his environment. He showed a complete lack of progress in neuromuscular abilities and moderate to marked regression in social and adaptive abilities. He was completely uncooperative during psychological testing, paying virtually no attention to the test materials or the psychologist. He achieved a social quotient of fifty-five on a Vineland Social Maturity Scale (questions asked his parents about demonstrated abilities at home).

Although this child did not show all the signs and symptoms, he was diagnosed as infantile autism.

Since the mother was aware of her rejection and yet intellectually and socially responsible, therapy was directed towards her gradual reassumption of care for her son. No effort was made to "force" her affection, but she was told that his greatest chance for re-integration of his personality depended on a re-establishment of her as his "mother." She was not asked to abandon her career, but some planning was done concerning sharing of time. A warm and motherly housekeeper was found by the parents and she replaced the day help that had been employed before the evaluation. With these factors in operation the boy began to respond to a limited degree. Sufficient time has not yet elapsed to warrant any prognostication, but it is felt that this mother will be able to overcome some, if not all, of her negative feelings towards her son and that he will reverse his course and re-assume a more normal developmental course. There are other parents who neglect their children and even some who physically abuse their children. Space does not allow a discussion of these more extreme forms of rejection. The end point of rejection is complete abandonment of the child.

Non-Compensatory

There is one other attitude in parents that may resemble compensatory overprotection but lacks any rejection. These are parents who have had difficulty in conceiving or who have lost children. Their child is too valuable and the investment of love is overdone. Such children are infantilized and "spoiled." These are often difficult problems in therapy and challenge the pediatrician's skill, ingenuity, and patience.

Extra-Familial Tensions That May Affect the Child

Not all children's problems are in response to intrafamilial tensions, although they are the point of emphasis of this chapter. Many other factors will affect an infant's or a child's adjustment. These include: socio-economic deprivation, including cultural deprivation; racial or religious minority groups with secondary social pressures; type of neighborhood; frequent change of environment; or restrictions of religious dogma (a family in which there is a great deal of emphasis on the form of religion without any force, i.e. a stringent set of rules and regulations without any application of the basic principles of love, compassion, or forgiveness). Any one of these may exert strong and continuing pressures on the child's personality. The end result may be clinical symptomatology, either physical or emotional or both.

The Pediatrician's Responsibility and the Holistic Attitude

The pediatrician's responsibility is more than preservation of health, prevention of disease, and restoration to health if illness has occurred. The "new pediatrics" is holistic in its approach. The pediatrician's field of interest has been broadened in recent years to include home and school safety, accident prevention, emotional problems, retardation and other handicapping conditions, education, delinquency, athletics, and others. These newer areas require the alert pediatrician to question beyond the "present illness" level and do more than treat the signs and symptoms. He must be aware of, knowledgeable about, and prepared to deal with environmental factors. No infant or child lives in a vacuum—he lives in a family or in a family substitute. Such must be considered when the child and his problems are in focus.

When to Suspect Marital Problems

There are some "ground rules" that may be helpful in leading the busy practicing pediatrician to suspect marital problems as possible factors in the production of symptoms and signs in a patient.

Suspect marital problems:

1. When the child's symptoms are out of keeping with any discoverable physical signs or laboratory findings.

2. When the child's symptoms, unsupported by signs or laboratory evidences, show recurrence or chronicity in spite of therapeutic attempts.

3. When the symptoms begin to show a relationship to time, season, or regularly-scheduled events.

4. When the mother or the father seems annoyed by, rather than worried about, the child's symptoms.

5. When one parent seems to blame the other for causing or increasing the symptoms.

6. When the parents show disagreement concerning discipline or a divergence of opinion regarding the importance of the symptoms.

There are obviously many other factors and findings that might raise the suspicion that the marriage is disharmonious, but those listed are perhaps the more frequently encountered.

Accessory Clinical Findings

In those cases where the pediatrician suspects marital problems as causative or contributory to his patient's problems, he will do well to look for some "accessory clinical findings." These are those small items of information seldom voluntarily contributed to a history, yet often crucial to a thorough understanding of the child's environment. Who "lives" in the home? There are the obvious permanent residents, yet often grandparents, neighbors, and household help are such regular and frequent visitors that they constitute a meaningful part of the child's environment. Are there elements in the family's social history that may have some bearing on the parents' problems or on the child's? Did they move in one generation from socially humble to socially prominent? Did they go from a higher level to a lower one? Have they had some sudden socio-economic reversal? Any one of these things could be the cause of marked parental emotional disturbances and the basis for parental disharmony.

There are some further factors that can cause marital problems and they are seldom obvious at the time of initial history-taking. Do the parents have similar socio-economic, cultural, and educational background? Are there major denominational or religious differences? Was there agreement among the grandparents at the time of the marriage? These may be brought to light with gentle guiding of the interview and any one of them could have a real effect on the parents' interrelationship and, through that, on the child.

The Mother Who Works Outside of the Home

The problem of the working mother must be considered. There are many situations in which this is a well-accepted and desirable arrangement and there are no discernible intrafamilial reactions. The mother's job serves as an outlet for her own needs, adds needed income, and does not interfere with her play or training times with her children. On the other hand, there are many women whose careers are of primary importance and marriage and children secondary. Sometimes such a mother is not consciously aware that she has given up that which she most wanted and does not really know why she has difficulty with homemaking and child-rearing. Some are aware of a recurrent longing for the "excitement" of their premarital occupation or profession but feel they should prefer motherhood. They may have some rather marked and serious problems in their marital adjustment and may show overprotection or perfectionism, rarely overt rejection, towards their children.

There have been, as yet, no satisfactory answers to the many questions about working mothers. Research into attitudes about women in occupations and professions and mothers as job-holders has revealed that a prejudice seems to exist against them. There would appear to be a broad distrust of placing women in positions of great responsibility in industry or in the professions and many positions remain virtually closed to women applicants. Many studies have been pursued regarding women's attitudes towards working after marriage and after childbirth, but it is difficult to evolve any comprehensive "moral judgment" or social ethic concerning working mothers.

The Attitudes of Husbands

It would be difficult to discuss fully the genesis of the many complex attitudes husbands have towards their wives' employment without reviewing a great amount of basic masculine attitudes. However, there are some generalizations that may serve as guides and should suffice for the pediatrician's investigation of the parental relationship as a possible source of his patient's difficulties. At a superficial level, it is usually possible to determine whether the husband approves or disapproves. By indirect questioning of both mother and father it is not difficult to determine whether they have "equal rights" in the home, in matters of discipline, in monetary management, and in regard to employment and creativity outside the home. Economic necessity may force an attitude of "approval" on the husband, but he may have rather deeply-seated resentment, prejudice, and envy. His own self-identity and confidence may be threatened and he may reflect these barely conscious feelings of insecurity in attitudes and actions that will gradually undermine the mother's sense of achievement within and without the home. Criticisms of hurriedly-prepared meals, poorly-controlled or undisciplined children, inefficient mother-surrogates, or lack of energetic "wifeliness" can act insidiously, yet continuously, to widen a marital breach.

The Emancipated Mother

The pediatrician should be aware of the many cross-currents in present-day motherhood. The American mother has been emancipated, but from what and to what? She is no longer needed as a producer of necessities for the home. These can be bought at the store. She is no longer the primary source of education for her children. They are now early exposed to and assimilated into extra-familial groups. She is no longer directly involved in her husband's economic productivity in non-farming families. Her absolute work load in home-making has been drastically reduced by labor-saving machinery and instant meals. To what, then, has she been emancipated? Frustration, a feeling of relative uselessness, a lack of a place to apply creativity and productivity, and an exaggerated sense of inferiority to the socially better-accepted male may become strong undercurrents in her emotional life. The pediatrician would find it easier if all mothers held child-bearing and child-rearing as their most important roles. Such is not really so and to naïvely hope to find it so will greatly hamper the doctor's ability to help, to counsel, and treat his patients and their parents.

The Reasons for Working Mothers

The pediatrician dealing with a situation in which both parents work may have his own personal bias about working mothers and this may interfere with his ability to be objective in his differential diagnosis of the child's problems. It is not possible to review the literature concerning the "rightness" or "wrongness" of the working mother, but it would seem germane to the emphasis of this chapter to list some of the factors involved.

1. Mother's job is an absolute economic necessity because—
   a. father's income is inadequate for even marginal family existence
   b. father is unable to work
   c. father is dead, divorced and not contributing to the family's support, etc.
2. Mother's job is a relative economic necessity because—
   a. parents want a better standard of living than father's income would allow
   b. parents have high educational goals for children and father's income is insufficient to finance them

      c. the father is in training or school and the parents de-
         sire to avoid indebtedness, to maintain a reasonably
         high standard of living, etc.

3. The mother's job is not an economic necessity but fulfills a
personal-social need because—
      a. she was highly-trained or had a special talent before
         marriage and feels a continuing obligation to society
         to use that training or talent
      b. she feels that being just a wife and mother is not a
         sufficient contribution and wants to add the creativity
         or productivity of her occupation or profession
      c. she is part of a husband-wife team or the business is
         family-based and her non-participation would de-
         crease socio-economic success or necessitate the em-
         ployment of someone outside the family.

4. The mother's job is neither an economic or personal-social necessity but results from emotional factors—
      a. some mothers appear to be unhappy in what appears
         to them as a submissive, dependent role, regardless
         of society's views, their own biological sex, normal
         heterosexual role in marriage, and normal attitudes
         towards childbirth and motherhood
      b. some mothers must assume a dominant role equiv-
         alent to or greater than that of their husbands be-
         cause of deeply-rooted feelings involving crossed-
         identification, antipathy towards their own mothers,
         inability to allow their husbands to replace their
         father figures, etc.
      c. some mothers find little challenge in homemaking and
         mothering, since modern technology and the usurpa-
         tion of much of the teaching roles of mothers and
         fathers by schools and organized activities for chil-
         dren have greatly decreased the need for creativity in
         these two areas.

It is not feasible nor possible to cover all the many facets of the
problem of the working mother. Neither is it possible to do more
than mention the non-working mother, although the frustrations

and unhealthy attitudes that she may have may contribute greatly to her marital problems and through them to symptomatology in her children.

The Need for Questions Beyond the Standard History

"Standard" pediatric histories will give considerable information about birth, growth, and development. The doctor will learn when and in what amounts certain foods were taken. He will record the time and type of illness. Yet he may not ask more than age and state of health of the parents. Often the important information that begins the identification of the problems that are causing, augmenting, or intensifying the child's physical and behavioral complaints are just a question or two beyond the usual new patient history. Not all pediatricians want to involve themselves in the emotional problems of a family, yet all desire to practice comprehensive pediatrics. There will be patients for whom "going the second mile" is vital.

What to Do After Making the Diagnosis

After the pediatrician has recognized that intrafamilial tensions are causing or intensifying the child's physical and/or emotional problems, he must begin to think therapeutically. He has several avenues down which he may travel. Treat the situation directly and personally; refer the patient to a child psychiatrist, a child guidance facility, or refer the parents for marital counseling or psychiatric help; or ask for a consultation from any of the above sources. It would be difficult to establish any rules in this since the decision must be modified by the type and severity of the problem, the physician's own skills and his security in approaching a counseling situation, the availability of other help, and the family's willingness to be referred for consultation or therapy.

Interpretation to Parents

However, the doctor making the diagnosis must take the first step, that of interpretation to the parents. Quite often, this is done by strong reassurance that no discoverable organic causes or factors are present.

If, to do this emphatically, many laboratory tests and procedures are enlisted as "evidence," the child's and parent's index of worry and apprehension may be raised to unnecessary levels. On the other hand, most physicians do not feel overly-secure in a psychosomatic diagnosis until they have done a reasonable amount of structural and organic investigation. The point to be emphasized is that of a balance in the investigation of any set of signs and symptoms. If the physician is alert to the possibility of emotional causes and attempts to evaluate their importance during his initial evaluation of the patient, some unnecessary studies may be avoided. The other side of the balance is often overloaded by a premature "snap" diagnosis of psychogenic illness without due consideration and investigation of the possible structural or physiological causes. Balance is, therefore, needed. A willingness and the ability to consider all types of factors as possible etiologic or contributory agents in any symptom or illness must become an integral part of every physician's diagnostic armamentarium and acumen. When the doctor has satisfied himself as fully as possible, he can be far more effective in his approach to the parents and the child. If he is not strongly convinced that the emotional entanglements in the home are of realistic importance in the causation or continuation of the child's illness, he cannot be very sincere or effective in interpretation to the family.

There are some approaches that have been effective in cases where marital problems have been a major factor in a child's illnesses. Most people have been educated sufficiently in the concepts of psychiatry to understand that feelings can be transmitted non-verbally. Most people know that they themselves have inner feelings of unrest when someone around them, particularly someone in authority, is tense, angry, or depressed. It is not usually difficult to establish a verbal agreement that such an effect is possible. Having done so, gentle leading from an extrafamilial occurrence to the existence of such an emotional impact within the family can be effected. Most mothers and fathers are aware that their children's behavior is quite different when they are away from their parents, e.g., in school, at the nursery, or with friends or relatives, than it is when they are with their parents alone. It is often profitable to present the adult corollary of this, namely that we are all too frequently one sort of person in public and quite a different sort at home where people should love us enough to understand our need sometimes to be selfish, irritable, and even uncontrolled.

Taking the first point, that is the reality of non-verbal communication of emotion and feelings plus the second point that we act differently in our home than we do in other situations, it is possible to bring many parents to the conscious realization that their own behavior, their individual attitudes, and their combined parental image will have a strong and penetrating effect on their child. In some families, this realization may be sufficient and they will take steps toward attitudinal changes and environmental modifications that will act as gradual modifiers of the stresses that have precipitated or augmented the child's problems.

Referral to Other Help

Other families may not be helped this easily and they may need length and depth in the discussion of intrafamilial attitudes and their own personal needs. For such situations, the practicing physician often has insufficient time and inadequate training. Should the family refuse the initial interpretation that the disharmony in the family is involved directly in the production or prolongation of the child's symptoms, an attempt to refer them to a guidance clinic, to marital counseling, or psychiatric help cannot be made immediately. The physician must attempt to hold the line momentarily. He has planted the seed and it may take time and the continuation of symptoms in the child before the parents will even consider additional professional help.

Many situations respond to simple suggestions that do not seem to involve any deep feeling-levels in the parents or the child and are aimed at relief of stress in only one or two small areas. Mealtime storms when each parent disagrees with the other's concept of proper diet or manners for the child can be avoided frequently by an authoritative explanation that the child will never eat if he feels he can play one parent against the other and that his manners will always be an imitation and not a response to what he is told to do. When this one area of disagreement has been avoided, the physician can then work slowly on other discrete areas, such as bedtime, study habits, etc.

Some parents are too disturbed maritally to be able to modify anything very important for their child or his illnesses. They feel that the physician's job is curing the child and that he has no right to involve the parents' problems in the therapy. For parents who feel thus, referral to other professional help is the doctor's only choice. His role is limited by the parents and he will find it difficult to change them sufficiently to allow him to operate as anything but the child's doctor.

Summary

In summary, there are several points worthy of re-emphasis. (1) Environmental tensions may have a direct and symptom-producing effect on infants and children. (2) Parental attitudes are potent modulators of children's environmental homeostasis. (3) Pediatricians have an absolute responsibility to be aware of environmental and emotional factors and they must include such as a part of their differential diagnosis of the child's illness. (4) There are some facets of history and symptomatology that often lead the physician to suspect marital problems. These are concerned with the type and timing of the signs and symptoms; the lack of any laboratory support for biochemical, infectious, endocrine, or structural disturbances; the quality and quantity of parental reactions to the illness; and the physician's awareness of subtle degrees of disagreement between the parents concerning the importance of the child or his illness to either one or both of the parents.

In addition, there are the accessory clinical findings concerning other people with strong emotional impact on the child, the presence of socio-economic problems or religious and educational disparities. (5) Having diagnosed the illness or symptoms as resulting from or aggravated by marital discord and intrafamilial tensions, the pediatrician must interpret this to the parents and the child and decide whether to treat the problem himself, seek a consultation from other professionals such as marital counselors or child or adult psychiatrists, or refer the family for therapy.

A bibliography is not appended to this chapter. There is little specifically written about marital problems as seen through the pediatrician's eyes. What has been written is scattered in time and place and deals with marital problems primarily or child psychiatry primarily. Interactions between the two must often be inferred. The "standard" texts of child psychiatry discuss the impact of separation, divorce, and "broken homes" but do not usually correlate these with physical as well as emotional symptomatology. In short, any pertinent bibliography would either be extremely short, and hence of little value, or so diffuse, extensive, and covering such a wide range of publications and years that it would be overwhelming and confusing.

10

How Teen-agers, Their Parents, and Their Doctors Can All Grow Up

Edward J. Hornick, M.D.

Locating the Adolescent

Adolescents are growing up through that hyphenated age, the age between the family they are in and the family they are going to make. That this in-between period is important to the adolescent everybody knows. It is a time when ideals are focused, when the dreams of childhood begin to be forged in the realities of school, work, and grown-up sex. What is not recognized so easily is how significant adolescents are to other members of the family. They are an eruptive force with parents, and they are upsetting to the younger children. It is insufficiently noticed, for instance, how the departure of a teen-age boy or girl to school or the army is followed by emotional difficulties of one sort or another for younger children in the family. But it is unfair to adolescents, their parents, and their brothers and sisters to regard their growing-up time as a phenomenon of doom. It is also a time of efflorescence, of increased energy, of increased reality, and of initial accomplishment in adult terms. There hangs over it the threat and the promise of maturity.

This portrait of an age group should be meaningful to doctors be-

173

cause they are necessarily responsive to the various vital facets of an individual. It is entirely human for them to feel differently toward different patients. According to his taste, a doctor may prefer a pretty woman, an intellectual woman, or a charming woman as a patient. It is an advantage to see the patient with all his qualities rather than to see him just as a disease or an "annual physical examination." So it is appropriate in human terms that the doctor should respond differently to and treat differently patients of different age, sex, class, and degree of illness. Among these variables, adolescence in a patient is often very evocative. That the physician is alive to and sometimes nettled by the pressure, impudence, and seductiveness of the adolescent is useful, if on the one hand he can control his own behavior and on the other hand can use such evocative stimuli to enhance his understanding of those he is examining and treating.

Dr. Millikan (I'll call him this), a family doctor of wide skill and intuition, had as a patient a teen-age boy whom he had brought into the world and cared for effectively and sympathetically ever since. At the age of fourteen, the boy refused to go to him any more and violently insisted that this doctor was "no good" and that he had to have another doctor. At first, Dr. Millikan was irritated. Then he thought it out. The boy's younger brothers and sister were going to him. He represented childishness. He relaxed and let time go by. In three years the boy came back to him and they got along as well as they had before.

Adolescence is the supremely turbulent period. A recent national conference, sorting out meaningful approaches to growth and crisis, settled on the following categories:

1. There are normal *periods* of crisis in the developmental history of all people. These include infancy to the age of five, puberty, pregnancy, and menopause.

2. There are normal *situations* of crisis such as the school, the job, or marriage.

3. There are *special* situations of crisis, such as disaster or death, particularly within the circle of one's family or friends.

4. There is the disaster of war or famine.[1]

If we examine this highly useful division of difficulties in relation to adolescence, it becomes very clear why adolescence is tough on everybody. It represents a violent change from an earlier edition of the body. During this period, crucial problems about school, about jobs, and about marriage are all decided. Happily, disaster and death are uncommon at this age, but with Universal Military Training in America, the issues of total war are not alien to this group.

The issues of military training are pertinent to all young men. The draft favors men who go on to college and men who marry. Since about 50 per cent neither go on to college, nor are married, they are caught in a no-man's-land where the military is not ready for them and prospective employers are reluctant to take them on. This profoundly affects their first chance of getting rooted in the adult world. On the more optimistic side, the draft does enable a great many young men to travel, to come to know other young men from other parts of the United States, and to experience living and working with men of all races, creeds, and colors.

The Adolescent Leaves Home

The first way in which the adolescent leaves the family is that he himself changes into a new edition at adolescence. The hormonal revolution initiated in the hypothalamus and transmitted through the anterior pituitary to the gonads and other glands produces widespread changes in primary and secondary sexual characteristics. This process according to the Stolzes is likely to run over a four-year period, with marked variations in duration and intensity. The growth spurt may be gradual over the four-year period, or the bulk of it may take place in one single summer. It is equally normal for the boy to grow fast as early as eleven or as late as eighteen or nineteen. What is true of growth is similarly true of voice changes, size of genitals, size of breasts, and other phenomena of adolescence.

In the course of this developmental process, the teen-ager constantly changes his notion of himself, his friends, his foes, his girl friend, whom he is most like, and who he would like to become. In more academic language, his body image, his identity and identifications, and his sexual and non-sexual alliances change rapidly and frequently. There are pleas to be treated as a baby and insistent demands to be treated as an adult. Those about him are hard put to it to know which part of the adolescent to address. If they answer the call from baby, they are reprimanded for condescension. If they grant the courtesies and prerogatives of the adult, they are considered indifferent and cruel by the adolescent. Often rebellion is a feature of this age group.

The teen-ager becomes disenchanted with his parents and yearns toward people and values at opposite poles from theirs. Rather than become disconcerted, it is far better if parents can see this as both developmental and temporary. By developmental I mean that it is necessary for the young person to disown his parents in order to find himself.

Judy Cohen was a second-year student in college four hundred miles from home when her parents learned of an affair she was having with a Christian boy. They practically kidnapped her from the college and placed her in treatment, at least partly as a punishment. It was rapidly apparent that Judy had been the darling of her family all her life, that her family had been an extraordinarily warm and interested one, and that she was having great trouble graduating from her family of origin. The counselor suggested a hands-off policy by the parents and refused the punitive role assigned him by them. Judy tested this once or twice, taking secret trips to see her forbidden lover. Then when she no longer needed him to establish her independence from her parents, she gave him up gracefully and became engaged to a young man of her own economic class and personal religion.

The particular battleground on which the issue is fought may be choice of dress, hour of curfew, or selection of friends. It may be a decision about a vocation or about a religious affiliation, but although the child's wish may have merit of its own, it is primarily used to establish a separate person. Once the separateness is accomplished, it tends to be temporary. There is the wonderful Mark Twain story about the college student who returned home after four years, amazed at how much his parents had learned during his absence.

One of the cushioning devices to which adolescents resort in their transition from one family to the other is the use of the teen-age gang or clique as an intermediate social solution between their earlier position as a dependent child and their later responsibility as a giving adult. The telephone wire has been called an umbilical cord connecting teen-agers to each other.

There are many kinds of peer groups, and most youngsters take part in several varieties. The commonest of all is the friendship between two boys or girls. They are likely to go places together, to play together, often wearing the same clothes, and certainly sharing the majority of their free time together in person or over the phone. It is not uncommon for these friendships to have a transitory character. In pre-adolescence, youngers frequently get together in informal play groups. These indulge in sand-lot baseball, epidemics of Hoola Hoops or yoyos, or stunt riding on bicycles. Most of their activities hinge on some show of strength by the boys. Then come the organized youth groups with a variable degree of adult leadership. Those in which the adult sponsorship is heavy protect the adolescents who are reluctant to leave their parents' supervision. They also provide cover for boys and girls to get together, allaying the anxiety of both parents and children. Secret clubs and gangs represent the most intensive teen-age group activity and within them there is the most room for teen-agers to try out the assorted roles they will be taking later in life independently of both their parents and the gang. In delinquent gangs as Redl pointed out,[6] a great deal of attention is given to elaboration of techniques that shield gang members from parental value systems. For instance, friendliness with adults is looked down upon, or it is allowed only under very special circumstances and "forgotten" when it challenges gang goals.

There is a resurgence of problems of eating and dieting. Obesity and concern with weight are common at this age. Anorexia nervosa is a rare disease which usually begins in adolescence. Even when it occurs later in life, there is commonly the history of a transient period of anorexia in adolescence. Perhaps the most common illness of this age in both sexes is acne, because of the increased secretory rate of sebaceous glands without adequate duct formation. Unfortunately for the adolescent, the acne often appears on the face where it impresses its owner as a hallmark of ugliness and inner badness. Often boys believe that it reveals their masturbation.

The onset of menstruation is a signal of coming of age to all girls, and a happy signal to girls who are ready. To those who are not ready, it often becomes the prime example of life as pain, illustrating how women are those born to suffer and to bleed and eventually to bear children in agony. Menstrual irregularity is the rule for one to two years after the onset of menstruation. The physiological as well as the psychological centers of the body require time to adjust and coordinate change.

By far the leading cause of deaths in adolescence is accidents, with cancer a poor second. Automobile crashes cause the largest number of accidental deaths, followed by drowning and hunting. While it is true that the adolescent is keener of eye and stronger of muscle than any later age group or any prior age group, he is prone to dispose his energies impulsively and the consequences are often tragic. In this department, it is interesting that adolescents have often been described as gawky and this time of life as the "awkward age." Actually objective tests of skill and dexterity show a progressive improvement during the teen ages. To return to the accidents, it is notable that adolescents in a jam tend to act out or to act up. A child of five in a jam tends to become fearful—of the dark, ghosts, witches. An adult in a jam is likely to become anxious or depressed, but an adolescent *does something*. If he happens to be in a car at such a time, he guns it, or he stops it, or he turns it. In any event, he is active. There is also a predilection on the part of adolescents to seek out playgrounds for action. Their restlessness leads them into sports as well as into playing "chicken" on the road (riding the center line until one "chickens out"). It is also true that by the time they begin to drive, they are also experimenting with drinking and sex. Alcohol in any quantity lowers the reaction time.

In the meantime, as the adolescent is maturing, there is a parental counterpoint, a series of crises frequently occurring in parents in their fifth decade. These crises have a life of their own, but inasmuch as parents and adolescents live in the same household, there is bound to be more projection and some scapegoating of the adolescent in the working through of the crisis. To begin with, parents themselves are decelerating. They are leaving life as the adolescents are entering it. It is not uncommon for parents to be jealous of their children's good looks, athletic prowess, or intellectual ability.

The family over a number of years establishes a given way of life in which the roles are set and the rules are structured. This way of life is shattered when an adolescent starts to make demands, to want his father's car, to use her mother's cosmetics, to smoke, and to drink. Moreover, adolescents ask for a different and greater part in the decision-making of the family. Especially their eventual departure or their threatened departure from the family may cause difficulty. For example, an Italian woman of forty had two teen-age daughters, both of whom had almost completed high school when the father of the family died. Within two months of the funeral, the mother purchased an expensive larger house for the family. The only justification for this was her hope of holding onto the daughters. It was the elder of these two daughters who was brought to the hospital with a depression, easily traceable to her rage at her mother's manipulation.

Often parents of both sexes become involved indirectly in the blatant sexuality of their adolescent children. Instances of actual incest are rare, but there is much prolongation into adolescence of childlike kissing and fondling by parents. It is most apparent, however, in the frequent and often unwarranted restrictions placed upon dating, curfews, dress, and allowances by parents. This is not meant to suggest that parents can or should relinquish their responsibility toward the adolescent. It is supremely necessary for the adolescent that the parents take a *mature and definite* stand on a great many issues. This provides him with limits within which he can find himself. However, there are many instances in which the parent exceeds his appropriate limit-setting. For example, a sixteen-year-old girl was brought in to the office by her father, who called her a whore. He felt that her hair was too bouffant and that her mascara and lipstick were unseemly in a girl of her age. Actually, the girl had no makeup on at the time he was leveling his accusations. Her father's eagerness to discourage sexuality in the girl was betrayed by his unwarranted accusations. When he tried, with some embarrassment, to wipe off the supposed makeup and found that, indeed, there was none, he was forced to realize to some extent his erroneous concept of his own daughter.

Parents are often involved in a "prime of life crisis" in which, much as the adolescent has to face the final edition of his or her physical self, the mother or father must come to terms with the limited life-achievement that he or she has attained. Up until the forties it may have been possible to expect greater wisdom, status, or wealth, but during that decade parents often experience the disappointment of many cherished dreams of glory. It might be more appropriate to say that many by-pass this let-down by pressing their expectations of themselves onto their children who will direct symphonies, run corporations, and become president. This is part of the destruction of Biff Loman by Willy Loman, that unfortunate salesman.

In all these categories the adolescent is easily scapegoated for parental life crises. It is the daughter who looks like a prostitute, not the father who is a lecher. It is the lazy college student who fails to make the dean's list, not the father who could not make his way past being assistant bookkeeper. It is the particular volatility of the adolescent that renders him available for the scapegoat role. Nor should it be forgotten that teen-agers do have real problems.

Betty Wilson is a nineteen-year-old girl who left high school after two years, at sixteen, and spent half the intervening time in a mental hospital. She has had two IBM punch-card jobs for two months each. When home, she sleeps all day, watches TV most of the night, refuses to wash her dishes or make her bed. Her own personal phone bill runs over twenty-five dollars a month, a sum her family can ill afford. She has entered the hospitals on three separate occasions following suicidal gestures. Her history sheds some light on her difficulty. Her mother was an alcoholic and neglected her so badly that the courts removed her from her mother as a malnourished infant of eleven months. She was placed in foster care with a childless couple who were permitted to adopt her when she was nine. In the meantime she had met her real father who was uncertain whether he wanted her with him and eventually decided against it. She was always a restless child, but she did well in school and with friends until she was sixteen. It is instructive to note that her adoptive mother also left school at sixteen and shortly thereafter moved out of her parental home.

These adoptive parents were about fifty at the time Betty was nineteen. The mother had lost a breast twenty-three years ago, had been rendered sterile by irradiation, and complained that she was unable to have any sexual relations because of pain after the irradiation. Betty became their whole life, and when she turned sixteen, they gave up what little outside enjoyment they knew—friends, walks, movies— in order to be available to Betty at every moment. Mrs. Wilson quit her job, and spent her time making Betty's bed and washing Betty's dishes, nagging Betty the while. In a family interview it became apparent that they had as much to gain from her illness as she did and that they were reluctant to provide any discipline to prod her from the crib, or any reinforcing experiences to convince her that grown-up life can be exciting. The parents' role is plain. However there are many parents like the Wilsons who try to keep their offspring children beyond their years. They were in the process of succeeding with Betty because Betty did not have sufficient integrative and adaptive stamina to make her own beachhead in the world outside the family. Her real problem was her developmental task of growing up. This would have been hard for her in any case.

The Adolescent Moves Toward His Own Family

We have been looking at the tremendous pull exerted on the adolescent by his sometime wishes to remain a child and by his parents' privately motivated desires to keep him a child. However there are also large-scale forces pressing him to grow up. These include his own need to develop, his parents' wish to help him, and the community's demand for his adult performance. Being an adult means jumping the hurdles—social, legal, economic, and emotional—that the society has defined for the achievement of adult status. The tasks of adolescence have been listed as separation from one's parents, definition of one's sexual role, selection of a vocation, and creation of a value system. Most adolescents accomplish these feats.

When difficulty occurs here, it may be laid partly at the door of our system. In Western culture the socialization of the teen-ager is accomplished by parents and teachers a generation removed from the adolescent, figures toward whom he has had both fearful and incestuous feelings during his earlier training. In Samoa they do things differently, so that the move from the nuclear family to the wider stage of community living is shepherded by the slightly older siblings. The disparity in age and power is less, and the friction is less too.

A more relevant critique of this process comes from Paul Goodman in his indictment of American society, *Growing Up Absurd*. "Growth, like any ongoing function, requires adequate objects in the environment to meet the needs and capacities of the growing child, boy, youth, and young man, until he can better choose and make his own environment.... With all the harmonious belonging and all the tidying up of background conditions that you please, our abundant society is at present simply deficient in many of the most elementary objective opportunities and worthwhile goals that could make growing up possible. It is lacking in enough man's work. It is lacking in honest public speech, and people are not taken seriously. It is lacking in the opportunity to be useful. It thwarts aptitude and creates stupidity. It corrupts ingenuous patriotism. It corrupts the fine arts. It shackles science. It dampens animal ardor." [4] These are strong words indeed and have a certain adolescent flavor themselves, but they indicate many of the features of adult society which impede the transition from the family of origin to the family of procreation.

Erik Erikson has followed the same theme in a different manner.[2] He has described the task of the late teens as one of coming to terms with a consistent subjective sense of self, which answers the "Who am I?" question of the mid-adolescent. Hopefully the adolescent seeks this sense of identity in an amalgamation of the significant adults and events in his prior experience which he holds together with the particular glue of his personality. He is himself. Erikson ascribes a special virtue to this time of life. It is fidelity.[3] It is compounded not only of the disillusion that the teen-ager has to feel about his parents and their values in order to separate himself from them, but also of the hopes and ideals and the sense of unique creativity that will guide his own life. Thus the adolescent is very sensitive to phoniness and hypocrisy in people and in institutions.

Perhaps the most important institution into which the late adolescent moves is marriage. More youngsters, especially more middle-class and upper-class youngsters, are dating earlier, going steady earlier, and marrying earlier than they did before World War II. This is related largely to increased wealth in the country, to the increased employment of mothers outside the home where they need not hold on to their children for their own needs, and occasionally to the subtle forcing of sexual and social maturity on teen-agers before they are equipped to deal with it. It is certain the divorce rate in this sample of early marriages is high. Margaret Mead has deplored the increase in early marriage for intellectual women, feeling that it deprives them of an opportunity for full intellectual growth. But early marriage may be an appropriate course for these young women, who may pick up their college careers later when their children are in school.

The Physician Confronts the Adolescent in Mid-Passage

The doctor is often consulted by the adolescent or by his parents at some state in this transitional period. It may be about a behavior disorder in the adolescent, about a depression in a mother, about the advisability of a marriage. There are two points to bear in mind about these situations. In the first place, the doctor inevitably belongs to the older generation and must be aware that his responses derive from this special point of view. His vision is likely to be blurred by half-forgotten memories of his own adolescent difficulties or distorted by the sense of threat, mentioned earlier, that he may experience in the presence of the younger generation. It is better to acknowledge these feelings to himself before he is moved to advise the young person.

Finally, rapport is not enough. The special knowledge of the family doctor comes into particular usefulness here. Whenever he sees a teen-ager in trouble he can explore tensions in the total family setting from which the teen-ager is emerging as well as the difficulties in the "family" (girl-friend, teacher, boss) toward which the adolescent is growing. The family doctor is in an excellent position to put the pieces together and to provide both the family of origin and the family of procreation with a framework for understanding that will emphasize the growth process and its difficulties rather than be caught up and entangled in the particular symptom which presents. In this worthwhile effort, he faces a hazard.

The Other Side

Parents, teachers, and the community at large are eternally blaming teen-agers for many of the ills of current life. Socrates said, "Children now love luxury. They have bad manners and contempt for authority. They show disrespect for elders and love chatter in place of exercise. They contradict their parents, gobble up dainties at the table, cross their legs, and tyrannize their teachers." Newspapers and magazines cry perpetually about the alarming increase in juvenile delinquency, mental illness, and drug addiction in this section of the population. A recent TV program reports that it is much easier to get communities to support grade schools than high schools.

The attitude of physicians toward this phenomenon is crucial to their understanding and dealing with it. One sage piece of advice is that of Pearson who counsels stoic patience, "I know of no way that the irritating behavior that arises from the raw wounds of both sides can be ameliorated. Wisdom, knowledge, judgment, all fail in the face of wounded self-esteem, and in the face of the partial amnesia all adults have for their own feelings as adolescents, and although the parent be given the best advice, he cannot put the advice into successful action any more than the adolescent can. One can only hope that both will survive for the few years during which these difficulties occur without either one doing the other too much harm.... Probably it is better for the adolescent if the parents close their eyes and lick their wounds in silence as much as they possibly can." [5]

Another and possibly more exciting approach to the conflict of generations is to regard the interaction as a screen that lights up both the adolescents and their parents. It is a new frontier in which the defiance of the adolescents may take many forms. They may be beatnik, delinquent, addicted, poetic, or political. They may join CORE and the freedom riders or they may horrify their liberal elders by attaching themselves to a right-wing movement. Or it may be a new physical or chemical theory about the nature of the world in which we live that attracts them. Regardless of the innovation that the adolescent generation proposes, within the family or within the arts, there is always an answer from the adult generation. Sometimes this is a stiffening of the value system and of institutional prerogatives. Sometimes the adult can learn and gain directly from the adolescent contribution. More often there is a give and take and a compromise. One way of regarding all human history is that it is written in this counterpoint between adolescents and their parents. Certainly the key to a family history often derives from this fugue. Parents, the community, and society at large constantly learn and change, and there are few provocations more stimulating than those provided by their heirs.

References

1. Bibring, Grete, *et. al.* March, 1961. "Role of Psycho-Analysis in Programs of Prevention in Mental Health." Summary of interdisciplinary meeting sponsored by N.I.M.H.

2. Erikson, Erik H. 1950. *Childhood and Society*. New York: W. W. Norton & Co.
3. ———. Winter, 1962. "Youth: Fidelity and Diversity," *Daedalus*. Reprinted in *Proceedings of the American Academy of Arts and Sciences*, 91(1):5-27.
4. Goodman, Paul. 1956. *Growing Up Absurd*. New York: Random House.
5. Pearson, Gerald H. J. 1958. *Adolescence and the Conflict of Generations*. New York: W. W. Norton & Co.
6. Redl, Fritz. 1945. "The Psychology of Gang Formation and the Treatment of Juvenile Delinquents," in Anna Freud and others, *Psychoanalytic Study of the Child*, Vol. I. New York: International Universities Press.

Bibliography

For Physicians:

Erikson, Erik. H. 1950. *Childhood and Society*. New York: W. W. Norton & Co.
This is the book which made identity at adolescence clear. It is a combination of developmental and psychoanalytical thinking at its best.

Josselyn, Irene. 1952. *The Adolescent and His World*. New York: Family Service Association of America.
Possibly the most succinct account of adolescence in print. It is equally readable by doctors and laity. It is short (122 pages) and inexpensive.

Pearson, Gerald H. J. 1958. *Adolescence and the Conflict of Generations*. New York: W. W. Norton & Co.
Pearson spells out carefully how important for growth this conflict is, the several forms it takes, and how both parents and adolescents can benefit from an awareness of their motivations.

Redl, Fritz, and David Wineman. 1957. *Aggressive Child: Children Who Hate* and *Controls from Within*. 2 Vols. Glencoe, Ill.: The Free Press.
A study of some very disturbed adolescents in Detroit, from which the authors have made some penetrating observations about the ways in which group codes can be deadly to adult influence.

Stolz, William. 1951. *Somatic Development of Adolescent Boys*. New York: Macmillan Company.
A classic.

Stone, L. Joseph, and Joseph Church. 1957. *Childhood and Adolescence*. New York: Random House.

186 / *Edward J. Hornick*

This represents the best of the child development thinking, stemming from the Department of Child Study at Vassar College. Eminently readable.

For Parents:

Goodman, Paul. 1960. *Growing Up Absurd*. New York: Random House.
A tirade against our adult society for not giving adolescents a worthwhile set of opportunities.

Hechinger, Grace and Fred. 1963. *Teen-age Tyranny*. William Morrow & Company, Inc.
The education editor of *The New York Times* and his wife issue a blast against the less appetizing facets of teen-age culture, especially its conformity and repetitiveness, and proceed to indict the adults who not only accept it but obey its dictates.

Wattenberg, William W. 1955. *The Adolescent Years*. New York: Harcourt, Brace and Company.
A lucid description of what happens in adolescence.

11

The Medical Problems of
the Unmarried Woman

Robert N. Rutherford, M.D.
Richard Klemer, Ph.D.
Jean Rutherford, A.B.

In medical practice "the unmarried woman" covers everything from the teen-age dysmenorrheic to the elderly hysterectomy patient, and from the never-married spinster to the chronic divorcee who is currently unspoused. Among these women there are two in particular whose problems often are not well treated. These are (1) the deeply concerned adolescent girl, fumbling for some understanding of her new roles and functions, and (2) the still unadjusted thirty-five-year-old single woman who now finds frustration and depression in her singleness.

Both the troubled adolescent and the older unmarried woman frequently feel that their problems are not taken seriously. The youngster is sometimes dismissed with an "Oh, you will get over it" when she expresses her fears and feelings of inadequacy. She is assured that her dysmenorrhea will be a thing of the past when she gets married, and often no further treatment is offered.

While the older unmarried woman may be examined more elaborately, her real problems are just as often left untreated. She is given tranquilizers and may be admonished to "get herself a man" or to learn to "live alone and like it." In general in our society, women who would like to marry, but who have not, present a problem that is more joked about and less seriously studied than any other malfunction of our family system. Only a few physicians seem to be aware consciously of this great source of frustration, of loneliness, and of emotional disturbance. Physical problems grow from these unmet needs. Unfortunately, some of the best educated, best behaving, and theoretically most valuable women are unmarried.

The Physician's Role

With both the teen-ager and the older woman, we have found in our practice that it is necessary to treat both the physical problems and their emotional concomitants simultaneously if any lasting improvement is to be hoped for. In other words, it is important to treat the *whole* person. Sometimes this can be done by the physician alone. Often though, he may call upon a psychologically-oriented specialist for help with the emotional aspects of the patient's problems.

As in other areas of medical practice, in gynecology it is sometimes easy to illustrate the close connection between emotional tensions and physiological malfunction. The classic case is that of the amenorrhea of the unmarried girl who believes that her delayed menstruation may be caused by an unplanned and unwanted pregnancy. She is fearful of a criminal abortion and hesitates to tell the young man involved because she wants neither his pity nor a marriage that would begin under these forced circumstances. As a result, she delays visiting her physician for as long as she can. At last, because of nausea, vomiting, and general panic, she visits the doctor—only to find that she is not pregnant. In our experience several patients have started to flow before they reached home after such reassurance given only a few hours earlier.

In the case of the spinster who comes in with vague and unspecific physical complaints, however, it is often far more difficult to establish a causal relationship between tensions and her frustrations in interpersonal relationships. Nonetheless, it has been clearly demonstrated that personal counseling and psychotherapy can have a helpful effect upon her attitudes and thus on her physiological functioning.

The Apprehensive Young Woman

In treating the normal apprehensions of the usual adolescent girl, the physician can play a predominant role providing he has time, interest, and understanding. He can improve both the physiological condition and the emotional attitudes.

A typical young woman coming into the gynecological practice usually has functional difficulties as her presenting complaint. Rarely does she announce the cause of her visit as the result of emotional problems. In going over her carefully, the physician usually does not find much of anything wrong with the actual organs of her body. Their functioning may be abnormal, but in general we do not find major correctable defects that might be handled by the surgical knife. Psychic malaise may be the cause of physical malaise.

She comes in because of dysmenorrhea, easy fatigue, palpitation, constipation, migraine, insomnia, poor appetite, complexion problems, and the like. Usually she is not aware that these covering or concealing symptoms are revealing in themselves. She is somewhat confused when asked, "What is your complaint?" This is why she is seeking medical advice. As a more useful approach in our first inquiry, we question her in general about her work, her interests, her eating habits, her friends, her coffee and cigarette consumption, and finally her physical functionings. This allows the patient to find that her doctor is interested in her total functionings as an individual, that he is not going to probe her dreams with a Freudian microscope, and that he will leave her daydreams alone until another day.

After this friendly and relaxed interview, she is moved into a properly chaperoned examining room where the nurse checks weight, blood pressure and the like, gowns her, and in our office, teaches her self-breast-palpation. This latter device has had an amazingly quieting effect upon patients. For, in being taught by a woman nurse to do a cancer-type check on a sex symbol, the patient finds a new way of thinking about the breast—as a vital part of her body which, if sick, can be a serious threat to her whole being. The bosom's "Madison-Avenue" appeal has been changed somewhat in her understanding.

Then, the doctor makes his usual top-to-toe examination, not forgetting to peer into every orifice (with or without a head mirror—an ordinary otoscope will do as well, but possibly not quite as dramatically). By the time the doctor has looked into her eye-grounds, her ears, her nostrils, her nasopharynx, thumped her chest, listened to her heart, double checked her breasts to see that there is no ominous tumor therein, checked her reflexes, palpated her abdomen—the girl is ready for a pelvic examination as part of this orifice-checking routine.

It has been our practice for years to spend several minutes with the patient during the original interview and before the physical examination to review the elements of menstrual and reproductive physiology using a large line-drawing. This allows the simple statement, "Now, we'll check your female organs to be certain they have matured and present no problems."

If this cannot be done vaginally because of the virginal hymen, rectal examination can be explained simply as an equally satisfactory method of checking for normalcy of the organs. Actually, in the pre- and early-adolescent girl, rectal examination in our experience is far more informative. "This examination will disturb you no more than having your daily bowel movement" is a satisfactory reassurance. We take vaginal smears of all of our patients for both cancer detection and evaluation of ovarian function. In the virginal girl, it is but a matter of a moment to use a cotton-tipped applicator, already shown to her as a soft swab designed to obtain the necessary amount of leukorrhea.

After this examination has been completed, it is worth the statement "You certainly check out well as a mature woman with normal sex organs." Then the patient can be left with the nurse again, for final return to the doctor's office or consultation room. At this stage, the patient has been reassured by several devices that she is normal and has been checked carefully. She usually seems convinced that all of the examinations the doctor did were customary for every woman —not just for her—and were designed to exclude the large majority of physical problems.

At this point, her presenting complaints can be reviewed with her. In the large majority of cases, these are matters of personal eating habits, working habits, recreational habits, and the like. Those which are not solvable now can be helped by an explanation of the workings of our bodies.

The doctor's explanation of this latter subject may be like this:

"There are two systems of nerve control in our bodies which are in constant balance for our protection. One is the 'housekeeping' system or parasympathetic system. As we sit here talking, we are digesting our last meals, our hearts are beating, our minds are registering many different things going on about us, and the like. Now, suppose a tiger appeared at the door. The second system—the alarm system—would swing into action and all of our housekeeping would stop. All of our survival organs would be activated so that we could run like crazy to get away from the tiger. Even the brain does not seem to function in this 'blind panic' induced by the triggering of the alarm system. It would take several hours safely away from the tiger before we started digesting our meals again. If we saw the tiger again in an hour and a half—well, we might never get the meal digested.

"Our bodies are not able to distinguish between one alarm trigger and another. In our modern culture, there are not many tigers but there are many triggers. There are parents, men, difficult job situations, matters within the family where tensions exist. These and many other things can trigger this alarm system to the total confusion of the housekeeping system so that poor body function is thus *guaranteed*. Now, to find the alarm-causing problem so that it can be corrected. Temporarily, until we can, here may be several suggestions or possible medications that will help." Thus, the patient has evidence that positive medication is possible.

In this fashion, the first interview is one of reassurance, of sympathy, of evidence of the doctor's interest, and skill and optimism regarding a good result. From here on, it is obvious that while some temporary support from medications may be necessary, the over-all problem is one which can, and must be, solved by the patient herself with the doctor's help. Matters of frustrations, relationships with others—parents, dates, the-man-she-is-living-with, or whatever—can be explored in the future with great profit.

In other words, we have learned to treat not just the physical symptoms but the patient's adjustment problems that have caused her to seek the services of the physician. Sometimes, of course, these adjustment problems are so extensive that the physician is well-advised to refer the patient to a counseling specialist. In our practice this means a psychologist-family-counselor. The great burden upon the physician is to exclude organic problems as the first step. This is the golden moment when the adolescent may begin developing the healthy attitudes that are our best guarantee for an ultimately healthy emotional life in later years. Prevention still outranks correction in any treatment program. Education in these areas has been consistently rewarding.

The Late Teen-Ager

Most of the problems that are presented by these young women result from aggravated reactions to the typical apprehensions of the girl approaching maturity in a changing society. She has vague anxieties about her ability in social relationships. She is fearful that she will not be popular or loved. She is afraid of her own awakening sexual desires and of imagined situations in which a sexual decision is necessary. She is disturbed by parental conflicts, by contradictions in the values of her peer group, and by her own sense of rebelliousness. Even as she is facing all of these problems she is coming in contact with the adult world with its paradoxes, conflicting values, and unanswered questions. Small wonder that she feels the need for some additional reassurance that she—she personally—is going to be able to succeed in her feminine role. The counseling sessions can provide the insights and self-confidence that result in reduced anxiety and smooth the way toward maturity.

Sometimes, of course, it is not easy. But one thing is always clear: these are the patients who give us specific diagnostic clues that if their problems are not answered now—and they are appealing for help beyond themselves—in later life as women they may be most unhappy.

The Older Single Woman

In a very real way the woman who reaches thirty-five, unmarried and without having become adjusted to the unmarried state, faces a more anxiety-ridden private world then the apprehensive teen-ager. Often the functional illnesses that this older woman presents are even more difficult for the physician to treat. Organic physical complaints may have developed from long standing frustrations, often from chronic inadequacy in interpersonal relationships. No simple explanation or reliance on eventual maturity is going to be completely therapeutic.

Careful medical examination by a competent physician is the first step in helping the older unmarried woman. It is clearly imperative that all possibilities of organic pathology be eliminated, not only to protect the patient but also to provide some of the reassurance that will be a part of her eventual therapy.

Often, extended medical treatment is not the answer. Nor is hysterectomy. Nor is exhortation about the joys of living alone. For many of these women, psychotherapeutic counseling with an interested and qualified counselor is currently the best treatment.

It should not be assumed, of course, that all single women in their thirties have emotional problems directly related to their unmarried status. Some single women actually are well adjusted to their single state and are convinced that they have chosen the better way for them. There are others whose emotional and physical problems may result from tensions other than from their singleness.

However, for many of the thirty-five-year-old unmarrieds, the constant reminder they receive in everyday life of their "different" status is either a direct or indirect source of emotional difficulty for them. Perhaps it is only because they cannot buy the home they wish without a husband, or adopt a child, or be invited to parties with their married friends, or even share in conversations about babies that they have nagging feelings of incompleteness.

Successful counseling with these unmarried women can be directed toward one of two results: (1) the patient's readjustment through psychotherapy to the point where she can happily accept the possibility of—or perhaps, in her case the desirability of—remaining unmarried and still having a successful living experience, or (2) improvement of the patient's interpersonal relationships skill and/or her motivation to seek male companionship where finding a mate is a reasonable expectation at her age.

The first result often appears at first glance to be more attainable. It satisfies a therapeutic definition in that it reduces the present tension of the individual. However, this does little to enrich a woman's life or to provide her with improved skills in relating to other people even though she does not marry.

The second result—improving interpersonal relationships—obviously demands more from both the counselor and the patient since it requires much greater behavior change, more learning, some rigorous practice, difficult competition, and the further risk of failure. Since it is well-established that one out of every two single women over thirty-five *will* be married, encouragement toward that objective for relatively normal women is not only reasonable, it is often well-rewarded with success. Naturally, the individual's initial motivation, ability, and personality will play an important part in her ultimate goal in therapy.

The first function of the counselor is evaluating with the patient the reasons for her failure to marry. It is always possible that there is some simple straightforward answer, some circumstance wholly beyond the control of the patient which has absolutely prevented her from marrying. Usually, however, the problem is far more complex and involves disturbed emotional mechanisms or, at the very least, some felt personality inadequacies. The unmarried person, tired of being asked why she has not married, usually has adopted some ready explanation that *could* be true. She has repeated it so often that she really believes it herself. Two such reasons very often heard are that the patient has had too many "obligations" and/or that she has not had enough opportunity to meet men.

There are undoubtedly a number of women who have such unalterable obligations to care for parents or relatives that they cannot possibly consider marriage. One of the most frequently overlooked social changes of the last century has been the change in the status of the older unmarried daughter from being a dependent to becoming the supporter of dependents. Some of the women who talk about their obligations do not perceive that they emotionally needed to stay close to father and mother even before their parents became dependent upon them.

While it is true that some women, by the very nature of their location and occupation, do not have as much opportunity to mingle with eligible men as other women, the modern employed single woman in an urban situation probably comes within meeting distance of more eligible men in a week's time than her grandmother did in a year.

More probably the real reason why some women have had problems in interpersonal relationships with men is related to their personality development. Sometimes childhood conditioning, of which they may be totally unaware, has given them unconscious fears, inhibitions, and compulsions that just will not let them love or be loved. In these cases, extended psychotherapy is a necessary prelude to any improvement in their ability to relate to other people. Often, the cause of singleness is related to some relatively minor personality inadequacy, perhaps even some lack of social skill that is not necessarily helped by classical psychoanalytical treatment. Group therapy or individual counseling directly concerned with increasing social skills in interpersonal relationships is a better answer in these cases.

A careful evaluation of the woman's probable reasons for singleness will often dictate the type of counseling most suitable. In the process of this evaluation three major factors should be examined. One, the woman's motivation toward improving her interpersonal relationships with men; two, her personality flexibility; and three, her ability in social situations—her social "know-how." As has been clearly demonstrated many times over, each of these factors is more important than her "opportunity" to meet men. The highly motivated, adaptable, and socially skillful person will make her own opportunities even in areas where men are limited. The disinterested, rigid, and socially inept person would have difficulty in getting a date even at an American Legion Convention!

Once the evaluation has taken place and some insight has been achieved by the patient, corrective measures can be taken. Long-standing habit patterns are not easy to change. Very rarely are dramatic results achieved overnight. Moreover, the mature woman faces a very difficult situation with regard to motivation, flexibility, and increasing her skills as well. She may have to work very hard to relate to men. Most men over thirty either by preference or by deterioration have less motivation to marry, and therefore she may have to have even greater motivation than younger women. Happily, however, it usually becomes easier as she goes along. The intensity of her desire to relate well to men will increase as she becomes more meaningful in the lives of other people. Once she has been able to awaken deep emotional responses in men, she will become much more motivated to continue.

Becoming more flexible, like increasing motivation, often becomes easier as the counseling sessions continue. As a result of the release of inhibitions achieved in the therapeutic sessions, the patient feels freer to deal with new attitudes, ideas, and values. She is far more able to adapt her ways of responding to the realities of situations in which she finds herself. This is as true of meeting men and relating to them as it is of any other phase of her living experience.

The counselor is of demonstrable help in this process in our experience. He provides the medium for re-education and reassurance which may enable the woman to talk more readily with other people. He teaches her to accept something less than complete conformity to some pre-existing set of unreasonably high standards. This is not to say that ideals are not important, but rather that perfection is not always attainable.

Finally, the counselor may help the patient to decide her first steps in improving her social skills. Many patients are convinced initially that individuals are born "popular." The counselor helps these patients to a better insight into the fact that those who are popular learned to be popular and that the patients themselves are usually the source of their own inadequacies. Since many of these inadequacies have led to failure in past social situations and each failure in turn has led to an attitude of expecting failure, the difficulty becomes self-perpetuating.

Consequently, one obvious problem in dealing with the socially immature unmarried woman is to provide her with some initial self-confidence and success. Of necessity, this has to be done slowly. Sometimes it is a matter of finding one small step that she can take—like saying "hello" to a stranger in a protected situation or even smiling back when someone smiles at her. Sometimes it may be a matter of helping her to restrain her impulse to show how right she is, when being right could lose a friend. Once she has practiced these seemingly superficial little accomplishments until they have become an integral part of her personality, and can be done without thought or embarrassment, she is ready to take another little step, and then another, and another.

A great deal of very real encouragement from the counselor may be required all along the way. For, as in all social relationships, belief in success usually presages success, while over-dwelling on the possibility of failure makes failure inevitable.

Preventive Education

Obviously the happiest solution to these problems is to have each young lady so educated that she never arrives at this particular juncture in her life. In other words, the best way of winning at this particular game is prophylaxis rather than therapy—foresight rather than corrective hindsight. This is more easily said than done. Ideally, parents should be the best teachers of their young, both by precept and example. Unfortunately, this is not the case. Only too often our children grow into adulthood without a definite knowledge of the position and responsibilities of a man as a husband and as a father. Such can be said of the role of a woman in our culture. Without such strong identification, boys and girls end up confused within themselves, uncertain as to their own role as a man or as a woman, often without the blessed recipe of a happy marriage to follow for themselves.

As doctors and counselors, we must start somewhere to establish a baseline in order to educate parents to be educators.

Preschool parent groups create an ideal nucleus for first steps in this direction. These groups are eager, well-intentioned, and serious in their efforts to create a good environment. A most important point is that these groups usually include *both* the young mother and father. It seems to be a basic premise in work in this area that the sympathy and interest of both parents is of paramount importance. Failure of the one partner to work in this educational teamship is most disheartening to the other partner and to others educating the children.

An even earlier start in the right direction can be found in groups brought together for education for marriage and education for parenthood. The strongest motivation seems to come before marriage or before the birth of the first child. In many cities, courses of this kind are given under the auspices of public adult education, in the YMCA and YWCA, or through young adult church groups. It is growing more common for individual doctors to conduct courses for their own patients. In this latter case particularly, education of this kind is a great reassurance to the patient and a work-saver for the doctor.

In our own office, we have a course of five lectures for the prenatal couple. These repeat every two months on Wednesday evenings. The subject matter briefly is:

1. Physiology of pregnancy. Physiological changes. Proper supports and garments. Diet. Allowable life while pregnant. Movie of the physiology of reproduction.

2. Color movie of our own techniques: Normal delivery, caudal anaesthesia, epidural anaesthesia, hypno-anaesthesia, rooming-in.

3. Pediatric lecture covering physiology of the newborn, feeding schedules, nursing vs. non-nursing, Rh factor, baby handling techniques—demonstration with a live baby.

4. Post-partum period with emphasis on physical conditioning, physical exercises, resumption of normal married life, work loads induced by new child, philosophy of "the first baby must take second place."

5. Marriage adjustments in pregnancy and parenthood.

We have been challenged for the last ten years to determine whether parents and children, seeing the same films and hearing the same discussions, would develop a better communication in these areas. One of the great problems the schools have noted is the fact that the parents rarely if ever see or hear the home room educational efforts, even through PTA meetings. The result is the parents' inability to discuss easily this unshared material.

As an experiment, we undertook an office two-lecture series on Saturday mornings where parents brought their children.

The first lecture opens with a film "Human Growth" which gives all a common vocabulary and understanding of human reproduction beamed at the ten- to twelve-year-old youngster. The physician then opens the discussion period, stimulating it at first if necessary. A week later, the psychologist or marriage counselor leads a discussion with the group. This is designed to introduce the matters of social behavior as a young man or young woman, with careful discussion of the personality development that is beginning to quicken with approaching maturity.

These are not formal lectures but instead are discussion sessions to demonstrate to parents and children that these are vital areas, possibly even more important than the right diet or vitamin as far as later life is concerned. They introduce also the physician, the psychologist, and counselor as friendly, interested experts appearing in a non-threatening fashion to discuss matters in which we all have common interest. On other Saturdays, a similar program is presented for the thirteen- to sixteen-year-old age group, using two lectures again by the physician on physiology and by the psychologist on social development.

That communication develops between parents and children might be illustrated by this story. One of the mothers, a week or so after a series, told the doctor that her daughter loosed a torrent of questions the minute they left the office. When the mother asked why she had not asked the doctor these things the girl replied, "There wasn't any need, because I knew I could ask you." All of these steps toward greater understanding aid in producing a home environment that in turn gives the young greater self-confidence and a better basis for the interpersonal relationships spoken of previously.

We are aware that this process of educating parents-of-the-future leaves the current generation without an established pattern to follow. In a number of communities a social code has been developed by the students themselves. This is in relation to dating, hours, suitable dress, etc. This has been instigated by the parents but implemented by the students. In many instances this has been started in groups as low as the seventh grade. The school is not the ideal situation for sex education in the opinion of many people. However in the absence of "educated parents" in this field, classroom situations have proved salubrious. More and more teachers are coming to the point of view that an intelligent, sympathetic presentation of information in this field does a great deal towards the healthy adjustment of the early adolescent. Many times, if the teacher himself does not feel confident in this area, a doctor or counselor can be called upon who is an expert in the field. Again, this is a golden opportunity not only to teach facts but attitudes. Proper attitudes and convictions have a great deal to do with the molding of future life and its unfolding with minimal problems requiring prescription. If proper attitudes could be developed through education in adolescence the doctor's day sheet would have fewer psychosomatic red herrings to pursue.

Summary

An effort has been made to point to the demonstration of the value of team work by the physician and the psychologist and marriage counselor. Many seemingly physical problems stem from confusions, apprehensions, and frustrations occurring within the mind of the single female patient as a result of her inability to live happily as a fulfilled woman within her environment. Two illustrative groups have been discussed—the teen-ager and the thirty-five-year-old unmarried woman.

Once the physician can exclude organic disease, he assumes the role of educator. If further education, re-education, or long-term counseling is required, the value and techniques of our modern psychologist and marriage counselor have been reviewed.

Positive programs for preventive education are outlined using not only established community facilities but also the physician's office. Two key phases for this positive approach are mentioned—the teen-ager and his parents as well as the new obstetrical couple. Programs are outlined and reference material supplied.

Bibliography

TEACHING AIDS:

"Human Growth," 16 mm., color, sound movie, Portland, Oregon, E. C. Brown Trust.
  This movie is prepared for the education of the ten- to twelve-year-old boy and girl in simple reproductive physiology. Some of it is in excellent animated form. It is suitable for use in groups of that age or groups of that age plus their parents. It is very tastefully and well done.
"Human Reproduction," 16 mm., color, sound movie, New York, New York, E. C. Brown Trust.
  It is designed for the education of the thirteen- to sixteen-year-old boy and girl in simple reproductive physiology. This has been used very successfully in teaching couples about to be married, already married couples with infertility problems, and obstetrical patients.

READING MATERIALS:

For Teen-Agers

Duvall, Evelyn. 1950. *Facts of Life and Love for the Teen-Ager.* New York: Association Press.
  This now appears in a paper-back edition and is an excellent presentation of the physiological, social, and emotional problems of the teen-ager of today.

Duvall, Evelyn, and Reuben Hill. 1953. *When You Marry.* New York: D. C. Heath and Company.
This is a good book for high school classes in preparation for marriage or for individual late teen-agers. It starts with dating and later covers most aspects of marriage relationships including marriage adjustments and sex education.

Levinsohn, Florence, and G. Lombard Kelly. 1962. *What Teen-Agers Want to Know.* Chicago: Budlong Press Co.
This is a pocket-book sized presentation of both the teen-age problems from the standpoint of the physician and from the youth counselor. It is well-presented and well-illustrated in a very mature fashion.

For Adult Women

Duvall, Evelyn. 1960. *Being Married.* New York: Association Press.
A more advanced textbook on marriage relations, this book was designed for college students or more mature individual readers. While it gives considerable statistical data, it is easily readable and can be recommended for anyone who has finished high school.

Klemer, Richard H. 1960. *A Man for Every Woman.* New York: The Macmillan Company.
This volume offers some practical suggestions for the woman who would like to be married. It is based on Dr. Klemer's studies in the field of marriage counseling and interpersonal relationships. It helps the single woman to look realistically at the reasons she has not married and offers constructive counsel on what she can do about it. This book can be recommended both to patients and to professional counselors in the field.

Robinson, Marie. 1950. *Power of Sexual Surrender.* Garden City, New York: Doubleday & Company, Inc.
This book has a good deal to offer the patients who are without adequate sexual response. However, since Dr. Robinson is Freudian in her orientation, some patients will be made to feel inadequate by her discussion of the clitoral vs. the vaginal orgasm. This book should be recommended judiciously.

For Menopausal Women

Gray, Madeline. 1948. *The Changing Years: How to Stop Worrying about the Menopause.* New York: Doubleday & Company, Inc.
This is one of the well-recognized books describing menopause by a most skilled science writer. It is written from the standpoint of both husband and wife, with question-and-answer format in some of the chap-

ters containing material poorly understood or utilized by the individual. It is a classic and has been reprinted in many foreign countries.

Kelly, G. Lombard. 1959. *A Doctor Discusses Menopause.* Chicago: Budlong Press Co.

This is a useful pocket-book sized discussion of the physiology of menopause and is carefully interpolated with clinical problems. It is designed for both husband and wife—or for any individual interested in understanding this phenomenon.

12

Case Illustrating Co-operative Treatment
of Marital Problems by a
General Practitioner and a
Marriage Counselor

J. Kempton Jones, M.D.
Ethel M. Nash, M.A.

The family physician is daily, in varying degrees, involved in marriage counseling. He has to decide which couples he will work with alone and which he will refer. If he knows his community, he has access to a variety of sources of help. Should the problem seem primarily financial, help with budgeting can be sought from home economists or bankers. Certain lawyers give special care to couples seeking divorce, trying to find out first whether reconciliation is possible or desirable and, if not, enabling the client to work for a settlement that puts first the welfare of any children of the marriage. Ministers, especially those who have had training in pastoral counseling, can be very helpful. Psychiatric referral may be essential. A fertility clinic's resources are sometimes needed. Agencies such as Family Service, Inc., or the Welfare Department can be of great assistance. Professional marriage counseling does not supplant these but can, as in this case, prove very valuable.

Medical Report

Mr. and Mrs. Parsons became patients following their marriage. At this time, medical examinations indicated that both were in good health. Mrs. Parsons remained well, but in the sixth year of their marriage, Mr. Parsons began to have persistently high diastolic and systolic blood pressure. Following the initiation of treatment with Reserpine, he became depressed and entered psychiatric therapy. During this time his blood pressure improved but was nearer to normal at the height of his subsequent extra-marital affair than at any time before or since. Exhaustive hospital studies during two separate periods revealed nothing except a quite labile blood pressure, which returned to normal when the patient was under heavy sedation. Renal and related studies were all within normal limits.

Mr. and Mrs. Parsons, following her return to him (as explained in the case history to follow), consulted me about their unhappiness. Mrs. Parsons refused to consider a psychiatric consultation but accepted the suggestion that both see a marriage counselor. I told them whom to call, thus putting responsibility for taking this step on them. However, as is my custom, I alerted the counselor to expect this referral, indicated the circumstances, and requested that Mr. and Mrs. Parsons be seen as soon as possible.

Throughout the period of counseling, I remained this couple's health consultant. The counselor and I frequently exchanged medical and counseling data. There was no period during the following five years when one of us was not seeing either Mr. or Mrs. Parsons. In the management of the hypertension, it was invaluable for me to know the course of the marital problem. For the counselor, this close medical consultation permitted retention of this case, despite the highly neurotic and on occasions near psychotic reaction of Mrs. Parsons. Further, when Mrs. Parsons terminated counseling, she would come to me and attempt to explain her withdrawal by discrediting her husband and/or the counselor's motives and objectives. Mr. Parsons would come for reassurance and to ask that I communicate his feelings to Mrs. Parsons since he could not get any response from her.

Since Mr. Parsons' blood pressure, both diastolic and systolic, remained elevated to the extent of 220/120, additional medication was given. Reserpine, chlorothiazide, and hydralazine HCl with simple sedation were all tried in the usual dosages. They failed to produce any significant change. Special salt-free diet and the reduction of thirty pounds to ideal weight brought no better results.

The turning point came following an acute gall bladder attack, which resulted in a period of hospitalization following which Mrs. Parsons responded to her husband's ultimatum by asking him to stay, as we shall see later. Following this and paralleling the new state of marital harmony, his blood pressure returned to near normal level. Since then, his blood pressure has fluctuated above normal levels occasionally but is easily controlled with minimal doses of chlorothiazide in combination with phenobarbital.

CHART

Events relative to progress of medical and marriage counseling	Mr. Parsons' blood pressure (at one- to three-month intervals)
Initial visit	180/120
Reserpine prescribed and depression resulted	160/ 86
Patient referred to psychiatrist and all medical	180/130
therapy stopped	140/ 80
	150/100
Extramarital affair started and continued for	136/ 98
several months	140/ 90
	142/ 90
	136/ 90
First visit for otherwise annual physical after	220/120
extramarital affair had been terminated	
Started on hydralazine HCl and chlorothia-	176/118
zide and continued same for about twelve	170/130
months	180/140
	190/120
Mrs. P's extramarital affair started and at same	200/120
time Mr. P. lost thirty pounds and continued	170/104
above medications in varying degrees	162/ 94
	180/112
	170/120

Mrs. Parson makes decision to leave	172/116
She is hospitalized and depressed. During this	160/100
time he is switched to guanethidine therapy	170/120
	170/130
	170/104
	180/110
Mr. P. has gall bladder attacks and is hos-	170/116
pitalized	200/120

Counseling comes to an end and possible solution to problems evolves.

Therapy over next two years consists of mild	170/110	
sedation with phenobarbital and chorothiazide	160/106	At about
in combination	160/102	six-month
	150/100	intervals

Request for Marriage Counseling Appointment

An immediate appointment for his wife and himself was requested by Mr. Parsons, who said that he was phoning on the suggestion of his physician, who had instructed him to ask for the earliest possible appointment. Often a marital difficulty, even though it has been developing over months or even years, reaches, at least in the minds of the couple, an emergency state in which delay cannot be tolerated. Whenever this is so, if it is at all possible, the urgency should be respected. An appointment was, therefore, arranged for the following day.

Mr. and Mrs. Parsons on arrival were asked whether they wished to be seen separately or together. Mrs. Parsons insisted that her husband talk alone, thus making it immediately apparent that she regarded him as the one really in need of counseling. Even though the counselor may prefer to see the couple together at first, it is not difficult to defer to wishes for a separate interview since it will be necessary to have a joint interview in order to evaluate the situation with them and to make suggestions about treatment. What is essential is the evolution of a trustful climate between counselor and counselees so that the situation as it presently exists, as it develops, and each individual's feelings about and contributions to it can be investigated and the possibilities appraised.

The investigation involves an assessment of each partner as an individual; of the socio-cultural forces past and present in their life histories which have and are affecting their past and present attitudes and actions; and an evaluation of the ambivalent motivations that constitute the bonds and boundaries of the relationship. In the early interviews, the counselor is seeking to find out within which of three main types a marriage falls. Is it a marriage in which the tensions are unconsciously gratifying to both so that the present strain will later resolve itself as the couple again settles down to their "normal" pattern of neurotic interaction? Is it in reality a healthy marriage relationship that has been disturbed primarily by a contingency factor such as missing an expected promotion, the birth of a defective child, or concern about what to do with a widowed parent? In such cases often all that is involved is to find the best way of dealing with the contingency situation. Is it a marriage in which the tensions have become intolerable to one or both so that a change has to be made either into the development of a better relationship or out of the marriage? Mr. and Mrs. Parsons fall mainly into the third type.

Counselees: Mr. and Mrs. John Parsons, age twenty-eight and twenty-five, white. Married seven years. Three children.

Mr. Parsons is college educated, a pharmacist by profession. Reared as a Methodist, he now irregularly attends the Baptist Church of which his wife is a member. His parents' marriage was unhappy. His father's business failures and gambling were frequently referred to before and after his death (which occurred when Mr. Parsons was six) by Mr. Parsons' mother. His mother was a school teacher and Mr. Parsons was left in the care of an elderly aunt, an arrangement he greatly resented. He was the youngest of three siblings and convinced that his mother preferred his brother and sister to himself. During adolescence and college, Mr. Parsons dated infrequently. His wife was the only girl he ever courted. They were married following an acquaintance of seven months and were formally engaged during the last three months of this period.

Mrs. Parsons is high-school educated and for most of the marriage has been a full-time housewife and mother. For the first few months she acted as a typist but resigned because the hours were long and the work often uninteresting. She goes to church regularly but has never been active in church work or in any type of community service. Her parents' marriage was unhappy. Her father was moody, frequently not speaking for days. Her mother was a persistent complainer, frequently sick. She has one sibling, an unmarried brother five years her senior. In adolescence, Mrs. Parsons dated infrequently. Shortly before becoming acquainted with her husband, she had broken an engagement to a hemophiliac young man because her father had insisted on this, saying that he would never let her marry an invalid. Her father had strenuously objected to her present marriage and before and since refused to speak to her husband.

Present Marital Situation as Described
by This Couple in First Interview

On the evening of their seventh wedding anniversary, Mr. Parsons told his wife that he wanted a divorce since he was in love with Jane. His wife was silent for several minutes. She then shrugged her shoulders and said: "Well, I never really loved you anyway." Two weeks later when Jane had reversed her decision to leave her invalid parents, Mr. Parsons felt that he had made a terrible mistake. He could never have left his own children. He begged his wife to stay with him. She consulted her brother who advised: "Forgive and forget. He really loves you." To her husband her brother said: "Take her out to dinner tonight. She will realize that you really love her."

Mr. Parsons followed this advice. He took his wife out to dinner with all the trimmings—steak, music, dancing, and a corsage. On his return from work the next evening, he found the house deserted and a note saying that his wife had taken the children to her parents' home in New England. She indicated that she planned to file for divorce.

Mr. Parsons once more consulted her brother and followed the suggestion that he go to New England to try and persuade his wife to return with him. After several hours of talking, she decided that she could not deprive the children of a father and consented to return to their home. She now only spoke to him when it was absolutely inevitable. She made him sleep on the davenport in the living room. She gave up looking after the house and appeared almost oblivious of the existence of the children. She spent her time either gazing abstractedly out of the window or threading bead necklaces. It was after two weeks of this that Mr. Parsons consulted his physician, who, following sessions with both, suggested marriage counseling.

In his first session with the marriage counselor, Mr. Parsons spoke of his great desire to win his wife's love. To sleep on the davenport, to make the meals, wash the dishes, vacuum the house, look after the children as well as do his own job—these were small inconveniences compared to the joy of this second chance. Mrs. Parsons' attitude was the antithesis of her husband's. She felt imprisoned in a loveless marriage by her children's need for a father. Her father had been right; she should never have married this man.

Sex, she stated, had always been on her husband's mind. Their honeymoon was a nightmare. Penetration was painful, and even worse, the hotel sheets were stained. She felt very embarrassed. Why had not the doctor told her about bleeding when they went for a premarital examination? Their first apartment had flimsy walls and she was certain that neighbors could overhear their love-making. She had wanted to have sex relations only when she was certain that the neighbors were out, but her husband ridiculed this idea. Fortunately, he now certainly could not expect that she would ever want to have intercourse with him again. He must realize that when she had agreed to continue the marriage, it was only for the sake of the children.

Not that he was much good as a father. He made every meal miserable by his constant criticism of their table manners. He thought that the children should play quietly whenever he wanted to rest, which was practically all of the few waking hours that he was at home. He was constantly harassing them to put their toys away. Once in bed, they were never to get out again or to call for a drink of water because this disturbed his watching of TV programs.

She made it clear that she, at present, found it very satisfying to watch him struggling to look after the children and stay pleasant about it because of his fear that she would take them away from him. However, even now, he made it plain that her wishes for the marriage did not really count. The very Sunday afternoon of the first weekend after she returned, instead of going riding as he knew that she wanted, he went hunting as usual, saying that he could not disappoint the boys. He never wanted to go anywhere with her or to do anything as a family. He was completely self-centered. Even when he came to try and persuade her to return to him, he bought for her and the children small gifts, but for himself he had bought an expensive brief case.

Weekly interviews were suggested with indications that these would probably last for twelve months. A fee based on income was agreed upon. Mr. Parsons eagerly accepted the idea of counseling, but Mrs. Parsons was, from the first, extremely reluctant.

The counselor's task is to draw this couple out of their isolation as individuals, beyond the confinement of their childhood experiences, into thinking of marriage as a series of experiments in group living and sharing through which each will attempt to provide for the other a soil and a climate that will be conducive to mutual emotional and intellectual growth. In a joint session, it was, therefore, explained that since both were reared in unhappy homes neither had known as children how a man and a woman enjoy life together. Both had thus begun marriage without a model of how it works well. It would be necessary during the counseling to learn to regard the marital relationship as the patient and to explore the kind of marriage pattern that would give both maximum satisfactions. This would also mean trying to find out in what ways unresolved inner conflicts were contributing to the present marital unhappiness. One axiom that each would have to accept and absorb was that in a marriage relationship the only person one can change is oneself.

Sessions Two to Eight—"Ventilation"

Each separately described his feelings about the marital situation as it developed during these first weeks of attempted reconciliation; of how they had felt about problems arising in the marriage previously; of feelings about relationships with parents, siblings and in-laws before and during the marriage; and of their self-concepts.

It was not long before Mr. Parsons began to find the inconveniences involved in his second chance burdensome. When, he wanted to know, was his wife going to let him back in the bedroom? He could not be expected to do his work properly if he could not sleep, and the davenport was uncomfortable. When was his wife going to start doing the washing, ironing, and housecleaning? He could not carry these joint burdens of earning and home-making forever. When was she going to stop looking out of the window and do some sewing for the children? How long would it be before she stopped throwing his professional magazines and papers out into the trash can? When he asked her to be more reasonable, she retorted: "Pick them out if you want them." "When," he asked impatiently, "is she going to get back to normal?" Her rejection, he said, was making it almost too hard for him to keep the promise he had made to her and to himself not to communicate with Jane in any way.

Interspersed with these expressions of frustration were descriptions of their previous life together. The wedding ceremony was a disappointment to him. He had returned from two months of army duty during which time he had written his fiancee only twice. She was very angry and refused to agree to kiss him in the church at the close of the ceremony, saying she did not want anyone to see this. He had wanted especially that everyone see this. From the beginning, their sexual life was unsatisfying. True, their first apartment had flimsy walls and his wife was probably correct when she said that the neighbors could overhear them when they made love. Naturally, however, he had refused to agree only to make love when the neighbors were absent. Anyway, with the neighbors absent or present, his wife would lie motionless on her back, saying: "Get it over with as soon as possible if you must have it." She had rejected all foreplay, saying that it produced too much lubrication and reminded her of an embarrassing vaginal discharge in her childhood.

Her attitude made her husband feel that he was no use as a lover. He found himself thinking more and more about the need to disprove this. Their difficulties were not only sexual. Differences about expenditures had begun early in marriage. He preferred to buy inexpensive furniture and clothes and to make purchases of major equipment, such as a refrigerator, on a have-now and pay-as-you-go basis. When his wife bought, she wanted the article to be of good quality and she liked to make major purchases only when they had saved the money for these.

The household she had run more or less as he wished, but she expressed resentment of his limited food tastes and of his refusal to let her know when his return for meals would be delayed. Was there anything wrong in liking plain food and not fancy casseroles? Should he not retain personal freedom of movement when on the job? He liked to make extra money by working at night. She wanted him home more. Her complaint that you cannot dance with a dollar bill seemed nonsensical to him. Was not all his work for her and the children?

Recreation, either together or with other married couples, was nearly non-existent since Mr. Parsons worked almost every night and on weekends went hunting or fishing. He thought his wife's desire to go riding together on Sunday afternoons too silly to be worthy of serious consideration. What pleasure could there be in just driving around? Certainly with her habit of letting the children talk all the time, it would not be any pleasure for him. She was too easy-going with the children, not correcting their table manners and leaving it to him to insist that they pick up their toys.

Difficulties during the first six years of their marriage had made him feel more and more tense and disturbed. His doctor diagnosed hypertension, but the drug that lowered this increased his sense of despair and worthlessness. He had bad dreams and fits of uncontrollable rage. Psychiatric treatment relieved him considerably but when after six months he terminated this for financial reasons, he found himself falling in love with Jane. This relationship soon placed his marriage in jeopardy. However, he could never regret the hours spent with her because through her he had learned that he could satisfy a woman sexually.

His whole life, he said, was apparently to be a sequence of unhappy personal relationships. As a child, deprived of a father and left to the care of an elderly aunt by his working mother, who always seemed to have time only for his brother and sister and not for him, he always felt neglected and left out. When he made friends, he always felt obligated to do more for them than they did for him; an attitude that still persisted in all extra-familial friendships. He had never been and never would be liked just for himself. Even Jane chose to stay with her parents.

Mrs. Parsons kept the first four appointments and after that came irregularly. During the first three, she reiterated her resentment about her husband's affair with "that girl." She was happy that she now had a good reason for refusing intercourse. She had never enjoyed sexual relations. They had three children and after his adultery, her husband certainly could not expect that she would ever consent to intercourse again. She was only staying with him so that the children would not grow up in a broken home.

When an attempt was made to explore Mrs. Parsons' feelings about sex and about the influence on her of her parents, she became silent and began to break appointments. In only one session did she speak of her dislike of her mother and of her father's persistent moodiness. She talked of the weeks which went by when he would speak to no one except herself; and of his waiting for her when she returned from her first date and anxiously saying, "Be sure that no other man ever kisses you"; and of his refusal to speak to her husband before the wedding or since.

It is evident that Mr. Parsons is a basically anxious, sexually frustrated man. His self-esteem, never high, has been further depleted by his wife's rejection of him as a lover; and by his mistress' rejection of him as her future husband. His relationships with the children reveal him as over-controlling and inflexible. The picture is of a predominantly anally-oriented character, who certainly makes his own contributions to the sado-masochistic relationship in the marriage, however pleasant and anxious to please outside of it. He has, nevertheless, made clear his basic will to health. When he had uncontrollable attacks of rage, showing that his defenses against feeling and expression of emotion had become over-taxed, he sought psychiatric help. This same will to health and the treatment resulted in his acting in such a way as to endanger the marriage but again he sought help.

Mrs. Parsons shows considerable neurotic disturbance that has culminated in a definitely anti-sexual attitude, the result of severe neurotic guilt and anxiety. She rejects all attempts to explore her sexual difficulties. She shows a tendency toward severe regression (withdrawal), evidence of hostility to her mother, and bondage to her father. This would seem to indicate a quite severe oral frustration with a predominantly orally-oriented character formation.[6]

In the premarital backgrounds of both are situations that are frequently predictive of marital difficulty. Both came from unhappy homes; the courtship was short and the time was not used to prepare for marriage. The wedding ceremony was not symbolic of a launching by the parents since Mr. Parsons' mother did not attend and Mrs. Parsons' father was most reluctantly co-operative. Both had received negative sexual education and further the premarital medical examination had done nothing to alleviate this as it was only utilized to check for venereal disease. Before counseling, their marital interaction included sexual dissatisfaction, household routines satisfactory to neither, finances adequate but no mutual agreement about or satisfaction with expenditures, a recreational life satisfactory only to the husband, disagreements about child rearing, and no adequate relationship to their community.

After eight sessions with Mr. Parsons and six with his wife, her resentment seemed sufficiently decreased to attempt a consideration together of what changes would be needed for them to form a more satisfying marriage relationship. The goal at this stage was to get both to see marriage as an interchange of give and take with each other, as a pair with other pairs, and as a family who are part of an on-going community. Six components were suggested as part of a marital framework. The value of this framework is that it serves not as a rigid system to be accepted but as a tool whereby a couple may examine their type of pair living and decide wherein it accords satisfaction to both. Where it does not, they can plan a more agreeable framework. The new patterns usually require the assumption of more mature and, therefore, of more mutually acceptable pair behavior.

The components of the framework to which Mr. and Mrs. Parsons were asked to give consideration included: the evolution of a mutually acceptable set of household routines and schedules; the development of a satisfying sex life; the establishment of a recreational life mainly, but not exclusively, within the married pair set; the acceptance of some responsibility for the on-going life of their community; and the attempt to reach a degree of agreement about child-rearing practices sufficient to allay anxiety on the part of either. This would require a merging of the value systems that each brought into the marriage. A new value system of their own could, as a result, come into existence.

When these components of paired living become established by a dyad, a joint, but not identical, philosophy of life begins to emerge. The center for the pair is no longer in their pasts but in the life they are building together. The goal is the development of a vital but not of a conflict-free relationship since further growth will necessarily involve the successful resolution of differences. One essential, therefore, is that the couple become adept at disagreeing not destructively, as previously, but constructively.

At this point reading became a part of the therapy. Meares' *Marriage and Personality* [5] helped each to see how they interacted. Polatin and Philtine's *Marriage in the Modern World* [7] brought information about marriage as a functioning relationship. Even though Mrs. Parsons terminated counseling prematurely, and at the same time introduced a new area of difficulty, nevertheless, a more satisfying marital framework developed during the ensuing months as both read and discussed.

The establishment of a set of mutually acceptable household routines and schedules meant for Mrs. Parsons re-assuming the responsibility for these aspects of family living. For Mr. Parsons it meant developing more catholic food tastes, calling home when he was going to be late, and limiting his night work. Both Mr. and Mrs. Parsons liked the idea of taking more recreation within the married pair set. They joined a folk dance group and took bridge lessons. The decision to buy and clear a lot on which they would later build, resulted in the family's spending Saturdays and Sundays working on this. When Mr. Parsons felt a strong urge to go hunting or fishing Mrs. Parsons could, with this background of pair recreation, send him off with her blessing. Mr. Parsons joined the Jaycees and Mrs. Parsons began to give an afternoon a week as a volunteer worker for the Red Cross. Thus both started to link themselves to their community. They bought the Ilg and Ames book on *Child Behavior* [4] and borrowed Baruch's *New Ways in Discipline*.[1] The down-to-earth approach of *Child Behavior* which made clear to them the stages through which children naturally develop and the emphasis in *New Ways in Discipline* on listening to what children's words and actions tell about their needs, gave these parents new ideas about child rearing which they could discuss, agree upon, and then practice together. When, as often, they found that tempers flared up because communication proved difficult, they were introduced to the "changing-skins technique." This is a method by which, when a disagreement occurs, each is asked to write down how the other feels, then how they feel personally. They then exchange what they have written. The goal is to become adept at what is in the mind of the other rather than to settle the issue. Later, it becomes possible to do this verbally.

Using this technique, some merging of values began to appear. Only when this had taken place was a specific attempt made to explore the area around which the major difficulties had concentrated —sex. Since Mrs. Parsons resolutely avoided talking about sex, recourse had to be mainly to bibliotherapy. It proved fairly successful, eventually. Both read Greenblatt's *A Marital Guide,*[2] Robinson's The *Power of Sexual Surrender,*[8] and Hilliard's *A Woman Doctor Looks at Love and Life.*[3]

The first evidence of breakthrough came about five months after counseling was instituted when Mrs. Parsons said: "I cannot love John yet, but I now think that he is rather handsome." This was followed in the next session by her reporting a slightly pleasurable vaginal sensation during intercourse. She reported that reading about intercourse made her feel better about it. Her husband was delighted with their progress. He said that although he thought his wife would never enjoy love play and coitus as Jane had, nevertheless, a fairly happy sex life was developing between them.

From a marriage counseling standpoint, this is the stage in the relationship at which weekly appointments should continue since a future harvest is beginning to ripen. In view of Mrs. Parsons' withdrawal tendencies, it is not surprising, although disappointing, that she at this junction initiated termination by announcing that this was her last visit. She gave as her reason the fact that they were getting on so well that "it is just as if we were newly-married, practically sweethearts all over again. I know that I am happy and I think that John is. Everything has improved; our everyday life and our love-making. I don't think that I have any problems any more. I don't want to stay in counseling. We are going to have another baby." Not only is Mrs. Parsons terminating, but she is adding the complication of another family member. Thus she avoids dealing with her own problems by a flight into maternality. At the same time, she adds to the family's problems by increasing its financial and emotional liabilities.

Mr. Parsons feels defeated by his wife's determination to leave therapy. He wants both of them to continue; she wants both to stop. The outcome is that both follow their own desires. Mr. Parsons is even more dismayed by his wife's desire to have another baby. The added financial burden and the inevitable loss of some of his wife's attention are dual areas of concern. He believes that he cannot oppose her request for another baby since she insists that this indicates the return of her love for him and is symbolic of her belief in the future of their marriage.

A baby girl is born. At first all went well. Mrs. Parsons became increasingly sexually responsive, occasionally reaching orgasm and sometimes, even, according to her husband, initiating intercourse. He reports that he has never seen her so happy. Then, when the baby was nine months old, Mrs. Parsons' father had a severe stroke.

Relapse after Improvement

Major life crises may shake up any marriage. In this case, however, it would seem the relapse was mainly because of Mrs. Parsons' resistance to therapy. She avoided the most vulnerable aspects, her bondage to her father and hostility to her mother. Following the news of her father's illness, Mrs. Parsons began to find excuses for not having intercourse. At the same time, unknown to her husband, she began to make an obvious bid for the affection of one of his co-workers. She was successful and professions of mutual love were exchanged. A little while later Mrs. Parsons took the usual step of "making a mistake" so that her husband became aware of the love affair. He now faced her with the necessity of choosing between the two of them.

The pattern set by her husband was repeated. She and this man arranged to leave their respective spouses. At the last moment, however, her lover chose to stay with his wife. Mrs. Parsons was thus rejected twice. She became very depressed. She began to talk in a dissociated fashion and her conversation indicated that she believed that she was about to have her fifteenth birthday. Hospitalization was arranged but she would not agree to consultations with a psychiatrist while there. A crucial period for this marriage has begun again. The question is whether Mr. Parsons could sustain this unhappy situation over a lengthy period. This was made more difficult by the fact that he felt deceived not only by his wife but by life. All had seemed so good and, as in childhood, the good was snatched away from him.

Released from the hospital, Mrs. Parsons remained extremely withdrawn. She had no interest in herself, in the children, or the house. Recognizing that her actions were partly dictated by retaliation but even more by her bondage to her father, Mr. Parsons determined that he would find a way to reach her. He tried making life interesting for her by arranging mountain drives and taking her on trips whenever he could so arrange his work that they could go together. All was apparently to no avail. Her only response was to try and get glimpses of the man who had rejected her. She consistently told her husband that she had no feeling for him and was staying only for the sake of the children. She acted thus for a period of over a year. Mr. Parsons remained in counseling.

As his efforts to revive the marital relationship apparently proved unavailing, his blood pressure rose alarmingly. Finally it was decided by his physician that he must be hospitalized. It was at this time that he decided that, for the sake of the whole family, this way of living must be terminated. Before leaving for the hospital, he said to his wife: "When I am discharged, I am going to leave you unless you can tell me that you care enough for *me* to want me to stay. I realize the importance of both parents to our children, but this is no marriage. I have done everything that I know to make it clear that I want you and love you, but I know now that it is useless unless you take an active step to indicate to yourself and to me that you want me as your husband."

Mr. Parsons was surprised and joyful when, two days following his release from the hospital, his wife said shyly: "I know I don't want life without you. Please stay."

Mr. Parsons felt that no further counseling was necessary for him. A letter received recently, approximately three years later, reports: "Everything is fine with us. My wife is a much happier person than before all this trouble. For the first time, I feel she loves me. Anyway, we are doing fine."

Focus

The patient is the marital relationship. This focus does not minimize recognition that marriage is inevitably the heir of childhood relationships and that the close intimacy of marriage serves to bring to the surface unfaced internal conflicts. Often the most desirable approach to marital unhappiness would be, as it would have been in this case, a working through with each individual of the basic intrapsychic disturbances so that each could have outgrown the limitations of childhood experiences and have become more able not only to resolve the interpersonal conflicts of the marriage relationship but to function more fully as a person.

However, physicians and marriage counselors have to work not only within the limitations of available finances and personnel but also within the confinement of the type of treatment and referral that a patient will accept. It will be clear that Mrs. Parsons would have benefited from psychotherapy of a type in which she could have worked through her hostile feelings toward her mother and her bondage to her father. Yet, despite her repeated refusal to accept personal psychotherapy, her attitudes did not result in the destruction of the marriage. Today, three years after termination of treatment, the husband says how happy they are as a family and how different his wife is from the girl he married. Thus, although little basic change took place in this woman and her growth toward maturity remained handicapped, nevertheless, the marital relationship, in the judgment of the couple, is now mutually enjoyable. This is an important point in regard to the effectiveness of marriage counseling. Often one finds that a comparatively minor shift in either or both individuals results in a marriage relationship that satisfies their relational needs and provides a warm two-parent home for the children.

References

1. Baruch, Dorothy. 1949. *New Ways in Discipline*. New York: McGraw-Hill Book Company, Inc.
2. Greenblatt, Bernard R. 1959. *A Marital Guide*. Chicago: Budlong Press Co.
3. Hilliard, Marion. 1957. *A Woman Doctor Looks at Love and Life*. New York: Doubleday & Company, Inc.
4. Ilg, Frances L., and Louise B. Ames. 1955. *Child Behavior*. New York: Dell Publishing Company, Inc.
5. Meares, A. 1954. *Marriage and Personality*. Springfield, Ill.: Charles C. Thomas.

6. Personality diagnosis made by D. Wilfred Abse, M.D., Department of Neurology and Psychiatry, University of Virginia Medical School.
7. Polatin, P., and E. C. Philtine. 1956. *Marriage in the Modern World.* Philadelphia: J. B. Lippincott Company.
8. Robinson, Marie. 1959. *The Power of Sexual Surrender.* New York: Doubleday & Company, Inc.

PART TWO

Premarital Medical Counseling

Steps in the Evolution of the Premarital Examination in the United States

Prepared by R. Farrer Meschan, M.D.

1935 Connecticut was the first state [6] to enact legislation requiring an examination of couples about to be married. The aim of this legislation was to detect potentially infectious syphilis; 80-90% of those individuals who had syphilis and who had applied for a marriage license were unaware of their infection at the time of testing.[12] Many would have passed this infection on to spouse and children.

1941 Dr. R. L. Dickinson,[3] dean of American gynecologists, realized that the premarital examination could also prevent marital problems. He urged a complete physical examination including that of the pelvis. He felt that impotence and frigidity could be averted by adequate sex information.

1947 Dr. Lovett Dewees,[1,2] writing in *Successful Marriage,* stressed the importance of the attitude of the physician who conducts the premarital examination.

1953 Dr. Eleanor Easley [4] addressed the North Carolina State Medical Society on this subject. She stated that her premarital examination covers three visits. At the first visit the history and blood tests are taken and generalities discussed. The complete physical examination, including that of the pelvis, is performed at the second visit, and the bride and groom are interviewed together at the third, when conclusions and advice are given. She indicated the importance of dilatation and surgical treatment of a tight hymen. She stressed the importance of physicians working with family life educators in this field.

1954 Dr. Nadina Kavinoky [7] mentioned the use of Dr. McHugh's [9] *Sex Inventory* as a guide to counseling. She advocated the introduction of a lubricated Pyrex tube by the bride, who needs reassurance about the length of her vagina. The teaching of methods of contraction of the vaginal sphincter to the bride was also mentioned.

1956   Dr. Abraham Stone [11] and Dr. Lena Levine [8, 11] co-authored *The Premarital Consultation,* a manual for physicians. Their manual covers the whole subject of the premarital examination in a comprehensive manner together with a suggested history sheet. This latter includes period of acquaintance, courtship and engagement, family attitudes toward marriage in general, and parental adjustment to the engagement. Sexual history in regard to autoeroticism and premarital experience are noted with the history. A chapter on genetic counseling is included.

1958   Dr. Paul Sholten,[10] in addition to other pertinent facts, pointed out that the premarital examination can be conducted adequately by any physician who has basic gynecologic training, who is prepared to spend adequate time with the patient, and who has sufficient interest in this subject.

1962   Dr. Charles Flowers [5] stressed the importance of including the Papanicolaou smear as a routine, even in this young age group. He pointed out that the dilatation of the hymen under local anaesthesia makes the fitting of a diaphragm possible before marriage and that virginity should not preclude this.

References

1. Dewees, Lovett. Personal Communication.
2. ———. 1955. "The Premarital Examination," in Morris Fishbein and Ernest W. Burgess (eds.), *Successful Marriage.* Garden City, New York: Doubleday & Company.
3. Dickinson, R. L. Nov., 1941. "Premarital Consultation," *J.A.M.A.,* 117:1687-92.
4. Easley, Eleanor March, 1954. "The Premarital Examination," *N. Carolina Med. J.,* 15:105-10.
5. Flowers, Charles, Jr. July, 1962. "Premarital Examination and Counseling," *Obstet. Gynec.,* 20:143-47.
6. Johnson, Bascom. May-June, 1938. "Laws Relating to Venereal Disease and Marriage," *J. Social Hygiene,* 24:409-10.
7. Kavinoky, Nadina. Oct., 1954. "Premarital Medical Examination," *J.A.M.A.,* 156:692-95.
8. Levine, Lena. Personal Communication
9. McHugh, Gelolo. *Sex Inventory.* Available from Family Life Publication, Box 6725, College Station, Durham, N. C.
10. Sholten, Paul. Nov., 1958. "The Premarital Examination," *J.A.M.A.,* 167:1171-77.
11. Stone, Abraham, and Lena Levine. 1956. *The Premarital Consultation.* New York: Grune & Stratton, Inc.
12. Talbot, Henry. Feb., 1937. "Certificates for Marriage," *J. Social Hygiene,* 23:87-89.

13

Premarital Examination and Counseling

Charles E. Flowers, Jr., M.D.

It should be considered a privilege as well as a duty for the generalist and the obstetrician and gynecologist to make available to each bride and groom an adequate and realistic premarital examination.* A mere Wassermann test and a congratulatory farewell are neither realistic nor adequate. The premarital examination should include a review of systems, a reproductive history, an adequate physical and pelvic examination, and contraceptive advice compatible with the patient's desires and religious preference. Finally there should be premarital counseling for both bride and groom.[2, 4]

Periodic health audits are the most important aspects of preventive medicine. There is no better time to make such a complete examination than before marriage.

A review of systems is directed not only toward diagnosing various medical disorders but also toward making an estimate of the patient's reproductive potential. The emphasis of the review is placed upon the organs directly related to conception and pregnancy. It is important that a young couple be advised if there is a cardiac lesion that may limit the number of years of childbearing. It is also important to know if there has been any renal impairment due to glomerulonephritis or chronic pyelonephritis.

* Reprinted by permission of the editor, *Obstet. Gynec.* (July, 1962), 20(1): 143-47.

The history gives an opportunity to assess normality of menstrual function. The patient should be questioned about the age of onset of menses, the interval between periods, the duration and character of flow, the number of tampons or perineal pads needed each day, and the occurrence of dysmenorrhea.

It is particularly desirable to know the attitudes toward menstruation which were inculcated in the patient by her mother, as well as whether the mother was a warm and affectionate person and whether she had marital difficulties. These important questions give an assessment of the patient's psychic adjustment to marriage and assist the physician in counseling.

The various methods of contraception should be discussed and the patient given the opportunity to ask questions that will allow her to make a decision as to the type of contraceptive she desires. Fortunately the majority of couples have reached a decision as to types of contraception, but sufficient time should be allowed for questions so that such a decision can be changed or reaffirmed.

The completion of a detailed history and discussion of contraceptive technics set the stage for the next, very important question, which should be asked directly. This question is: "Have you begun intercourse?" If the answer is in the affirmative, one should determine if any difficulties have been encountered with coitus, whether orgasm is occurring, and whether the patient has any questions. If the patient has not begun coitus, it is desirable to know the extent of lovemaking as well as the patient's thoughts and possible anxieties concerning the impending initiation of coitus. Free conversation will occur only if the patient senses a real interest in her problems.

The patient is finally asked if there are any questions concerning the physical examination, so that if necessary a particular system may be examined in greater detail. The patient may be unduly concerned about a previous physician's comments concerning such things as a heart murmur, a curved spine, or an infantile uterus.

Physical and Pelvic Examination

The physical examination should be a complete one, including the head, neck, breasts, heart, lungs, abdomen, and extremities.

The pelvic examination should be carefully performed, and the patient assured concerning her reproductive potential and her ability to initiate coitus without difficulty.

Virginity should not preclude adequate pelvic examination, a Papanicolaou smear, and the fitting of a diaphragm if it is desired. The hymen can be easily and almost painlessly infiltrated with 2% Xylocaine,* beginning at six o'clock and proceeding around the entire periphery of the hymeneal ring. This procedure, which allows the hymen to be stretched and makes incision or excision of the hymeneal ring unnecessary, can be safely and easily done even when the vagina will allow the entrance of only a fingertip. Naturally the hymen should not be stretched without the prior approval of the patient and groom. But it is indeed a rare and poorly adjusted groom who must reassure himself at the expense of his wife's dyspareunia.

Following stretching of the hymeneal ring a speculum can be inserted, the cervix visualized, and a Papanicolaou smear made. A two-finger vaginal examination will allow adequate palpation of uterus, adnexa, and cul-de-sac.

Fitting the Diaphragm: Contraceptive Counseling

If a diaphragm is desired, this can be fitted with the knowledge that in three months a larger size may be necessary. The prospective bride should not be denied a diaphragm because of the shortness of her vagina.

A diaphragm can be fitted with greater ease if a patient is shown a plastic model of the pelvis. It is important that she understand how conception occurs and that the cervix must be covered by the diaphragm for the method to be effective. The majority of failures of the diaphragm occur because the patient believes that there is a "safe period." Over 60 per cent of unplanned pregnancies are a result of this fallacious idea, which is unfortunately perpetuated by some physicians and marriage courses. Conception can occur at any day in the menstrual cycle since sperm may live seven to ten days in the cervix and tubes. The patient must also understand that the contraceptive jelly or cream has equal importance and must be used each time the diaphragm is inserted. Finally the patient must understand that when the diaphragm is inserted it must be checked so that the

* Astra Pharmaceutical Products, Inc., Worcester 6, Mass.

patient can feel the cervix covered by rubber. Placing of the diaphragm behind the symphysis does not indicate correct positioning. All too often the diaphragm is inserted anterior to the cervix without the patient's being aware of the faulty positioning. At the time of the initial fitting, the patient should examine her vagina and feel the cervix before the diaphragm is inserted, so that she will know the sensation of the cervix being covered by the diaphragm.

When the patient is sufficiently oriented concerning her pelvic organs, the proper size of diaphragm should be inserted and the patient told how it should be removed. The physician should then leave the room and allow the patient and the office nurse to remove the diaphragm and insert it at least twice, leaving it in the vagina the second time so that the physician can be assured that the diaphragm is properly placed. Occasionally, it is necessary for a patient to take the diaphragm home to practice, and return for later checking. Nothing can be more disconcerting to the young bride than to attempt the insertion of the diaphragm for the first time on her wedding night. She must understand the system thoroughly before leaving the office and she should sleep with the diaphragm in place at least two nights a week until marriage, so that she will become accustomed to its use.

The conclusion of contraceptive counseling and a general discussion of marriage should be carried out after the patient has left the examining room and had the opportunity to feel at ease in the office.

If a diaphragm is to be used she should again be cautioned concerning the reasons for failure. The basic points of its use should be reiterated. It is believed that the diaphragm has improved safety if approximately one-third of a vaginal applicator of jelly is inserted after the diaphragm has been placed. A third or half an applicator of jelly should be placed in the vagina if coitus occurs more than once during an evening. The patient is told that the diaphragm should not remain in place longer than twenty-four hours, since vaginal irritation may develop, and since the jelly behind the diaphragm may be dissipated.

She should be told that douches are generally unnecessary and particularly that a douche is not needed when the diaphragm is removed. The diaphragm may be removed when the patient takes a shower or bath, or it may simply be removed and the perineum washed with soap and water.

If a condom is to be used, the patient should understand that it alone is a poor means of contraception. The condom may rupture, or if withdrawal is not practiced immediately upon ejaculation, the decrease in size of the penis will allow sperm to be deposited in the vagina. However, the patient can be assured that an applicator of vaginal jelly or cream in addition to the condom is an excellent contraceptive means.

Increasing numbers of patients desire oral contraceptives. It is believed that these may be prescribed and advocated with assurance. Oral contraceptives are effective in three ways. The progesterone interferes with the passage of sperm through the cervical mucus; ovulation is inhibited; and the endometrium is ripened early in the menstrual cycle, precluding implantation even if ovulation should occur. Oral contraceptives fail only because patients do not take them regularly on their medication days, or forget to begin the tablets within seven days if menstruation does not ensue after a cycle of medication is completed.

The use of oral contraceptives demands that the physician explain in detail the proper use of the tablets, to be taken between the fifth through twenty-fourth days of each cycle. The patient should be provided with a menstrual calendar and an instruction sheet. She should also be told that there may be some side effects such as intermenstrual spotting and nausea during the early months of oral-contraceptive use, but that these are correctable and usually occur only during the first few months of use.

The Catholic bride can be given some contraceptive assistance by information concerning the less fertile days of her cycle and the significance of changes in the cervical mucus and breast engorgement.

General Marital Counseling

The foregoing procedures should provide the physician with a good idea of the patient's needs concerning premarital counseling. General discussion should concern the problems that may be anticipated in this marriage.

If the patient has already made a satisfactory sexual adjustment with the future husband, little need be said. The couple can then be seen together and their questions answered.

If coitus has not been initiated, the prospective bride should be seen alone. She is more apt to have unnecessary fears, anxieties, and guilt feelings concerning the initiation of coitus. She must be assured that coitus will cause her no physical pain, discomfort, or injury. Moreover, she must clearly understand that she is a normal woman without sexual defects or inadequacies.

Other aspects of marriage counseling can proceed according to the patient's needs. Each physician must develop his methods of premarital counseling according to his own ideas and personality.

The prospective bride should understand that the average female is much slower than the male in being sexually aroused. She may be told that this is probably due to past training in the home, customs of society, and the fact that during the many years of evolutionary development the female has realized that the basic responsibility of pregnancy is hers. However, the bride should understand that coitus is a beautiful and tender expression of affection in which she achieves the giving of herself and body.

It is particularly important that she understand that there is no such thing as sexual perversion in marriage, and that she should share sexual stimulation with her husband. She should let him know and understand the ways she becomes sexually aroused. Coitus is a method of communication between two individuals; it should be profound and complete.

There is much confusion among women concerning orgasm. This confusion is probably a result of the various sensations that women experience at the climax of coitus. No bride should expect a spectacular initial response to coitus. Initially, she should be happy with the warmth, the tenderness, and the closeness of her husband, and should realize that in time she will appreciate a rhythm in coitus that culminates in a beautiful conclusion of mature affection. Frigidity is never a result of physical abnormality, only an emotional one.

The prospective bride must also be counseled so that she will not be disappointed in her initial intercourse. She may be reminded of the first party or dance that she attended. The newness of the occasion, her excitement in wearing her first evening dress and high heeled shoes compensated for the lack of agility in herself and her dancing partner.

The bride should understand, however, that she has certain responsibilities concerning the sexual aspects of her marriage. She must keep herself attractive and feminine. She must not exhaust herself in her daily work and routine so that she has only the dregs of the day to offer her husband. Moreover, she should not enter intercourse with a condescending politeness, but with enthusiasm and the knowledge that coitus can create as well as affirm mature affection.

The majority of prospective bridegrooms have a good foundation for initiation of the mechanical aspects of coitus, but some require private counseling. All should clearly understand the slowness of the female in being sexually aroused, and that the husband should assist her, in making the adjustment, with tenderness, understanding, and delicacy.

One of the major problems of the bridegroom is premature ejaculation, which is the result of lack of confidence and control. Time and understanding of both marital partners allows improved coordination and control, and eliminates premature ejaculation.[2]

It is important that for the conclusion of premarital counseling both partners be present. What is said will depend upon the problems of the particular couple, but there are a few points of final advice that are important.

The bride and groom must understand that one should not make love by mechanical plan, as one uses the manual of arms in a military drill. The various steps indicated in a marriage manual are not the prerequisites of successful coitus. Sexual intercourse is a beautiful and mature expression of love that should be expressed according to the personalities of the two individuals; it should be expressed with warmth, understanding, tenderness, and originality. It is by no means the most important aspect of marriage, but it is a relationship that affirms the physical as well as the emotional aspects of marriage. When the many trials and tribulations in life seem insurmountable, they can be made to fade into nothingness when true affection is appreciated and expressed.

The couple may be told two truths: that marriage is a logical and beautiful union, blessed by the church and approved by man; and that mature love is like good wine, properly tended it improves with age.

References

1. Butterfield, O. M. 1962. *Sex Life in Marriage.* New York: Emerson Books, Inc.
2. Easley, E. B. March, 1954. "The Premarital Examination," *N. Carolina Med. J.,* 15:105-10.
3. Israel, S. L., and J. B. Roitman. Sept., 1959. "Sexuality and Fertility," *Clin. Obstet. Gynec.,* 2:900-6.
4. Stone, A., and L. Levine. 1956. *The Premarital Consultation.* New York: Grune & Stratton, Inc.

14

Group Counseling with Engaged Couples

Charles E. Flowers, Jr., M.D.

I have been asked to discuss what one expects of a good premarital examination.* It is important for each person preparing for marriage to have an estimate of his general physical condition. This involves a complete physical examination and a thorough medical history. By first discussing each organ system and the past medical history, the physician is able to get an estimate of particular medical problems the patient may have had. Thus we know better how to conduct our physical examination.

In the female, particularly, we are interested in the function of the

* The contribution which physicians can make toward increasing the potential for a satisfying marriage cannot be over-estimated. From the standpoints of time-saving for the physician and effectiveness for the couples, group counseling is, for many, the method of choice. This chapter is an edited account of a tape recording of how one physician, Dr. Charles Flowers, who has been working with groups of engaged couples at seminars on the Duke University Campus, talked to them.

These seminars are for couples to attend together, when their wedding date is set for not more than six months ahead. Most of the couples are within two to three months of marriage. The number attending is limited to thirty individuals, who meet for three two-hour periods one of which is with a physician. The other two sessions are under the guidance of a marriage counselor, Mrs. Ethel Nash. These center around the adjustment to be expected in the first year of marriage.

Similar seminars have been offered at Wake Forest College in Winston-Salem, at which Dr. R. Farrer Meschan was the physician. This chapter represents the result of collaborative editing by her and Dr. Flowers.

heart and lungs. Any history of rheumatic fever or a congenital heart lesion is of great importance. Signs of these diseases should be evaluated because there are occasions when the girl should really not have children until she has had cardiac surgery. There are times, of course, when it would be important for her to begin her family at an early age, because aging makes the heart less efficient as a pump. It would be wrong and improper to fit such a person with a diaphragm or prescribe contraceptive tablets, for she should begin her child bearing and finish it in a few years.

We are also interested in any history of kidney disease. A severe kidney infection in childhood could set the sub-soil for the later development of high blood pressure during pregnancy and would again indicate the necessity for child-bearing early rather than in the mid-twenties or early thirties. A history of repeated urinary tract infections such as cystitis, with burning and frequency of urination, would also indicate the necessity for evaluation of the urinary tract before marriage and treatment of any existing lesions that would interfere with child bearing. One should not be alarmed, however, if a mild urinary tract infection develops soon after marriage, "honeymoon cystitis." This should be promptly treated by a physician, but it is in no way dangerous nor does it lead to kidney damage.

The system review is equally important to enable the physician to reassure the patient that she is normal and healthy. All too often a girl may have been told things that may prevent her from making a reasonable adjustment as a wife or which may cause anxieties concerning marriage and child bearing. For instance, young girls have been told that their breasts are too small and that they never will be able to nurse their babies. This should not cause a great amount of anxiety, but it is important to reassure girls that the actual amount of breast tissue needed for lactation is about the amount that would fit in a French champagne glass. The rest of this organ is largely fat and is unnecessary.

Some girls have been told that they have a small or infantile uterus, and they wonder whether they can ever become pregnant. They wonder also whether the vagina is so small that they will have considerable difficulty in initiating intercourse. I think it is important that they be reassured about these organs. We know now there is no such thing as an infantile uterus. It is true that some uteri are smaller than others, but as normal hormonal stimulation occurs, particularly after marriage, this is a very rare cause of infertility. Other girls may have tried to insert tampons without success, and this may cause considerable anxiety about intercourse. These problems should be discussed and they can be worked out very simply.

We also need to evaluate the girl's menstrual function and discuss this in the same detail as we would heart lesions, lung diseases, kidney infection, or digestive disorders. There are many variations in attitudes about menstruation, and I think that the physician who is doing a premarital examination should give the girl an honest appraisal of her menstrual pattern. Many girls believe their periods are quite irregular, but when the pattern is discussed, one finds the variation is only from twenty-five to thirty-two days. This is perfectly normal menstruation; no one is supposed to menstruate to the hour every twenty-eight days. I think of normal menstruation as anything from twenty to forty days, and the girl who misses an occasional period is again perfectly normal.

We would also like to know how much bleeding occurs during menstruation. Some girls are very much upset by the fact that their menstrual flow is very scant, while others are concerned that they bleed quite profusely. An answer to both of these can be given by comparison to fertilizing a lawn. If a quantity of fertilizer is added and the lawn is watered profusely, more grass grows and there are more grass clippings. On the other hand, if not quite so much fertilizer is used, and not quite so much water, then the grass clippings are not quite so plentiful. There is a similar principle underlying the amount of blood lost in menstruation. The more hormone stimulation there is to the lining of the uterus, the greater will be the blood flow during menstruation. Menstrual function has no fine line of normality. If variations are extreme, it is possible to utilize hormones to regulate this. We can also insure that menstruation can be avoided during the honeymoon.

After menstrual function has been discussed and the system review taken, the individual feels much more secure with the physician. We then proceed to discuss sexual adjustment in marriage, contraceptives, and the initiation of intercourse. At this stage I ask a very direct question since we are dealing with individuals who are interested in obtaining a reasonable sexual adjustment in terms of marriage. I ask my patients whether they have begun intercourse. The answer to this question directs the subsequent course of the interview. It is not always possible for a physician to tell from his examination whether or not a patient has or has not had intercourse. Obviously there will be a few patients, with a tight hymen, in whom penetration will be difficult; others will have what we call a marital introitus. But there is no point in discussing the initiation of coitus with an individual who has already had intercourse on numerous occasions. It is better to spend the time talking about how both are getting along and whether the woman is achieving orgasm. We take an entirely different approach with an individual who has not yet initiated coitus.

The next thing we would like to know, and again we ask in a very straightforward manner, is how the couple is getting along in terms of the sexual adjustment of courting. Has petting commenced? If so, are there any particular guilt complexes about it? Is petting or intercourse occurring as something that is necessary to maintain the interest of the fiance or as a method of expressing affection? I think it is important for us to take an entirely different approach with the girl who feels guilty about petting or coitus from the one we take with the girl who has accepted intercourse in terms of this expression of affection and whose petting or coitus is not associated with guilt complexes and anxieties. I think it is important merely to mention these questions during history-taking in order to get an answer; after the physical examination we may go into these problems in more detail.

I like to ask a couple the type of contraceptive they plan to use. Some patients have already decided on a particular type of contraceptive that they desire. Others are undecided and would like the physician's opinion. I do not like to tell someone what type of contraceptive they should use since the sexual habits of people differ. The advantages and disadvantages of each should be discussed forthrightly. First let us discuss the use of the diaphragm and jelly; this is an excellent method of contraception. Actually, there are very few failures when a diaphragm is used properly. During my practice as an obstetrician and gynecologist I have only had one person say that she became pregnant when using a diaphragm exactly as prescribed. The proper use of the diaphragm will be discussed along with the pelvic examination.

Another method that is becoming popular today is the use of the oral contraceptive. This is the most effective contraceptive method available. No pregnancies occur when these pills are used properly. The contraceptive pills that are available contain two hormones. One is an estrogenic hormone that is produced during the phase of the menstrual cycle before ovulation. The other is the progestational hormone that is produced by the ovary after ovulation. When these hormones are taken by mouth, the body is not required to produce them and the complicated pituitary-ovarian axis stimulation for the production of ovulation is suppressed. But they also do two other things. They over-ripen the lining of the uterus, or endometrium, and make this an unfavorable medium for development of the egg should implantation occur. Thirdly, these hormones change the characteristics of the cervical mucus so that the spermatozoa are discouraged from reaching the uterine cavity or Fallopian tubes.

These pills are taken from the fifth to the twenty-fifth day of the cycle. The first day of bleeding is the first day of the cycle. On the fifth day, whether menstruation has ceased or not, one begins to take one pill at bedtime each day until the twenty-fifth day of the cycle. Within a few days after the pills are discontinued, menstruation begins. The body naturally produces these hormones in a parabolic manner; at the end of the cycle, they decrease in amount causing a decrease in the blood supply and sloughing of the endometrium. When the pills are discontinued, the endometrium sloughs; when they are started again on the fifth day the lining of the uterus begins to heal.

Occasionally patients will miss a period when taking the oral contraceptives; this is no different from patients occasionally missing a period when not taking the hormones. If this should happen, the tablets are resumed seven days after they are discontinued. The absence of menstrual bleeding during this interval does not mean pregnancy and should not cause concern, but the pills should be resumed after seven days because ovulation may occur if the pills are omitted for as long as ten or twelve days.

Every sword has two edges; the effectiveness and the aesthetic features of these pills is one edge. They eliminate the necessity for the mechanical introduction of jellies and diaphragms; they give the user a sense of security and they generally reduce menstrual cramps. Menstrual cramps are reduced in two ways. First, the endometrium or lining of the uterus does not have the opportunity to accumulate and is less in amount than that normally passed. Second, the hormone in the pill has a quieting effect on the uterine muscle.

The other edge of the sword cuts differently since there are several side effects that can occur. The basic side effect is irregularity of menstruation during the first few months. A patient may spot or bleed enough to wear a tampon during the last ten, twelve, or four-teen days of the cycle. This generally ceases in about three months; the body learns to adjust to the new hormones. It may also be neces-sary to make adjustment to more frequent menstruation. A patient who normally menstruates every twenty-eight to thirty-five days might have a period every twelve or fourteen days during the first few months of taking the pill. Again, the body adjusts and there is abnormal bleeding in only 3 to 4 per cent of patients after three-months' use. For premarital purposes, I like to start the pills two or three months before marriage so that the patient may become accustomed to them. Nausea may occur in about 10 per cent of the patients but it occurs only during the first ten to twelve days.

Another drawback is that an occasional patient may have fluid retention and becomes edematous. Certain women retain water more easily than others during the later portion of the cycle and this is associated with premenstrual tension. This can be prevented by re-ducing the amount of salt in the diet toward the latter part of the cycle. The physician can prescribe a diet that is low in salt and suggest the use of diuretics. Unfortunately, the tendency to retain fluid can-not always be overcome in three months, and we do have a number of patients who have to stop taking the tablets because the retention of fluid is more than they really want. They feel the tablets are more trouble than they are worth.

There are some individuals who feel reluctant to use the pills be-cause of magazine articles or family pressures. I feel that no one should be persuaded to use the pills. However, if there are particular ques-tions about their efficiency or safety, I can offer reassurance. Ninety-four per cent of women who want to use oral contraceptives can; about 6 per cent will find them unsatisfactory.

The question has been brought up as to whether the contraceptive pills produce emotional tension. I can only quote our series at Chapel

Hill in which we had two emotionally disturbed women among 250 patients who were taking these pills. This percentage would probably be found in a similar group who were not taking contraceptives. The only side effect of taking these pills, which is of any concern, is that they may affect the clotting mechanism of the blood. This question is being investigated, but at present there is no statistical evidence that they cause clinical abnormalities.

Whether the taking of the pill reduces menstrual tension is difficult to assess since this is such a complex problem. If the tension is associated with fear of pregnancy, then this tension should be alleviated.

So far the first generation of babies conceived after their mothers had been using this form of contraceptive have been completely normal. I am not concerned that any adverse effects will be seen in the second generation. I believe that the pills are perfectly safe. The only thing that is really unfortunate about them is that they are not the answer to our population explosion.

We are conducting two parallel studies on oral contraceptives at the University of North Carolina. First, we are giving them to patients who have had twelve years or more of education; oral contraceptives have worked magnificently in this group. We have had no pregnancies in two years despite the fact that they are all young people with high fertility. The second group consists of women who have had four to twelve years of education; we have had a 25 per cent drop-out rate in this group because of lack of motivation and intelligence. These are the people who are responsible for the population explosion. They should be the ones taking the contraceptive pills, for they are the ones who have less interest and less motivation for caring for their children and are less concerned about trying to educate their children.

I might say in passing that a contraceptive pill for men is now under investigation. The inmates of several prisons have volunteered their services for research purposes. These pills are also taken by mouth and appear to decrease spermatogenesis in the testicle, as shown by testicular biopsy. Although the sperm are decreased in number it is not yet certain that they are reduced below the level at which fertilization can occur. Various side effects are also described, similar to the effect of taking Antabuse for alcoholism. Patients taking these pills are unable to tolerate alcohol because of nausea, vomiting, and congestion of the eyes.

We should now discuss some of the older methods. One is the use of jelly alone. This is a fairly effective method of contraception. Actually, this form of contraception will give a failure index of about eight to ten pregnancies per one hundred years of exposure. That is, if one hundred women use this contraceptive method for one year, one would find eight to ten pregnancies in the group.

Another method is the use of the condom and jelly. This is as effective as the diaphragm and jelly method for the following reason. Should rupture of the condom occur, or should it remain in the vagina with accidental leaking of the spermatozoa, they will be killed by the jelly. I cannot recommend the condom alone as a good method of contraception. First, the condom can break. Second, unless withdrawal occurs right after ejaculation, the penis decreases in size and sperm therefore can swim down the shaft of the penis and be deposited on the vulva and migrate up the vagina into the cervix. But the use of condom and jelly is an extraordinarily good method of contraception. Of course, some patients will not use it since it is not as aesthetic as other methods.

Many men do not know how to use a condom properly. The condom has a small nipple at the tip. The tip should be grasped so that there is a free space between the nipple and the end of the penis. When ejaculation occurs, the ejaculate accumulates in this area, which is free from pressure. Rupture of a condom may occur when it is placed tightly onto the penis and is subjected to the movements of coitus plus the accumulation of the ejaculate.

Another method of contraception that is receiving attention is the use of the intrauterine device. One of these is a small stainless steel ring which is about the size of a nickel and is inserted inside the uterus and stays there for an indefinite period of time. Plastic devices are also being tested. These are designed to prevent implantation. Although the sperm and ovum unite, implantation of the embryo in the uterus does not occur. This type of device has a great future for the lower social groups. It is effective for years and cannot be removed by the patient although it is easy for the physician to remove it. An intrauterine device is difficult to insert unless the woman has had at least one child because the mouth of the womb is rather tight until it has been dilated by childbirth.

The use of vaginal foam is probably the most aesthetic approach to contraception which we have at the present time. Vaginal foam resembles shaving cream; it is inserted via an aerosol container and disappears in the vagina as coitus is initiated. The only problem is that we are not yet exactly sure of just how effective this is going to be. The initial reports suggest that this is as effective as jelly alone. We must await further information. This will be available in a few years from the Planned Parenthood Federation.

Finally, we should discuss the so-called safe period or the rhythm method of contraception. This method is associated with a pregnancy rate of twenty-three to twenty-five per hundred years of exposure. It is the least reliable of any method we have discussed, but is the only method that the Catholic church will accept at present. This method is based on the fact that women are fertile during that time in their menstrual cycle when there is an ovum in the reproductive system which is capable of being fertilized. If intercourse occurs before or after this time, when the ovum is no longer viable, pregnancy will not occur. The crux of the situation is the determination of the time of ovulation, and this is characterized by a preliminary fall and subsequent rise in the body temperature. A person planning to use this method of contraception should commence a chart a year before marriage, using a specially graduated thermometer and charting the temperature each day, before rising from bed in the morning. She should also write the Planned Parenthood Federation in New York for their excellent booklet on the "safe period."

We used to think that the sperm could live in the uterus and tubes for only about forty-eight hours. We now think that they can survive for as long as seven days. Even if we know the precise time of ovulation by our temperature chart, the time during the cycle when intercourse is "safe" is very short. Also, there is some evidence that coitus itself may initiate ovulation, irrespective of the time of the cycle.

These are the reasons why the rhythm method of contraception results in such a high failure rate. It might be said in passing that it is possible to have intercourse during menstruation with a high safety factor and there are no medical contra-indications to coitus during menstruation.

There are other methods available to women to determine whether ovulation has occurred, apart from the temperature chart. The breasts in some women become tender at the latter part of the menstrual cycle, and this period is relatively safe. There is also available a litmus paper that comes with an applicator which the wife places in the vagina. This changes color with the change in acidity of the vagina which occurs at ovulation. Thirdly, women may notice a change in the character of the normal vaginal secretions. Nature has so devised these that at the most fertile period the secretion has the lowest surface tension and contains more sugar, providing a medium that is favorable to survival of the sperm and promoting their passage into the uterus. Unfortunately all of these methods have limited reliability but should be mentioned to Catholic couples.

Let us say a few words about the physical examination and, in particular, the pelvic examination. The latter is performed after a thorough physical examination. Actually the premarital examination should be made well in advance of marriage since stretching of the hymen is occasionally necessary. Unfortunately there are physicians who feel that virginity precludes a pelvic examination and that a virgin should not be fitted with a diaphragm. This certainly is not true, and while the hymen will vary from individual to individual, the vagina beyond the hymen is relatively constant in size.

If the hymen should be tight, it is an easy matter for the physician to infiltrate this with a local anaesthetic and stretch the hymen sufficiently so that the initiation of intercourse is no problem. It is possible to fit a diaphragm. It is no longer necessary for a girl to go to the hospital and have a general anaesthetic since the above procedure is performed in the office. I do feel that the well-adjusted male will certainly wish his bride to be spared any discomfort during the honeymoon period. But the decision to have the hymen stretched and dilated before marriage is for the bride and groom to make. The following case illustrates why premarital stretching of the hymen is important.

A young co-ed at Carolina was seen because of menstrual dysfunction. At the time I examined her, she had a very small hymeneal introitus that would admit only one finger. This will allow a person to do an adequate pelvic examination, but it is certainly not satisfactory for coitus. The menstrual dysfunction was regulated, but I told her that before she got married it was very important that she have her hymen stretched. I did not see her again until much later, but here is the story she told. A month before marriage, she went to see her family physician and he was horrified to think that anybody would ever even examine a young girl who was about to be married and certainly nothing should be done for the hymen. She took his word for it. They had a nice wedding and an expensive reception in her home town and flew off with great anticipation to Bermuda. Well, to make a long story short, they had to get a physician out in the middle of the night to suture her hymen because she was bleeding so much. The episode was so upsetting that they flew back home and she was so frightened and so tense that coitus could not occur for about three months. This could easily have been corrected by an adequate premarital examination and elimination of the obstructing hymen.

I think that a Papanicolaou smear or cancer test should be done premaritally. This should be done once the hymen is stretched and the adult speculum can be introduced. We like to instruct our patients to have this test performed once a year.

Also, we estimate the normalcy of the uterus, the cervix, the tubes, and the ovaries so that when we have finished we can make a very straightforward statement to most patients in saying that the physical examination and the pelvic examination show things to be entirely normal.

Our next point of discussion is how can we properly use these normal structures. At this stage of the examination, and if the girl desires this form of contraceptive, I demonstrate to her the fitting of the diaphragm. This is facilitated by the use of a transparent plastic model. In demonstrating this, the salient features of the female anatomy can be pointed out.

This particular model * represents a cross-section of the pelvis. We see the labia, or folds of tissue that have to be separated before the entrance to the vagina can be seen. These represent in the female the same developmental area that forms the scrotum, in which the male testicles are contained.

We can visualize the vagina, which is expanded in this model to

---

* A plastic model of the female pelvis is obtained from the manufacturers of the products pertaining to feminine hygiene.

demonstrate the position of the diaphragm. Normally the vagina is a tube of skin that is completely closed. The cervix or mouth of the uterus or womb is easily seen, and this area is all important in the fitting of the diaphragm. You will notice the cavity of the uterus and the Fallopian tubes with their frond-like ends that lie free in the peritoneal cavity. These are ready to sweep the ovum, which escapes from the surface of the ovary, into the tube, where the ovum and sperm meet to unite in the development of the future baby, which is housed in the uterine cavity. We can say that the Fallopian tube acts like a vacuum cleaner in that just before ovulation rippling movements commence, and the fimbria or fronds at the end of the tube sweep across the surface of the ovary to sweep the ovum into the tube. Some women are more highly fertile than others, because their husband's spermatozoa survive in their bodies for a long period of time—as long as ten days—and the conditions of the bride's cervix and vagina are such that the sperm finds it an easy matter to complete conception.

Let us now discuss the use of the diaphragm and jelly. A typical spermicidal or sperm-killing jelly is thin and colorless, since the manufacturers have tried to create a jelly that resembles the natural vaginal secretions. The average bride will find the jelly a little messy and the diaphragm a little difficult to adjust at first. But when an item is effective, we can overlook these defects. That is why we like to fit the diaphragm several weeks before the marriage so that the insertion can be practiced and become familiar to the bride. It is obviously preferable to insert the diaphragm as a nightly routine when bathing rather than as a last minute procedure.

The distention of the vagina varies considerably in different individuals. It is for this reason that proper fitting of the diaphragm is important. The method of using the diaphragm is as follows: a teaspoon of jelly is placed in the hollow of the diaphragm, and the margin is encircled with jelly. The diaphragm is now squeezed so that its two sides approximate (in some brands the diaphragm is marked so that one approximates the marks). It is then inserted into the vagina in a downward and backward direction till it slips behind the pubic bone in front and up behind the cervix in the vagina. The forefinger is used to test the fact that the cervix is covered by the diaphragm. It is important to let the patient feel the cervix herself while in the office. This feels firm like the cartilage of one's nose and has a small opening in it. She then feels the sensation when it is covered by the rubber of the diaphragm. The function of the jelly in the center of the diaphragm is to destroy any sperm at the entrance of the canal to the uterus; the function of the jelly at the margin of the diaphragm is to prevent any sperm from working their way around this barrier. In addition, we instruct the bride to insert about a third of an applicator of jelly into the vagina as an added precaution. While in the office, the nurse or physician will see that the patient places the diaphragm in position and takes it out on several occasions, so that she has confidence in using it. A failure of the diaphragm in contraception will occur if the wife has not bothered to use it, trusting in the "safe period" which does not really exist, when she has inserted it so that the cervix is not covered, or when she has failed to use jelly. The diaphragm should not be removed for six hours after coitus in order that the sperm are killed. Douching is not necessary then or really ever at any time. The vagina cleanses itself very well and after coitus all that is necessary is to place tissue between the legs and roll over and go to sleep. If, with young people, intercourse is desired on several occasions during the one evening, all that is necessary is to check again that the cervix is covered and to insert another half applicator of jelly into the vagina. The diaphragm should not be left in position more than twenty-four hours as irritation of the vagina may occur, and also the teaspoon of jelly at the mouth of the uterus will be dissipated.

To sum up the contraceptive situation, we have to say that if contraceptives are going to be used effectively they have to be used at each coitus.

Let us now return to the general theme of sexual relations within marriage. I like to think of sexual experience as a very simple thing. It is not complicated; it is very normal. One of the major difficulties is that the majority of girls have had a mental barrier erected that is incorrect biologically. This barrier is an artificial one erected by our society which has rightly decided that education and the development of a profession should precede the establishment of home and family. By physiologic standards, girls should have been having intercourse since the age of ten or eleven, and should have had four or five babies by age twenty, as was actually the case not too long ago when women were in a state of pregnancy or lactation the greater part of their married life.

While electing to postpone the joys of married life to a later period, some of these feelings of awe about intercourse may remain, but taboos instilled by Victorian standards must also be regarded as a thing of the past. Intercourse is a beautiful expression of affection between two people who love one another. It is certainly in no way abnormal, but one must not be disappointed if this expression lacks the dramatic aspects that the lay press would lead us to expect, but rather is a reaction of enjoyment that may take months or years to reach its zenith.

Most women get their greatest joy out of giving; giving in the preparation of a home, keeping it clean and nice, the preparation of food, doing things for other people. You have done things for other people all your life and therein lies great joy. In this instance, you are giving yourself to your husband and this is a natural and normal thing for a woman to participate in and enjoy. Moreover, it is not complicated but resembles any particular feat that requires muscular co-ordination. Coitus at first may be a bit awkward; it is something that improves with time; it should always be expressed with tenderness and affection; it is something very beautiful.

There is confusion in the minds of women as to what they should achieve in terms of coitus and what is the normal sensation of orgasm. I think the confusion results from the fact that it means different things to different people. Some women have a fairly violent action with orgasm. But to most women it is a sensation of release of great pleasure and is associated with the feeling of relaxation. It is not necessary to have an orgasm with each coitus. To some extent, it is a learned reaction. The sensation of orgasm is enriched with time, by the alleviation of anxiety and the guilt aspects of coitus, and with the improvement of the mechanical aspects of nearness and completeness of the act. One should not be disappointed if orgasm does not occur initially but be reassured that, with time, orgasm takes care of itself if fairly simple aspects of sexual stimulation occur before coitus.

I think it is important that we realize that this is not the day of Victorian virgins and there should be no such thing as sexual perversion in marriage. There must be free communication in terms of that which is pleasant and enjoyable to each other in the art of love-making. Moreover, sufficient time should be taken to allow mutual stimulation.

It is unfortunate that some couples make love in a regimented manner. I have had girls come in for a premarital examination after having read books on sexual techniques who have said, "Now I want to get this straight, how do I do this and how do I do that and when do I do the other?" That is not the way one makes love. One might have intercourse that way, but making love is something entirely different. It is an expression of one's own personality and one's own tenderness. How this is done depends upon one's own feelings and expression. Let us regard the relationship as one of making love, not merely having intercourse.

It is interesting to compare desire for intercourse in animals with man. In the lower animals the female will only receive the male during the time when she is in heat, that is, when pelvic vascularity is greatest. It is natural that nature constituted women so that their greatest sexual desire would be around the period of ovulation; it is also great just before menstruation when there is pelvic congestion. However, with the development of the higher centers of the brain with which man is endowed, we recognize that love-making is a process of mutual enjoyment quite irrespective of the aspect of pro-creation. While the girl does have these periods of maximum desire, she is also anxious to give and receive affection at other times of the cycle. Many women may enjoy daily intercourse, but orgasm may not be achieved on each occasion. The average young man is quite prepared for insemination every other day, whereas the female's time for greatest sexual excitement is twice a month. There will be times of stress, as far as the male is concerned, when erection will not be possible. There will also be many times when intercourse is far from the mind because of bodily fatigue and emotional stresses.

There are no hard and fast rules laid down for frequency of intercourse, but rather it is a meeting of minds and bodies that are attuned to each other and find each other mutually desirable.

Next we shall concentrate on the male because so rarely do we have an opportunity to talk to him, and I like to let the girl know that the male also has problems in initiating coitus. Often the bride can be of particular help to her husband. The greatest problem that the male generally has is premature ejaculation; there are several reasons for this. Again, the awe of intercourse is built up into something that causes great stimulation initially, but stimulation is really an abnormal ingredient of love-making in that it is excitement rather than a firm, affectionate stimulation. So like the over-anxious football player, he fumbles and misses the pass. He had not learned some of the coordination aspects of coitus and therefore ejaculates early. The wife can be most helpful in this by having him merely enter her body which is warm and succulent without making any mechanical movement. After he becomes adjusted to this new environment, coitus can develop in such a manner that premature ejaculations do not occur. Thus his reaction can be attuned to that of his wife. It is a good idea at the close of the premarital examination to bring the couple together and ask if there are any final questions or problems that they would like to discuss.

We have spent considerable time on the premarital examination of the female; it is important to discuss what the male can expect from such an examination. Again, he ought to expect a review of systems, as we have discussed, basic laboratory tests, and a complete physical examination, including an examination of the genitalia.

We might, at this point, describe the difficulty which might be met in trying to find a physician to carry out the type of premarital examination we have discussed. Dr. Nash Herndon and Mrs. Ethel Nash conducted a survey of a large sample of practicing North Carolina physicians. Only 12 per cent give this particular type of premarital examination; an additional 50 per cent will do this if it is requested. It is important to tell the physician the type of examination that is desired. The age of the physician is often an indication of his ability to give this type of examination. At present the greatest chance of having this done properly is by a young obstetrician in a city practice.

Actually, in North Carolina the marriage license will be given if the physician will certify that there is freedom from venereal disease, tuberculosis, epilepsy, or mental illness. Freedom from venereal disease means usually a negative serologic test for syphilis. Incidentally, in many states, only tests carried out by certain laboratories are recognized, and physicians should be familiar with those laboratories which are acceptable.

Let us now talk about various aspects of childbirth.*

About three days after conception, the union of male and female cells, an organ known as the placenta begins to develop as an integral part of the embryo. The maternal system has no control over the placenta; it functions as a separate organ. The placenta produces hormones in an amount almost five hundred times that produced in the normal menstrual cycle. One of the functions of these hormones is to prepare the uterine muscle and birth canal for subsequent delivery of the baby. The normal uterus weighing two ounces has to increase to an organ weighing two pounds; this is achieved by the individual muscle fibers growing, multiplying, and stretching. The small cervix, which we indicated on the model, has to be able to distend to ten centimeters in diameter, to enable the baby's head to descend through it. There must be a reduction of fibrous tissue within the cervix and an increase in the fluid content to enable it to become more elastic. These changes are directly under the control of the placental hormones.

Secondly, the vagina, which normally allows the introduction of two or three fingers, has to be prepared for the passage of a seven-pound baby, with a shoulder circumference of thirty-five centimeters.

Thirdly, the breast tissue is stimulated by these hormones to prepare for lactation. One of the most remarkable things about the organization of the animal kingdom is the fact that each species will deliver its offspring at the appropriate time when the offspring is able to survive the external environment. This occurs in the elephant when the fetus weighs five hundred pounds and in the mouse when it weighs only a few grams. The mechanism that prevents delivery until the appropriate time is quite complicated and not fully understood but is probably related to some extent to the placental hormones. To some extent, the placental hormones prevent contractions of the uterus during pregnancy and prevent the expulsion of the baby prematurely. During the latter weeks of pregnancy the placenta ages and gradually produces fewer hormones. At the same time, with the release of progesterone, uterine contractions commence, mild at first and only felt when a hand is placed over the abdomen. Later, as true labor develops, awareness of these contractions enters consciousness and becomes pain-

* This is preliminary to showing to the group the film "A Normal Birth," produced by Medical Films, Inc., P.O. Box 402, Stockton, California.

ful. The period when contractions commence occurs over the last few weeks of pregnancy. It almost seems that the uterus is getting into practice for the final test of delivery.

These minor, or Braxton-Hicks, contractions produce the effect of softening the cervix and making it more easily distensible. Finally, when the complicated temporal and chemical factors of labor are joined, the uterus produces its own pace-setting mechanism for contraction, just as the heart does. The remarkable thing about the uterus is that it does not merely contract and then relax, which could mean that the baby could slip back to the starting point. The muscle fibers in the fundus or top of the uterus contract and hold their advantage, so that progress of the baby down the birth canal is constant, and at the same time the cervix is being thinned out preparatory to its eventual dilatation.

Another thing that occurs in labor is that the baby is maneuvered to the most favorable diameters of the pelvis through which it must pass. There are three levels in the pelvis, one at the inlet, one in the mid-pelvis, and one at the outlet. Each of these levels has different diameters of measurement. The average diameters of the baby's head are 11.5 centimeters and 9.5 centimeters, respectively. The maternal pelvis has a leeway over these measurements of about two centimeters in each diameter taken at these three levels, but the greatest diameter at the pelvic inlet is practically at right angles to that at the outlet. The baby prepares for the descent with its head flexed, which is the optimum position for delivery. We can compare it with a football player in the tackling position who might be injured unless he flexed his head. As birth occurs, the head is extended and the obstetrician assists this procedure. The shoulders follow and then the trunk and legs, each position of the baby accommodating to the most favorable diameter of the maternal pelvis. The cord is then tied and cut, and the placenta or afterbirth is delivered a short time later. The average length of labor for the first baby is about ten to eleven hours.

The message I would like to emphasize is this. If the woman will learn to relax and have confidence in her body and in her obstetrician, labor and delivery is safe, simple, and reasonably rapid. The time of pregnancy is one time when the advice of friends is completely out of place and their remarks and adverse comments are uncalled for. I personally would like to hang a placard around the neck of each patient after I have conducted a prenatal examination saying: "I have just seen the Doctor. He says I'm normal and everything is fine."

You are all interested, I am sure, in obstetrical pain relief. There are three methods: no analgesia or drugs during labor and delivery, medication to relieve the majority of discomfort without being asleep, and drugs to induce sleeping during labor and delivery. There are certain cities where the obstetrical patients prefer general anaesthesia and others where saddle block is preferred. The whole question often revolves around individual preference and local custom. Medical science has now reached the stage of being able to allow a mother to sleep during the greater part of labor and delivery. However, I feel that patients should elect their own programs of obstetrical pain relief after the various types have been explained by their physicians. They thus may receive no medication, or they can be asleep during most of the labor. I regard the selection of analgesia as an intellectual decision. If a mother would enjoy participating in labor and delivery, it is worth the effort.

There has developed a fashion in some sections of the country of allowing husbands to be present at delivery. I personally feel that the husband's role in pregnancy is twofold, that of initiating the events of the pregnancy and that of being a comfort and support during the early stages of labor.

About 10 per cent of pregnancies end in miscarriage. Human reproduction is not perfect. If an individual has had one or even two miscarriages, her chances of going through a pregnancy normally are almost the same as a woman who has never lost a pregnancy. One of the most common reasons for miscarriages is that conception occurs at the wrong time of the month when the lining of the uterus is not ready for implantation. In addition, there can be defects in the ovum or sperm which may prevent normal development.

I have welcomed this opportunity to talk with young couples before marriage. I find in practice that many girls are afraid of the premarital examination. I feel that this reluctance will pass and that, with further education along these lines, a meeting with the physician who will give an adequate premarital examination will be accepted and appreciated.

PART THREE

Concepts of Marital Diagnosis and Therapy

15

Concepts of Marital Diagnosis
and Therapy as Developed at the
Tavistock Family Psychiatric Units,
London, England

H. V. Dicks, M.D., F.R.C.P.

Introduction

The aim of this chapter is to present a synoptic view of what we, at the Tavistock Clinic, have contributed to a new field of mental health action—joint diagnosis and therapy for marital cases.* Marital work at the Tavistock Clinic and Institute developed from two separate projects around 1949, which have gradually come closer together.

1. First I shall mention the Family Discussion Bureau (F.D.B.), a marital case work agency that grew out of a large voluntary agency, the Family Welfare Association. It is staffed mainly by psychiatric social workers. Their training in marital work, aside from personal

* Based on a paper given at the International Congress for Mental Health, Paris, France, 1961, in collaboration with Alison Lyons, Mary Welch, and Douglas Woodhouse of the Family Discussion Bureau.

analysis which many of them have undergone, originated with Dr. Michael and Mrs. Enid Balint. This bureau has, for reasons I need not detail, been joined for some eight years to the Tavistock Institute.* Its main tasks have been therapeutic and educational; in the latter activity the staff conducts seminars and offers case experience to many social workers in the preventive health services in Britain. Their therapeutic work has dealt with some 2,500 couples, with encouraging results in a gratifying proportion of cases. All work is regularly supervised at case conferences held by psychoanalyst psychiatrists.

The work and its theoretical foundations have been described in two books.[2, 7]

2. The other unit dealing with marriage problems was created by me at the Tavistock Clinic at a time when F.D.B. was still outside it. The impetus came from the same source, the request of the Family Welfare Association to assist in understanding problem families. This unit has also been concerned with therapy, but was first planned as a research team for gaining insights and concepts useful to the development of inter-personal diagnostic methods, seeing fewer cases in consequence.[4]

This unit is part of the regular service offered to the public under the National Health Service. It is staffed by a multi-professional team and has attached to it doctors, social workers, and psychologists in postgraduate and more senior status. We do not claim that the units described do more than a small fraction of marriage counseling in Britain. Much of this burden is borne by another large voluntary organization of lay people, who do valuable work in the easier problems. Our Magistrates' Courts, also, have attached to them probation officers—trained social workers—who have the statutory duty of attempting marital conciliation in cases applying to the courts for legal relief in marriage conflicts. Probation officers handle a large number of cases with increasing skill and success. Our team's role in the education of probation officers for this task is of long standing.

What we may justly claim is that the Tavistock projects have

---

* When in 1948 the National Health Service came into operation, the Tavistock Organization decided to split into the Clinic, which entered the National Service, and the Institute, which remained a private corporation, pursuing research, training, etc., in mental health and in social and community studies not strictly medical. But the two bodies are as two sides of a coin and in closest working touch.

been concerned to apply a fairly consistent psychodynamic approach by professional persons to problems of marital hygiene, interaction, and pathology in Britain. It is this conceptual framework that I wish to present. It is unnecessary to stress the central importance for the health of individuals or groups of a community of stable, secure family life. I spoke of this at the Toronto Congress (1954) in a paper devoted to the more sociological background of this work.[5]

What we have to offer is not a finished system, but a set of working hypotheses whose validity rests on our clinical experience. We are none of us paid to engage in full-time research, and our ideas are the by-product of wrestling with the interpretation of the clinical phenomena presented by our clients when they ask us to help resolve them.

It remains to mention briefly that our sample of cases consists always of married couples (or persons who live as married couples even if not legally wed). We accept in our units only persons whose problems are not primarily recognized by themselves as psychiatric illnesses. Inevitably, in the course of such investigation and therapy, personality or character problems are encountered which are often quite severe. But it is the marriage that is the sick unit we study.

Our clients are people, on the whole, of the more successful sort, above the median of intelligence, often in adequate social and economic circumstances, mainly middle- or upper-working-class, and ranging from late adolescence to the seventh decade in age.

I do not wish here to enlarge on the statistical aspects of the population studied. We regard it of much greater importance to talk of "what goes on" between married partners and to draw what insights we can for a helpful approach to such problems in the clinic, the community, and even the court of law.

The Framework

The late Harry Stack Sullivan defined psychiatry as the "operational statement of interpersonal relations." This broad and challenging definition might have been invented to describe our psychodynamic approach to the study of marital interaction. Not only does it stress the proposition that mental life *is* relation to objects of which the most important are other human beings, but it can also be referred to the manifestations of deeper levels of relatedness and its disturbances, in the transference situation between patient and therapist which has, so we think, yielded the largest measure of understanding of the phenomena with which psychiatry and psychology as a whole are concerned.

Thus we state at the outset that our orientation to the study of marital problems has been based on psychoanalytic personality theory, especially on contributions from later writers such as Melanie Klein and W. R. D. Fairbairn, and on Jung's ideas on complementariness and on unconscious "opposites." It follows from this that we have not conceived of our function as therapists in this or in any other field as consisting of exhortation, persuasion, or decision-making for our clients, not even, often, of giving advice—a role which our clients would wish to assign to us and which might be implied by the appellation of "counselor," which, in consequence, we do not use.

Rather we regard our task as that of ourselves first gaining some insight into the phenomena we meet and then applying this insight in helping to clarify them for the partners involved in conflict by interpretation and comment. In other words, ours is an interpretive psychotherapy based on psychoanalytic principles applied to a two-body unit—a dyad—the married pair. It is a group-psychology for the smallest numerical group!

We conceive of the marital relationship (1) as an interaction *sui generis* between two persons who have consciously agreed (at "ego" level) to play certain social roles (first of spouse, later of parent) in ways which not only satisfy the needs of each other but also, to varying degrees, fulfill the requirements and mores of the cultural background in which each developed and of the changing society of which they form a part—a society that may not, in the circumstances of modern social and geographical mobility, be the society in which the spouses grew up. (2) We further conceive of the marriage relation as a more unconscious "transaction" of forces in two persons, each with a developmental history in the course of which their primary biological and social needs for security, dependence, sexual gratification, and self-assertion had been structured by the influences of their milieu upon the given genetic predispositions.

It will be seen that this concept involves us in viewing marital relationships and their disturbances, from three angles:

1. The personality assessment of each partner in the dyad as a separate individual
2. The socio-cultural factors and stresses affecting the couple from their separate "past" as well as in the "here and now" of their position in social space
3. The attempt to evaluate the more unconscious bonds of motivations which we have called "the transaction" between them.

It is, as my colleagues would agree, a clarification of this third level which constitutes the distinctive contribution we are hoping to make to social psychology, the nature of the bonds which hold a heterosexual pair together.

Let me now be more precise about each of these.

(1) *Intra-personal Conflict*

The assessment of each partner as a separate being follows the more or less classical path of a psychoanalytic, psychiatric anamnesis, deepened and enriched as contact with the case-worker evolves. Here we look for the strengths and weaknesses, the harmonies and conflicts, in the partner's capacity for sustaining relationships to objects. The capacity for, and the interpretation given by, the person to the roles that he or she will have to play in the marriage is in large measure an outcome of the learning process, the preparation for object-relation in childhood. At the risk of stating a platitude, we start from the position that a young adult's readiness to commit his personality to a lasting heterosexual union is a result of maturation against the background of his experiences in the family of origin. Here the child, who will become the marriage partner we are studying, will have felt and internalized the images that I like to call "interaction models" or "role models" of relationships: first between self and his mother; next in the wider circle of self and father and brothers and sisters (if any); and of the parents to each other and to the other siblings. As I have stated elsewhere,[5] in our modern urban-industrial societies, this nuclear family retains the all-important function of giving the child this experience, of socializing its relational needs and demands, even though much of its traditional power and influence have been diminished by the encroachment of public schooling and of the economic system that makes the growing members increasingly independent. The child acquires the level of emotional maturity that the parental interaction models were capable of helping him to develop.

We can think of this developmental process as the secure passage through a succession of positions of ambivalence and conflict, from the total, crude and undifferentiated earliest feelings of "good" and "bad" objects, through a gradual lessening of absolute contrasts as reality-testing by the growing ego becomes strengthened, toward a tolerance of ambivalence both in the self and in the object. In a healthy outcome of this conflictful growth-process, the bio-social object-and-goal-seeking drives have not been seriously obstructed by the unresolved tensions of the preceding phase. Relations with objects are felt to contain the promise of satisfaction of needs or goals. The preponderance of secure, loving outcomes of reality-testing and conflict-resolution creates in the growing personality a reservoir of relational potential with figures of his world which we term *good internal objects*. With these the child can identify, and they form his strength of inner resources. Through them he learns how to love as an adult because he has felt adult love nourish and sustain him. The child has come to tolerate within himself and others ambivalent feelings because he has experienced the parents' tolerance and mastery of their own anger as well as the child's in a mainly loving way.

In the less fortunate outcome there will remain certain unresolved, not outgrown need-demands towards the parent figures, who were experienced as frustrating, hence as objects of hate. This hate is felt to be both inside the self *towards* the object, as well as outside the self, *in* the object towards the self. It is from this kind of situation that there arise the typical rigid psychic mechanisms of defense as described in psychoanalytic literature: guilt and anxiety which produce or maintain splitting of the objects into good and bad; hysterical dissociation and denial (a splitting of the internal object world); projection resulting in paranoid attitudes towards love objects; depressive anxiety about one's own deep fantasies of hate; and the emergence of covering attitudes of idealization, obsessive restitution-making or false detachment and intellectualization. The growth process is deformed or even arrested by the crystallization of such rigid defenses that "interfere" with the secure flow of the drives towards their bio-psychic goal-satisfactions. The rigidity of a hard shell hampers the flexibility of creative and adaptive responses to the love-object. The individual remains unconsciously still at grips with the object of conflict and with his own complex of feelings surrounding that figure (termed *the bad internal object*).

This means that in marriage the partner so handicapped will have an inner interaction model that includes infantile, hostile, and contradictory attitudes towards his own and his partner's role performance derived from earlier levels of personality development. We recall that, with few exceptions, observers have noted the presence of bad parental relations or broken homes as the most constant factor in marital breakdown. Our own sample showed it to be 95 per cent.

(2) *The Importance of Social and Cultural Distance*

My earliest cases were problems in mixed marriages in a certain run-down area of London. Hence I do not ignore the difficulties as well as the enrichment of a marriage between persons of widely different cultures or social levels. People have never liked "mixed marriages." Traditionally in-groups have always had fears about their children marrying out of their faith, race, nation, or socio-economic class. The risk of marriage to a "stranger" is precisely this doubt about the disparity in the partners' inner role models, in the tacit assumptions about how one plays the part of a "good husband" or "good wife." Apart altogether from neurotic conflict inside each partner, the widely differing norms and values assigned to various items of role behavior in the different cultures can lead to paradoxical and frustrating responses in the other. It is, in simple terms, the situation produced by the man saying, "You can't make apple-pie like mother's"; or the wife's being shocked that her husband does not go to church or rise when she enters, like the men in her community.

But this is not a simple matter of fitting culture pattern to culture pattern. Just as people from the same parish can quarrel in their marriage, so can persons from widely disparate backgrounds get on well. We have to allow that where there is friction in a trans-cultural marriage it can then most easily be blamed on culture distance. Where culture distance leads to major conflict in marriage, it is because the culture norms are too rigidly tied up with the persisting parental attachments that represent the culture "inside" us. The denial of their continued power, ignored during courtship with the "stranger," was part of a rebellion against the parental norms one did not know one was still unconsciously ruled by. It is part of the defensive rigidity at deeper levels which links this factor to our first category of unresolved ambivalent parent ties, when these are reactivated by the experience of frustrating role behavior, of "missed cues."

Matters become complicated when the actual parents still try to exert a pull on partners from one or both sides. There are still psychological Montagues and Capulets. Modern marriages in Britain are no longer dependent on parental choice or approval but are, at social level, independent or autonomous agreements between the partners. Many couples are married without having met their in-laws. Children are in theory brought up with a view to becoming independent psychologically and economically. But in practice, at a deeper level, the atomization or isolation of the modern urban family makes the emotional dependence of parents and children *on each other* very strong. The phenomena of the over-protective or possessive parent are familiar to us all. For example, I am at present treating a couple in which the wife was the favorite, over-protected daughter. When her mother heard that she was pregnant she at once gave her an (ineffective) abortion pill—horrified at the thought that her pretty child should become a woman and mother. Since this time the unfortunate woman, though she has had three children, has been tormented by the fantasy of her mother's being in the room when coitus was taking place, and envying and disapproving of the daughter's sexual maturity. This is a graphic example of the way in which a persistent tie with an ambivalent object can "interfere" with the normal performance of the marital role.

Lastly, on the topic of social factors, a few words on economic conditions. Social workers in England who deal with problem families and the crude violence and "unhappiness" of their marital life often assert that poverty and bad housing are "causes" of marriage breakdowns. This is a confusion. Not only have rich and over-privileged people the same troubles, but there are plenty of poor couples who meet adverse conditions with solidarity and loving co-operation. It is our opinion that adverse social conditions do not *cause* but activate the emergence of latent childish needs that are displaced from the partner to the frustrating environment. "If it wasn't for this bad fortune I could be a good spouse." Indeed, there is evidence to show that re-housing slum populations of London in hygienic new settlements has produced much tension and unhappiness because of the isolation of the families from their social roots in the "bad neighborhood." I stress that it is human relations, not bricks or marble or family budgets, that are the chief concern of the mental health service.

(3) *Marital Interaction and Collusion*

Let us now turn to the third area of study of marital relations—one perhaps most characteristic of what our teams are trying to define and clarify. This, as I stated earlier, relates to the interaction of the two personalities of the partners at conscious and unconscious levels.

One may say in quasi-mathematical terms that the marital relationship will be a product, or a parallelogram, of the mature capacities for sustaining an on-going, interdependent relationship, and of these forces which I described a moment ago as "interferences" from residual internalized preoccupations with past object-relations. Modern marriage, no longer buttressed by moral compulsions and social mores universally valid, is perhaps the greatest test of emotional maturity. It is not enough that the family of origin has prepared their son or their daughter for independence in the social and economic sense, hard though that is. For marital success the crucial problem is how, in addition, to conserve and make available to them the tolerance of the need for dependence. I will cite two paradigmatic instances:

1. Consider an insecure man who cannot accept the feminine emotionality of his wife. He has to belittle her for not having a masculine rationality. We can often trace such intolerance to rigid defenses in the man against his own repressed emotional dependence on his parents, which he has come to despise by identification with parental figures who rejected such feelings or behavior in him as "sissy" or "cry-baby." He uses his marital relation as a means of denying his own dependence or emotionality or homosexual trends by projecting this despised part of himself to his wife.

2. Similarly, we often see a woman with unconscious masculine identifications who has difficulty in overcoming these on marriage and who now projects these "phallic" attitudes onto her man. He must, in consequence, be a hero, and if he fails to live up to such a

fantasy role expectation, such women will persecute and belittle the husband to the point of psychological castration for his despised more tender or soft qualities.

(a) The *first hypothesis* that can be derived from seeing many such situations is that in conflictful marital relations a spouse does not *confirm* the partner's real personality, but requires him or her to behave in accordance with the inner role model, and directly or indirectly avenges failure to conform. Much marital conflict can be shown to stem from strivings to mold the partner to conform to the self's inner expectations, meeting with the resistance that is sooner or later evoked by such pressure as well as by intolerance of the real person. The converse hypothesis is that in marriage the partners need to be confirmed and accepted by the spouse as they are. But matters are not as simple as this preliminary hypothesis suggests. From it we would only derive *one* partner with unhealthy demands, evoking "healthy" self-protective reactions in the other.

(b) Our clinical experience has established beyond doubt a fact that we cannot fully explain—namely the *reciprocity* or *collusion* between partners, often at unconscious level.

This proposition involves the whole complex field of mate selection or marital object choice. We can think of the differences between the successful and unsuccessful partnerships as lying along a scale of mutually tolerable degrees of ambivalence and perhaps also along a scale of "fit" or congruence between the internal object and the real partner's personality as deployed in the marital relationship.

This collusive reciprocity emerges in a variety of forms. Let me give some brief examples:

(i) A handsome, quite prosperous couple, husband aged forty-two, wife thirty-five, consult us because of the husband's *ejaculatio praecox* often *ante portas*, which they state is the only cloud in their happy marriage of nine years' duration. He is a conventional "English gentleman"—good at sport, with the dream of country life, elegant and relaxed. He has followed his father both at school to gain sporting distinctions and into a tense, gambling career of a risk-involving business. He is not fitted for such a role. He has a profound libido-split. He was potent only with "casual" women—a prostitute in Cairo, a "pick-up" in Italy. He was impotent, as with his wife, in attempted sexual affairs with "nice" women of his own social level.

The wife has a less conventional social background. Before marriage she was in fashion business and often traveled to Latin countries. Here she had exciting and sexually very satisfying but guilt-laden affairs with "naughty" men who were competent lovers. But her religious background and her insecure childhood home made her yearn to be free of guilt feelings and to be "very safe" and taken care of. Meeting her kind chivalrous husband, she said, was like finding a safe anchor. She liked him because he did not make sexual advances; he treated her with so much respect, showered her with gifts. He was, she said, so "different," but because of his fine physique promised healing of her split between the parental and the sexual—between security and allowed sexuality.

And the husband also had hoped for a resolution of his split: here was a girl the parents could accept, yet also with a "flavor" of "Latin" naughtiness. It is significant that he can be potent with his wife when they go abroad for holidays. It is also interesting that the only partial fulfillment of their sex needs maintains a very tender bond. The wife said: "It is like being perpetually engaged—how can I fall out of love with somebody from whom I am still expecting fulfillment?"

We see in this situation, which I have greatly condensed, a good example of a collusive process. There is a lot of general affection and idealization. There are dovetailing splits in both partners' object-relations between tender and sexual aspects of love. Their marriage allows them to keep these splits in being. Their more mature needs bring them to seek help for this neurotic collusion to be superseded by full genitality. Both are, in this way, appeasing their guilt feelings while also managing to have some sexual stimulation from each other.

At the same time it also gives the wife the satisfaction of her strong need to control and mold the rather passive husband over whom she is gradually establishing an ascendancy of the "long suffering, but forgiving woman." So far the hate of their ambivalence is never directly expressed. But he insures his life heavily and she said, "I will be quite a rich widow." We can guess that at least part of his motivation for *ejaculatio praecox* is withholding something of himself lest she take everything.

(ii) Another example of such a collusive mate choice and relationship was that of a couple aged twenty-three and twenty-one, married one and a half years. The reason for coming to the Clinic was that the wife would not permit consummation of the marriage. She had a strict, old-fashioned father who chased boy friends away from his attractive daughter. She had had some furtive exciting affairs with a few enterprising young men who braved the old man.

Then comes the husband, a polite, well-brought-up boy. The father selects him as suitable because he is "decent" and dependable.

Indeed the young husband fitted these epithets. He also had a stern father, who had taught his son the utmost deference and chivalry for women—the mother being an invalid. He could not bear to "hurt" his young wife and treated her with great delicacy and propriety.

The wife confessed she found the husband too quiet and unexciting, and wished he would be stronger and beat her for being so stupid. As it was, she had lost all interest in him as a sexual partner because he did not have the strength to overcome and control her. She had dreams of being chased by gangsters.

The stern, controlling father-figure inside both these young people formed a major bond maintaining the collusion. To the wife he was the model of the powerful man, while he was also the authority to defy and castrate in fantasy. This Oedipal conflict made her choose an object of the opposite, non-libidinal type. To the husband, the stern father was himself a split internal object: he was the model for identification in so far as he presented the considerate and chivalrous protector of frail women; but he was also the super-ego figure who would punish any sexual aggression. Again, we note the close fit of the unconscious interaction models to form a neurotic collusion. At ordinary worldly level people might, with equal truth, assert that they did not fit at all: "he was not passionate enough for her" if they were on the wife's side; or "she was too inhibited and squeamish for him" if they were on the husband's side.

These two examples, taken almost at random from recent case material will, I hope, illustrate what we mean by the "dyadic interaction" or collusion. The second case points to an increasingly prominent concept in our thinking—the bond of the shared internal object.

(c) We may express this kind of insight in another proposition or hypothesis: marital problems arise, sooner or later, when the interaction does not permit the working-through of relations with bad internal objects through the marital relationship. The partners choose each other *because* in the other they sense the promise of such a work-through but also, paradoxically, as a guarantee that it will not need to be worked-through, because there is an unconsciously shared deterrent figure.

In widest terms the need for working-through is probably true of all marriages. The marital relation is an experience most closely resembling the parent-child relationship. It contains the complementary needs for total and unconditional acceptance of self by the other and the other by self. When someone can securely affirm himself in commitment to another, he or she thereby makes it safe for the other to do the same. Each confirms the other's identity at the level to which they had matured and so makes possible a congruent growth individually and as a dyad.

To those of us who are aware of the growth stages of human beings, it will be clear that such a relationship involves the *freedom to regress*. It means that with the partner there is an open pathway that can be shared, backwards and forwards between present and past, between ego and the earlier stages of emotional development. This freedom to bring into the adult relationship the deepest elements of infantile object relations is a precondition of growth. As Balint has stated,[1] this persistence of tender, soft, and immature feelings requires to be fused with mature sexual drives. The fulfillment of these requirements is the basis of marital happiness, to be able to regress to mutual child-like dependence, in flexible role changes, under the security of knowing that this is fully accepted by one's partner and congruent with adult responsibility and commitment to one's social roles of provider, home-builder, parent, and citizen. The foundations for such a freedom of role playing are built, as I have said earlier, in the experiences of the "interaction models" of the parents.

And so it is that when the pre-Oedipal and Oedipal relationships with the parents have been lived through and securely repressed by the happy and united images of parental interaction, there will be a reservoir of unfulfilled but not condemned erotic needs which is released by the courtship and mating behavior. In this respect mating is a crisis not unlike puberty and adolescence which follow the stability of the latency period. Apparently stable attitudes go once more "into solution"—childish needs and ambivalencies break through to the surface and are offered for reality-testing to the partner who seems so fitted to receive them. Lovers notoriously tend to "baby" one another. A psychological transference is made on the grand scale.

(d) This description is, of course, a theoretical model. In practice no such smooth and undisturbed flow between the conscious and the unconscious of two persons is to be found. The nearer to this model a relationship is, the fuller and more powerful is the marital bond—although not always the most conflict-free, because in such a close interaction there are necessarily included the aggressive or hate-containing bonds with their charges of guilt and paranoid anxiety. The further from this theoretical model the relationship is, the more the partners must rely on defensive collusions to maintain a harmonious or at least co-operative co-existence without the deeper knowledge of each other's real personalities. Such "phony" marriages are always vulnerable. It remains true to say that modern Western people cherish the ideal of "completeness," of committed "for better for worse" interaction, and are often not content with more sensible and modest requirements. Somewhere there is, they feel, an ideal person who is all-loving and permissive, who will make it safe for one to release the earlier feelings in one stream, to fuse and give expression to all part-object relations. They long and seek for such a marriage, behind all the defensive cynicism of the modern world.

In the less successful marriages, as we have seen, this deep need of an "ideal relationship" still holds good. In fact it is demanded more persistently. It is here that we see the expression in marital behavior, direct or disguised, of the unresolved needs of the partners for the working-through of an unfortunate unconscious relation to a "bad," or at best highly ambivalent, internal object. This latent "interaction model" is repressed until the mobilization of much extra libido under the stimulus of the bio-psychological mating urge. As I said, in these troubled relationships the mate-choice must have been achieved by a mutual signaling system enabling the future spouses to recognize each other as possessing some sort of complementary or shared internal object problem which the other fitted. We saw an example of this in the young couple whose shared father-fixation constituted such a bond and was the source of their symptomatology. In most marriages the degree or quantity of such fixations to ambivalently loved-feared-hated figures is not so great as to prevent the partners from containing their hostile feelings in a framework of love and adult give-and-take.

It is not necessarily the fact that both partners have predispositions to generalized neurosis that threatens marital stability. It is their need to use each other, or the family setting, to work through dovetailing ambivalencies that seems to constitute the essence of collusive marital systems.

Martha Winch [9] (Part II, pp. 310 ff.) has discussed the interesting question of why "unhappy" couples stay together. She urges us to apply Robert Winch's theory of *complementary need systems* to these couples who cannot do without each other. No useful service is rendered to them by exhorting them to be more "normal." In Mrs. Winch's study we find independent support for our concept of collusion which is based not only on what she calls the psychodynamics of frustrations, "the negatives," but also on the gratifications, or "positives," contained in maintaining and provoking the partner to maintain an apparently destructive or belittling role behavior.

The answer to this question at the level of collusive transaction systems is at present not complete. I would like here only to venture a statement in most general form. It is that, social values and duty to children apart, there is a need in each partner to wring out of the other the response that signifies to the unconscious the typical interaction model with the internal object or objects which have come to be vested in the marital relationship. For a woman with a hated tyrannical father-relation the unconscious satisfaction of being a shrew may lie in repeated demonstrations of her power over a weak and ineffective man with sporadic outbursts of violence that serve to appease her, but which to the husband is a way of continuing an ambivalently submissive/rebellious relationship to a powerful parent-figure. To an intelligent man who chooses marriage with an empty-headed little woman whom he despises, the neurotic gain is to his unconscious fear of a woman of equal stature and his compensatory need to demonstrate his superiority. To his wife the same relationship may represent a masochistic satisfaction of her own inferiority feelings and a need for a belittling parent figure, which may be all she ever knew of father love. Some women are content, as was recently shown in one of our cases, to be parts of their husband's anatomy. M. H. Stein [8] (pp. 65 ff.) has shown how such a gratification of being a plaything, which is also resented as a humiliating derogation of personality, corresponds to certain male fantasies of the woman as their "bad" phallus, to be alternately excited and denigrated.

On the whole it is rare for this fateful bondage of sado-masochistic feelings to be apparent before marriage. More often the secret, latent interaction model is covered by a conscious idealization. This is in part a function of cultural values, as I have stated a moment ago. But the determining factor is idealization with its need to deny the recognition of the partner as possessing the qualities or exciting the projections of the bad inner object. "Blind love" asserts that the chosen mate is the opposite of the bad object or only represents the gratifying, loved, or longed-for attributes of such an inner object. Retrospectively, many such persons will be able to recount the "warning signs" they chose to ignore during courtship.

Once the reality testing of close symbiosis has brought the unreality of such idealizations to the surface (not necessarily to full consciousness) and the regressive demands made upon the ideal object are frustrated, then sooner or later the denial cannot be sustained. There now occurs a reactivation of the mechanisms of defensive behavior characteristic of the latent object-relation unconsciously sought for in the partner. The spouse receives the transference of irrational hate as the representative of the original bad object. With the entry into the new social role, young lovers with these difficulties will begin to act as if they were child to parent, or parent to parent. The complex symptomatology of such interactions is then revealed in all its protean forms. These phenomena of marital stress and conflict are well known and need not be detailed.

I regard it as a major conceptual break-through in solving the problem of marriage difficulties *to be able to understand the varieties of this attribution of idealized expectations to the partner and the varieties of reacting to the disappointment or frustration of such expectations* when their partial or entire lack of factualness becomes apparent to one or both partners.

(4) *Some Clinical Variants of Marital Tensions*

We come in this way to ask ourselves: How far are we towards being able to distinguish varieties or syndromes of unhealthy or undesirable marital interaction states? This is no mere academic question, for we are not collectors of the specimens we wish to label. The ability to assign not persons but marital dyadic stress to genotypical categories, at least as harmless or destructive to the personalities of the spouses or of their children, affects our prognosis, therapy, and social case work and orders our ideas of causation and etiology. Classification is a help to the researcher's mind in abstracting what is recurrent and typical from the bewildering variety of rich idiosyncratic material presented to us. He is the better able to make predictions and begin to claim scientific status. I must confess to severe limitations of knowledge.

At the ends of the scale we have little experience. Successful interactions, whether near the ideal I sketched or well defended by good social technique of the partners, do not come for help and thus do not afford us ready opportunities for close study. At the other extreme, marriages in which the decision to end the relationship has already been made offer only rare chances of an "inquest."

a) *Age Groupings:* In England and Wales in the 1956 official figures, there were two great concentrations of divorce: in the youngest age group and in the age group averaging thirty-five years, in which it was highest of all. This was also the age predominating in the sample seen by the Tavistock Clinic's marital team. These are not the age groups in which the majority of married couples in Britain fall. The latter are a good deal older, statistically. It appears to take either very little time or about 12.8 years to discover that one cannot continue a marriage. We are entitled to conclude that these very young people had married largely on fantasy expectations that were rapidly dispelled by reality testing. I will return to this point later.

Our interest as therapists and mental hygienists has necessarily lain with the group whom we have been asked to help, i.e. neither the very satisfied couples nor the unequivocally broken marriages who had solved their conflict by the surgical method of divorce.

b) *Descriptive Genotypes:* It is relatively easy to construct a number of dyadic interaction pictures at a descriptive or phenomenological level. Thus we can go along with Mittelmann,[6] (pp. 81-100) when he classifies the following variants:

1. One of the partners is dominant and aggressive; the other, passive and masochistic.

2. One of the partners is emotionally detached; the other craves affection.

3. There is continuous rivalry between the partners for aggressive dominance.

4. One of the partners is helpless, craving dependency from an omnipotent mate; the mate is endlessly supportive.

5. One of the mates alternates between periods of dependency and of self-assertion; the other between periods of helpfulness and of unsatisfied need for affection.

This classification has the merit of including several others we have met, such as that of Community Research Associates [3] (p. 25) in their study of disorganized families in St. Paul, Minnesota (which was a transitional attempt, now superseded) or that of Robert F. Winch [9] (pp. 310 ff.) who uses four literary analogies: "Mothers and Sons," "Pygmalion," "Torvald and Nora," and "Thruberian" couples as his main categories of collusive complementariness. I have already alluded to the division of roles, by which one partner comes to represent all sweet reason, the other turbulent emotions, just as if the dyad were one human being.

We could go on enumerating many such interactive systems deriving from earlier part-object relations that clash with the felt needs for mature genital love and confirmation of one's identities. But a list is not a useful etiological classification. It would be valuable to analyze this problem in the future and especially to go more deeply into the question of a shared internal object that binds the partners as well as sabotages the mature interaction.

For the present I, personally, limit myself to a much more lowbrow division of my case material in terms of likely prognosis and response to therapy. I use the categories: (1) early adaptation troubles (in the recently married); (2) acute transitional crisis in a good marriage; (3) acute crisis in chronic difficulty; (4) chronic difficulty (is the term *dysgamy* worth using?); (5) dead marriage. Within these one still has to use individual clinical appraisals as to degree of severity, except in the last where all the fires are burned out.

I also use the scale of (a) acting out; (b) "holding back"; and (c) "mixed." Acting out can be the resort of simple characters early in the development of trouble, in which case it need not be of ominous significance. It contrasts with desperate acting out late in a disturbed marriage of educated and fastidious persons. In the latter it is like the bursting of a defensive dam slowly eroded by chronically suppressed hate. I refer to such phenomena as physical or verbal violence, desertion, purposeful adultery, and all other forms of overt damage to the other. "Holding back" is the obverse—withdrawal, coldness, tension, often under preservation of the externals of considerate or "correct" behavior. It is this class, or the mixed (namely the regretted episodic "acting-out" by one or both partners), whom we see most frequently in our clinics. The acting-out group is more frequent in the police court, and dealt with by probation officers, without necessarily having a worse prognosis. We may remember that while laborers go on strike or smash windows, their bosses have ulcers or depressions. It does not follow that the interaction patterns between spouses in the two categories are different—only the way in which they deal with the resulting tensions. We also remember the old Russian joke of the wife who says to her husband, "Don't you love me any more? You have stopped beating me."

In regard to severity of stress, I estimate this from interview data describing areas of interaction or task sharing. I use a rough score on a set of fairly obvious social criteria of current co-operation in primary and secondary level roles for maintaining the marital unit. The list is: tender concern; respect; sexual intercourse; sharing of domestic work; sharing in child rearing; policy decision-making and financial responsibility; attitudes to each other's kinship groups (especially parents-in-law); sharing of friends, leisure pursuits, and the aesthetic, political, religious, and philosophical moral value systems.

The degrees of congruence or distance, of satisfactions or dissatisfactions, of the partners in role-sharing or role-differentiation and the distribution of power and social maturity that inquiry can help to assess are of considerable help in arriving at a prognostic assessment before making a decision on how much professional time to invest in a given area.

Principles of Therapy

As my main concern has been to offer a conceptual framework, I shall have to be brief on the subject of therapeutic technique. The main guiding lines will have become obvious from what was said earlier about our role as interpreters and clarifiers, rather than advisers or moralistic manipulators.

The emphasis in both our units has been on interpretative interviews with each partner, on a once or twice a week basis. The beginning of such therapy out of the diagnostic interviews has, perhaps, differed. The F.D.B. has tended to assign each partner to a therapist *ab initio*, with whom the therapeutic relationship has been established from the diagnostic interview. The stress has been placed on the developing transference, with interpretations aimed at relating the insights back to the marital interaction rather than to the individual. Correlation has been by frequent conferences "behind the scenes" of the two therapists, colleagues accustomed to work in parallel and trained and supervised in the same "stable."

In my own unit the distinctive innovation has been the extensive use of the *joint interview* as a diagnostic as well as a therapeutic tool. The method in its essentials is described in my 1953 paper.[4] Since that paper we have experimented with the joint interview as a continuous method of therapy (without separate interviews); as a first diagnostic approach omitting individual assessments of the partners separately, usually by *one* interviewer; and the joint interview as a periodic interlude in otherwise mainly one-person therapy, to be used for gauging progress or change. It is worth mentioning that the F.D.B. is coming round to the freer use of this method of getting the feel of the couple's transactions and of the success of therapy. For marriages with much paranoid projection the use of joint interviews throughout appears to me the method of choice.

We have been timid in forming groups of married couples or of marriage partners distributed in "marital" therapeutic groups but not sharing the same group as their spouses. A recent beginning has been made, but no data are yet available.

One wishes one could cite firm follow-up data. The difficulties of evaluation in this work are so well-known that we have not thought it possible to institute this time-consuming and unreliable procedure in the absence of ample research funds. The status of this work is really still that of learning skills and drawing generalizations in the shape of working hypotheses from it.

Conclusion

In this paper I have tried to convey some idea of the concepts with which our group approaches the investigation and therapy of cases in which *the marriage is the patient* rather than either of the two partners as individuals. My concern has been to open up the field rather than make definitive pronouncements that would be out of place in the modest state of our knowledge. Stress has been laid on the existence of *collusion* through shared unconscious need systems that are in conflict with the growth and integration of an adult dyadic system. There is a tentative theory that continuing conflictful marriages may be based on a *shared* internal object, such as a parent image.

Much has been left out: all symptomatology and the role of children, especially. My hope is that others may build on our ground plan.

References

1. Balint, M. 1948. "On Genital Love," *Int. J. Psychoanal.*, 29:34-40.
2. Bannister, K. (ed.). 1955. *Social Casework in Marital Problems*. London: Tavistock Publications.
3. Community Research Associates. 1953. *Classification of Disorganized Families*. New York: Community Research Associates.
4. Dicks, H. V. Sept., 1953. "Experiences with Marital Tensions in the Marital Clinic," *Brit. J. Med. Psychol.* 26:181-96.
5. ———. Feb., 1955. "The Predicament of the Family in the Modern World," *The Lancet*, 1:295-97.
6. Mittelmann, B. 1956. "Analysis of Reciprocal Neurotic Patterns in Family Relations," in Victor W. Eisenstein (ed.), *Neurotic Interaction in Marriage*. New York: Basic Books, Inc.
7. Pincus, L. (ed.). 1960. *Marriage: Studies in Emotional Conflict and Growth*. London: Methuen & Co.
8. Stein, Martin H. 1956. "The Unconscious Meaning of the Marital Bond," in Victor W. Eisenstein (ed.), *Neurotic Interaction in Marriage*. New York: Basic Books, Inc.
9. Winch, Robert F. 1958. *Mate Selection*. New York: Harper & Brothers.

16

Concepts of Marital Diagnosis and Therapy as Developed at the Division of Family Study, Department of Psychiatry, School of Medicine, University of Pennsylvania

Hilda M. Goodwin, D.S.W.
Emily H. Mudd, Ph.D.

In recent times, the understanding and treatment of marital problems has become the focus of ferment and research within many interdisciplinary fields. Attempts to define underlying principles, methodologies, techniques, and experimental approaches have been numerous. Marriage Council of Philadelphia, established in 1932, has had a long experience in attempting to help couples with their marital and premarital difficulties and in analyzing the method employed. In 1950 Marriage Council was officially affiliated with the School of Medicine, University of Pennsylvania, by becoming the operational unit of the Division of Family Study of the Department of Psychiatry. The counseling staff is largely made up of professionally trained and experienced case workers. Throughout its experience, Marriage Council has availed itself of medical, legal, and psychiatric consultation as the need arose. At the present time, the agency utilizes the services of psychiatric consultant for both training and case consultation. In addition to counseling, the agency carries an active family life education and research program.

The essential emphasis that has emerged through the years is the necessity for understanding and evaluating marital interaction within a different framework from that used for evaluating an individual's intrapsychic difficulties. It has become increasingly clear that counseling with marital partners involves a three-dimensional picture of the couple's situation: (1) an understanding of social and cultural factors generally and specifically their impact on the marriage; (2) an understanding of personality structure and motivations; (3) an understanding of the many facets of a marital relationship, the reciprocal interaction, and the impact of time on the balance or imbalance in the relationship.

Philosophy

Marriage Council recognizes the importance of the family in our culture and that the stability of the family rests on a sound marital relationship. It is our belief that there is no one pattern for a sound or happy marriage but that satisfactions in marriage rest on the successful meeting of reciprocal needs. The modern form of marriage emphasizes mutuality of love and affection, equality of the partners, and freedom for personal development. Although permanency and stability are goals, equal value is placed on individual happiness and the right to move out of a marriage if it is not providing the happiness desired. For many modern couples, moral and religious sanctions no longer afford the support and degree of control that they exerted in an earlier time. Continuity of a marriage, therefore, rests to a much greater degree on satisfactions of mutual needs, and each partner carries greater personal responsibility for finding a way to stabilize the marital relationship.

Marriage requires two persons; therefore, it has been our philosophy, as in many other counseling services, to make every effort to work with *both* husband and wife. This approach is explained at application and reiterated during counseling. When one partner refuses counseling initially, we begin with the partner who desires help, but in 75 per cent of our cases, we have contact with both partners.

On the basis of experience, we felt it was often confusing and even separating in effect upon husband and wife to have different counselors. We have, therefore, for the last ten years, routinely scheduled one counselor to work with both husband and wife. Each partner is seen separately and together as part of the application process, and throughout counseling, as indicated, individual and joint interviews are held weekly with both husband and wife.

Process of Counseling

Marriage counseling is defined as the process through which a professionally trained counselor assists two persons (the engaged or marital partners) to develop abilities in resolving, to some workable degree, the problems that trouble them in their interpersonal relationships as they move into a marriage, live within it, or in some instances, decide to terminate the relationship. The focus of the counselor's approach is the reciprocal relationship between the two people in the marriage, rather than, as in psychiatric therapy, the reorganization of the personality structure of the individual. Marriage counseling has as its primary concern an understanding of the way in which each partner projects his attitudes, feelings, wants, needs, and daily behavior into the marital relationship. A marital relationship has unique properties of its own, related to but different from the individual dynamics of the two partners, i.e., the relationship itself tends to influence and change each partner and this in turn influences the relationship. The choice of a marital partner may represent the merging of many motives, some conscious and some on a preconscious or unconscious level. Each partner takes into the marriage relationship his usual pattern of attempting to meet his needs and the unresolved needs and conflicts from his childhood. Often one of the disguised motivations is searching for a mate who will, to some degree, allay one's personal anxiety. When the marital relationship does not afford an acceptable degree of satisfactions for each spouse's needs, or if conflict develops, several processes are set in motion which undermine personal identity and promote failure of each partner to alleviate the anxiety of the other. These processes may include: failure to meet each other's affectional needs, resentment, breakdown of communication, an upset in the balance of the relationship.

As the counselor is able to establish a continuing relationship with each partner, rather than with one partner only, he or she may recognize earlier in the contact when the material presented by each represents projection or reality. The focus is kept on those factors in the attitudes, feelings, and behavior of each spouse which precipitate disturbance and suffering in self or the other. In so doing the counselor is able to discern and to assist the client in handling those unresolved early experiences that may be putting an undue psychic load on the marriage.

In marriage counseling it is especially necessary that the counselor clarify in an early interview the confidential nature of his relationships with each partner. When each spouse has confidence in the counselor's integrity he or she can discuss feelings and behavior with freedom and candor, knowing that what is said will not be disclosed to the other partner unless this is desired and consent given. We recognize the importance of the relationship between counselor and client as the medium through which help is given and the processes of problem-solving and change take place. The theoretical framework behind this approach has the following hypothesis: as an individual can experience during counseling new understanding of himself and his marital partner, he may be helped to develop a more satisfying way of using himself and his daily relationships in the marriage and to achieve a more constructive balance.

The counselor may use various processes in his work with the marital partners. These may include—psychologic support and clarification of differing or shared concepts of the roles of each, of cultural orientations, of self-image, of capacity to estimate and respond to day-by-day expectations and responsibilities in an appropriate manner. Assistance in reopening or strengthening emotional and verbal communication between the partners and occasional direct advice, information, or guidance may be offered as indicated by the client's need and capacity to use this type of help. Joint interviews may be scheduled at various points in the process. Experience indicates that, if joint interviews are to be constructive, the counselor must assume responsibility for establishing limits, structure, balance, and focus during the interview. If used skillfully, the joint interview may aid clients in enhancing communication, in gaining perspective on painful areas of conflict, in reducing individual feelings of inadequacy and self-blame as the reciprocal interaction is held in focus. It also creates the opportunity for each partner to hear and accept the needs of the other partner which had not been perceived before, to discover that each can tolerate feelings in the self and the other without dis-integration, and to further future co-operative involvement and com-mitment. At the ending of counseling, a joint interview is used to look back, review progress, and help the couple entrench any gains.

In suggesting and scheduling joint interviews it is well to bear in mind certain procedures and certain aspects of each partner's per-sonality dynamics. After the intake process and during on-going counseling a joint interview should not be scheduled until a firm relationship has been developed between the counselor and *each spouse*. For constructive results from a joint interview the clients should be at least minimally free from projection, be able to tolerate some anxiety, have trust in the counselor's use of confidential ma-terial, have their hostility toward each other under minimal control, and have some ability to tolerate competition.

Discussion in the area of sexual relations can often be particularly rewarding in terms of understanding certain of the dynamics of marital interrelationship and the identity problems of each partner. Schedules, initiated in our research program to cover information concerning sexual feelings, attitudes, and behavior, are utilized dur-ing counseling sessions at the discretion of the counselor. These per-mit obtaining systematic material independently from both husband and wife about something jointly experienced.

Premarital Counseling

Counseling with premarital clients calls for the same awareness and skill as does counseling with postmarital difficulties and may, in some instances, place greater stress on the counselor. Very often premarital clients have very definite time limits in which to make major de-cisions concerning their plans and future. Because of the age factor involved, many may be economically and legally dependent on one or both sets of parents, and parents may be very active in the lives of the young people. In the majority of situations coming to the counselor today, premarital couples are conflicted or troubled about their impending choice of a mate or marriage and may have severe anxiety or doubts. Limitations of time often necessitate quick decisions on the part of the counselor who must weigh the advantages of stirring up sufficient anxiety to warrant acceptance of psychiatric referral—should this be indicated—or a delay in the marriage plan, or to go along with the couple's plans for an imminent marriage and lay the groundwork for assistance later. In cases where physical or mental health suggests the possibility of a dysgenic marriage, the counselor has to evaluate the total situation and the agency's responsibility in it. Consultation with a psychiatrist and/or a physician may be indicated.

Anxiety is a state the counselor must constantly take into consideration, and there is always the question as to whether it is the kind of anxiety the individual can handle and use constructively or whether it is a major problem, requiring psychiatric treatment. The counselor must be ready to deal with guilt over masturbation, over traumatic childhood experiences in the sexual area, over premarital play or intercourse, or homosexual activity.

The continued dependence on parents and of possessiveness on the part of the parents are among the most common problems in this group. The counselor's effort is to aid in the client's growth toward independence and maturity without loss of affection for the parents or a traumatic break with them.

It is important for all counselors to realize that some clients who focus their problems on their partners or their marriage may have personality disturbances, character pathology, or mental illness of a type that requires intensive personal psychotherapy and that for the welfare of the client should not be handled in counseling. Therefore, when at intake either shows obvious signs of extreme disturbance such as unrelatedness to reality, paranoid distortion, etc., every skill of the counselor should be focused on effecting a soundly interpreted referral to psychiatric treatment. Failing this, a psychiatric consultation should be sought immediately by the counselor. In other less obvious situations when, after six to eight on-going interviews, either partner gives evidence of more acute disturbance of an intrapersonal nature, psychiatric referral should be discussed. In such instances, the less disturbed partner may be continued in counseling with intermittent conferences between the psychiatrist treating the other spouse and, at times, conferences with both partners and therapists.

282 / *Hilda M. Goodwin, Emily H. Mudd*

Bibliography

Ackerman, Nathan W. 1958. *The Psychodynamics of Family Life*. New York: Basic Books, Inc.

Glick, B. 1959. *American Families*. New York: John Wiley & Sons, Inc.

Goodwin, H. M., and E. H. Mudd. 1958. "Marriage Counseling," in J. H. Masserman and J. L. Moreno (eds.), *Progress in Psychotherapy*. Vol. III. New York: Grune and Stratton, Inc.

Mudd, E. H. 1951. *The Practice of Marriage Counseling*. New York: Association Press.

————. 1957. "Premarital Counseling," in S. Liebman (ed.), *Understanding Your Patient*. Philadelphia: J. B. Lippincott Company.

————. 1957. "Psychiatry and Marital Problems," in C. E. Vincent (ed.), *Readings in Marriage Counseling*. New York: Thomas Y. Crowell Company.

————, M. Stein, and Howard E. Mitchell. June, 1961. "Paired Reports of Sexual Behavior of Husbands and Wives in Conflicted Marriages," *Comprehensive Psychiatry*, 2:3, 149-56.

————, A. Stone, M. J. Karpf, and J. F. Nelson. 1958. *Marriage Counseling: A Casebook*. New York: Association Press.

————, and A. Krich (eds.). 1957. *Man and Wife*. New York: W. W. Norton & Company, Inc.

Rogers, C., and R. F. Dymond. 1954. *Psychotherapy and Personality Change*. Chicago: University of Chicago Press.

Stokes, W. R., and Robert A. Harper. Dec., 1954. "The Doctor as Marriage Counselor," *Med. Ann. D.C.*, 23:670-72.

17

Psychotherapy with Marriage Partners

Charles E. Llewellyn, Jr., M.D.

A study of the practices of North Carolina physicians in pre-marriage and marriage counseling conducted by C. Nash Herndon, M.D., and Ethel M. Nash, M.A., indicates that medical training of North Carolina physicians does not adequately prepare them for dealing with marital problems and that treatment facilities are inadequate. "It would seem that many physicians could profit from greater familiarity with the accumulated body of knowledge about family adjustment and sexual behavior, and with the principles and techniques of marriage counseling." [9] A survey of the literature in this field reveals publications pertaining to marriage counseling by a large number of authors. Many of these are primarily directed toward ministers, social workers, and physicians, in the form of books, articles in various professional journals, and pamphlets. Therapy with marriage partners and the management of marital discord has drawn attention from many sources and has become an enormous and multifaceted field. It would be impossible to attempt to survey the voluminous literature in the time allotted here. I shall attempt to focus on psychotherapy with marriage partners in this paper, rather than on pre-marriage counseling, various types of marital discord, or discussing other techniques and resources available.

Qualifications of the Therapist

Much literature [2, 4, 7, 10, 15, 18] has emphasized the consideration of the personality, training, and attitudes of the therapist as an important factor in the therapy of marital partners. Since all of us have some irrational prejudices that may influence our reactions, the ideal of complete objectivity can never be fully met. The physician should be aware of his own emotional difficulties and their role in influencing his judgments and his responses. If these difficulties are oppressive and interfere in his relationships to his patients, he would be unwise to try to help others in marital conflicts without first submitting himself to successful psychotherapy. The physician must have sufficient emotional maturity to be able to identify himself with the patient's troubled feelings and to accept their importance to the patient. He must be capable of showing the patient a genuine, dignified interest in his unhappiness and a willingness to investigate it with such thoroughness that really constructive interpretations and suggestions can be formulated. He must be able to permit the patient the feeling of being a free and active participant in whatever is worked out, rather than being the passive recipient of the doctor's wisdom. The physician must be capable of being an attentive listener. "Even repetitive and seemingly irrelevent talk by the patient can reveal a great deal about his personality . . . nothing will substitute for simply listening as a basic technique for generating warm feelings toward the doctor. . . . The busy physician in routine medical work is likely to feel so pressed for time that good listening seems impossible or merely a wished-for luxury. Yet the fact remains that successful counseling on emotional problems is seldom possible without some good, unhurried, attentive listening." [4]

The physician should have some understanding of the dynamics of human behavior and of the effect of environmental and social factors upon the development of the personality. He should know how to identify emotional contributions to psychosomatic symptomatology and the relationship of such symptoms to the stresses of life. He should know something of careful history-taking and the process of formulating the material that he hears and observes into dynamic concepts of the meaning of human behavior. He should have some understanding of the implications of the roles of husband and wife and, especially, concepts of roles among the various social levels in the sub-cultures of society as observed in his community. He should have a frank knowledge of sexual behavior between married partners and some understanding of the causes of disturbed sexual relationships.

The physician's attitudes and judgments resulting from value systems should be such that he can accept the varying needs and levels of expression of his patients. He should carefully examine his own values or positions concerning various problems that may arise in marital situations and evaluate whether he can be objective in his attitudes when attempting to work with individuals whose attitudes may be different from his own. It is important to recognize that it will not be his job to campaign or crusade for certain ideals of marital behavior, but rather to help to bring about a more comfortable solution to the marital discord that will face him, at the level at which it can be best accepted by his patient. A physician should carefully examine his own position concerning separation and divorce. He must recognize that, in some instances, separation may be healthier for the individuals involved than to remain in a chaotic, neurotically determined marriage. He must recognize that, in some instances, divorce may give opportunity for one or both marital partners to profit from their unfortunate experiences and find a more mature and happy level of life for themselves and their children.

The physician should also carefully consider his own marriage and its effect on his treatment of marital partners. If he is unhappy in his marriage, he should be very much aware of the possibility of seeking narcissistic gratification from the marital conflicts that he will be treating. If he has had a fight with his wife that morning, he may find himself over-identifying with the husband who has unrealistic and distorted feelings toward his wife. He may not be able to evaluate objectively the wife who complains of intolerable sexual aggressiveness on the part of her husband, if his own wife is frigid and rejecting sexually. If his marriage is happy and rewarding, he must be aware that others are not as fortunate as he and be willing to be tolerant of their difficulties.

From the standpoint of the physician, it seems that we are asking for a combination superman, psychoanalyst, and ideal husband. These are ideals, but these principles are not unlike the same principles that apply to all fields of medical practice, with variation upon the particular area concerned. I suspect that few of you feel that you meet all of these qualifications, and you wish to learn something more of the treatment of marital problems, because this is undoubtedly a real and a pressing problem of your practice.

Evaluation for Marital Therapy

In the psychotherapy of marital problems, the first step is that of evaluation. Nathan Ackerman has pointed out that

> ... a marital relationship is something beyond the sum of the personalities that make it up. The relationship itself tends to influence and change each partner, and this in turn influences the relationship anew. In confronting problems in this particular area, we shift our traditional focus from the pathology of the individual personality to the pathology of a human relationship as a social unit. . . .
> A corrective approach to marital disturbance cannot be a simple undertaking. It must be recognized that it is therapy for the disturbances of "husbanding and wifing", rather than straight therapy for an individual neurosis. If we agree to the proposition that neurotic interaction is a part, perhaps central, but nevertheless, a part, of total interaction, it is necessary to first find criteria appropriate for evaluating the total process of marital interaction and then to differentiate the neurotic components of that interaction.[1]

Perelman suggests that the treatment of married couples presents difficulties that few therapists care to overcome. In the first place, it is difficult to find a couple motivated for treatment. Most couples come to therapy as a last resort, just before seeing a judge, and not infrequently after they have seen one. Already the wounds are deep, the chasm is wide. Perelman notes another type of resistance that proceeds from the reluctance of one partner to participate, as exemplified by the statement on the part of one of the spouses: "Straighten him out and the marriage will be O.K." Frequently, it may appear that the neurotic interaction has become repetitive, increasingly bitter and hostile, blocking the working through of deeper elements. If the therapist intervenes, he is taking sides; to be helpful to one is to painfully ignore the other.[16] Several authors [1, 3, 6, 12, 13, 15, 20] have described various types of neurotic interaction in marriage. Ackerman points out that this is not necessarily to be viewed with alarm. There are many situations in which neurotics marry and find basically strong support and complementary functioning for one another.[1]

Early evaluation through careful history-taking is essential to determine if the problems are resulting from deep pathological personality interaction or from more superficial maladjustments in a basically stable relationship. During early evaluation, in addition to obvious psychotic or neurotic symptoms in one or the other partner, the patients may reveal evidence of maladjustment through subtle symptoms. Many patients with marital problems seen by the general practitioner may come to his office complaining of some somatic symptoms, and only an exploration of the cause of these symptoms, including an investigation of the marital adjustment will reveal that marital discord is present and perhaps related to the cause of the symptoms. Patients may reveal evidence of maladjustment through such symptoms as difficulty in communicating with one another, excessive sensitivity to possible injury, chronic nagging, lack of tenderness and affection, poverty of interests in common, attitudes of martyrdom, severe quarrels over management of children, in-law trouble, jealousy, various grades of sexual impotence and frigidity, sexual promiscuity or infidelity, wide variance between spouses as to frequency of sexual desire, and a host of psychosomatic symptoms. These psychosomatic symptoms may involve the genital organs, the gastro-intestinal tract, headache, fatigue, and symptoms related to feelings of depression. Whether the patient has come with the frank statement of marital discord or whether evidence of marital discord is picked up by subtle expressions or through the evaluation of symptoms, it becomes extremely important to explore the various aspects of the relationship of the patient and his spouse, the tolerance and understanding of each other's needs and roles in life, the compatibility or lack of compatibility in the sexual area, the degree of mutual interest in work, finances, etc. The history of the early developmental background of the patient is important in developing a picture of his personality structure. A history of the courtship and the early adjustment in marriage, with special emphasis on how and when did the discord seem to begin to become apparent, should be explored. The patient's present attitudes toward his spouse and motivation for the marriage should also be explored.

The evaluation should attempt to answer the following questions: Why does this patient come at this time? Is his marital disturbance the manifest reason for his visit or is his visit because of some more superficial reason, but with marital discord as an etiological factor in the background? Why did he not seek help earlier? What methods of problem-solving has he attempted before? What does he expect of the physician? Are his expectations realistic? Is he willing to make sacrifices to achieve and re-establish equilibrium in his marriage? Does he perceive his spouse as being the sole cause of all his troubles and is his perception realistic? Does the patient seem to wish help for himself or does he seem to wish help for his spouse? Has the patient come seeking help by himself or under pressure from some outside force such as neighbors, family, courts, lawyers, etc.? Affirmative answers or negative answers to any of these questions will not give the physician clear direction as to the next steps, but exploration of these areas will help the physician to better understand the patient, his problems, and expectations. They may guide the physician in determining whether or not he can be helpful. Stokes and Harper suggest that: "When sufficient data have been obtained to justify a tentative diagnosis, the clinician will ask himself two questions: Do I think it possible to help this patient through the warmth of my personal interest and understanding and through conferences with other members of his family, for the purpose of bringing about improved family insights and co-operation? Or should I accept it that the patient seems to have emotional disturbances of such depth that I am not qualified to cope with them but should refer him to a qualified psychiatrist or marriage counselor?" [18]

Marital Therapy Is a Complex Process

Once evaluation has been completed through one or more interviews with the patient and occasionally other members of the family, the decision has to be made as to what steps to take next. Laidlaw points out that

... if unconscious factors are discovered that necessitate long and involved psychotherapeutic techniques, the case ceases to be in the field of marriage counseling. It becomes a problem in clinical psychiatry.... Sometimes a relatively simple presenting problem will develop unforeseen complexities, while an apparently complex marital situation may yield to a simple short term approach. . . . Since psychiatry is now concerned with all types of emotional problems, properly, then, all marriage counseling falls within the domain of psychiatry. Yet, just as simple mathematical problems may be soved without calling the aid of a mathematician, so is it useful to define a field where the properly trained and personally qualified individuals with professional backgrounds other than psychiatry, as well as the psychiatrists themselves, may render useful service.[10]

Mudd defines marriage counseling as the "process through which a professionally trained counselor assists two persons to develop abilities in resolving, to some degree, the problems that trouble them in their interpersonal relationships as they move into a marriage, live with it, or (in a small number of instances) move out of it." She emphasizes that "the focus of the counselor's approach is the relationship between the two people in a marriage rather than, as in psychiatric therapy, the reorganization of the personality structure of the individual." [14] Others [1, 10, 15] have emphasized that the most effective approach to the therapy of marital problems is to look upon the difficulty as an interactional phenomenon between the partners.

Often the tactful giving of information concerning roles of the partners, expectations of male and female roles, anatomy and physiology, especially involving the sexual area, sexual functioning, and contraception, as well as other appropriate information may bring about resolution of the marital discord, especially when the underlying relationship apparently is stable. It has been suggested that assistance to the patient in developing avenues of communication and encouraging more open discussion of feelings with the spouse is often helpful. Opportunities for ventilation of repressed feelings and questions concerning earlier childhood experiences or guilt about childhood or other experiences and feelings may frequently reduce anxiety and tension and contribute to improvement in the marital relationship.

Many patients may display intense feelings at the time they consult the physician. These must be worked through before satisfactory results can be expected. The physician must be prepared to deal with the expression of overt hostility from some of these patients or their spouses. A dissatisfied wife may storm at the physician and accuse all men of being brutes. Another patient may accuse the physician of taking the side of the spouse against him. The physician may find himself the recipient of threatening telephone calls and possibly the threat of legal action from spouses who are disturbed because of the honest attempt of the physician to help the other spouse who is the patient. Frequently, the recognition of the feelings of the patient during these hostile attacks and the realization that the expression of the hostility is not originally focused around the physician but rather that the physician is being used as an object of expression may help both the physician and the patient or the spouse to weather the storm, and then constructive work can begin. The hostility that such patients express is not a reality, but rather a manifestation of the patient's own poor adjustment or inability to handle the intense stress he feels at that particular time.

The opposite reaction must be guarded against, especially by male therapists in regard to female patients and female spouses of the patients. The woman may try to get the physician to substitute in various ways, for the lost or denied satisfactions. She may flatter the physician or behave in very seductive ways, in an attempt to fulfill her own needs. She may distort and magnify the physician's attitude about her and perceive him as being fully in accord with her unrealistic complaints and ideas and convey these fantasies to her husband. The physician must recognize that these seductive and satisfaction seeking maneuvers are again manifestations of neurotic behavior and are not realistic. When dealing with these patients, the doctor must be very careful not to reveal his doubts and anxieties. He must be careful not to respond to these neurotic, unrealistic needs. Should he respond, he will find that the seductive behavior, the "please take care of me" attitude, may quickly change into "you are just like all the rest of them."

Many situations developing out of marital discord may create intense anxiety on the part of the physician. A patient may threaten suicide. A patient may create anxiety by his hostility; the physician may become anxious, feeling torn between the two members of the marital relationship. At this time the physician must be careful of projecting his own attitudes and defenses onto one or the other of the marital partners, thus interfering with his ability to understand the feelings and problems of the marriage. Some physicians become so anxious about marital problems that they indicate to the patient they only want to know about the patient's physical well-being and that they are not interested in marital problems. Often, by avoiding such problems, the doctor finds it impossible to help the somatic symptom or problem for which the patient originally has sought help. He finds then that his anxiety increases, and he only senses more frustration in dealing with his patient.

In many of these instances, as well as in others, the disturbance of the patient may indicate to the physician that he is not able to handle the problem. He may become aware that his own anxiety interferes with the proper management of marital difficulty. He may find that his own personality problems become stimulated and threatening so that he cannot maintain an objective point of view. He may find that he is frightened and anxious about the severity of the neurotic or psychotic disorder that he perceives is present. In these instances, he should make an appropriate referral to another physician whom he knows to be able to handle the marital difficulties with confidence and effectiveness. He may make referral to psychiatric resources when this is indicated and if they are available. He may make referral to marriage counselors such as Family Service agencies, social workers, ministers, etc., if he knows of such agencies or counselors and feels that they are adequately trained and that the type of problem presented by his patient can be handled in such a setting. This latter point may be difficult to define.

In the psychotherapy of marriage partners, the question often arises whether or not marital partners ought to be seen together or separately. This is always difficult to determine, and I think there is no obvious single answer. The approach to dealing with marital problems has to be evaluated in terms of each individual case. In some instances, these problems can be very effectively dealt with by seeing the couples together, and in other instances, they can be seen separately by the same physician. There are many times in which it is unwise for the same therapist to see both marital partners, and one of them should be referred to another physician or agency. A review of the literature does not offer an answer to this question. Busse warns that the physician should avoid seeing both husband and wife together and if both require a number of psychotherapeutic sessions, the procedure of choice is to have a colleague see one of the patients while you work with the other.[4] Eisenberg states "if the client is the marriage, unless both partners are there to represent the marriage, the client isn't there." [5] Stone argues that "the marriage is a unit in itself. When two people marry, it is a declaration of inter-dependence. It is a new relationship. Therefore, we are not looking at either the husband or the wife; we are looking at the total unit and we have to get a complete perspective of both partners if we are to evaluate adequately the situation. In marriage counseling, we have to keep one ear open for the other side, or at least have a third ear by which to listen to both sides." [19] Some agencies, such as the Jewish Family Service, do not undertake to offer marriage counseling unless both persons involved in the marriage are willing to come. Skidmore and Garrett have enumerated the values of the joint interview.[17] Mittelmann discusses the treatment of married couples by the same therapist seeing each one at separate times. She states that treatment of married couples by the same therapist makes more concrete both the realities and the neurotic interactions between mates.[13]

It is undoubtedly difficult to state categorically that one or another approach should be taken in regard to this. In evaluating a marital problem, it is often helpful if a spouse can be seen, but careful consideration should be given to whether or not the spouse should be seen with the patient or separately. I feel that it is best to recommend that they be seen separately until the physician has sufficient knowledge of the interaction between them and security in his own feelings to develop a plan for seeing them together. I often will see both together for the first visit and then arrange to see them separately in order to get a better understanding of their behavior and attitudes. Some of the factors that contribute to a decision to see them together are such things as the severity and extent of the marital discord, the basic relationship and strengths in the marriage and the means of solving previous problems with outside resources, and the degree to which communication can be established or exists between the marital partners and the physician and between the marital partners themselves. Where marital discord seems to be a reflection of longstanding behavior characteristics and where each partner seems to be projecting heavily upon the other, it will probably be most desirable to see only one member of the marriage and try to arrange for the other to see a different person. Communication between the two therapists may be very important in order to help each other in the evaluative process. If the couple has indicated an ability to seek help individually from different resources and then get together and work out their problems, it may be advisable to suggest that they each be seen by different people.

The therapist who attempts to deal with marital problems must be constantly aware that these patients frequently are fighting for their last hold on status, prestige, and integrity. Where marital problems have been fairly longstanding and severe, these patients will resort to extreme means to try to maintain some form of internal equilibrium. They will not hesitate to use the therapist against each other and to interpret his comments to the advantage of one and the disadvantage of the other. They frequently will re-enact their marital neurotic conflicts around the therapist. The therapist may find that the partners are playing the therapist off against one another, or they will try to play off their own individual therapists against each other, when each is seeing a different therapist. Patton *et al.* clearly indicated how skillfully marital partners are able to bring about an identity on the part of their respective therapists to the point of causing breakdown in communications between the therapists.[15] It is important that this possibility be recognized very early when communication is to be established between two therapists seeing the marital partners. Where there is a history indicating that the couple has solved a problem with the use of a single resource in the past, then one may try to see them together.

In regard to the role of sex in the marriage, I think it is important to point out that often times sexual disturbance is but a symptom of an underlying disorder. The frigid woman may be having difficulties because of her early childhood training, her fear of attack by aggressive males, or she might be using her frigidity as a way of retaliating passive-aggressively against her husband who she feels is not aware of her needs and who is not fulfilling her desires in other ways. "If you won't take care of me the way I want you to, then I will not meet your sexual needs." Often information clarifying misconceptions about sexual experiences will help to focus on the union between the partners and the freedom of emotional expression through the sexual relationship. The fact that sexual difficulties are often reflections of deeper problems may be recognized when information, instruction, and frank open discussion about sex does not seem to improve the marital problem.

In some instances, the marital difficulty may arise out of anxiety and neurotic reaction on the part of one or the other partner. This often becomes complicated by the lack of understanding of the other spouse so that marital discord erupts. The history obtained in such a case usually reveals a fairly effective relationship between the couple, but as stress is placed on one or both partners, one partner begins to react with neurotic psychological reactions and symptoms and the other partner then begins to feel rejected or disappointed and retaliates in a hostile manner. In this instance, supportive interviews with the patient, helping him to understand what has happened to himself and to the spouse, and indicating that he can be helpful to the spouse's understanding of himself as well as to his own needs by being more supportive and tolerant, will help to restore equilibrium in the marriage. Treatment of the patient should be focused around his neurotic reaction and in helping him to clarify and understand the emotional problems involved.

Often marriage conflicts grow out of maladaptation from very early in the marriage. In these situations it appears that the couple are not suited for each other and that their reasons for marriage were neurotic and selfish, independent of one another. They wished to get away from home, they were lonely, they had a strong need for sexual satisfaction and felt unable to achieve this outside of marriage. This is frequently seen in adolescent marriages, where the goals were to achieve a false sense of security and superiority or to escape from home. Once the couple realizes that they have a responsibility together and have achieved the goal of escape from home or other immediate satisfactions, they confront themselves with a lack of interest in one another and the battle begins. A high percentage of these marriages break up very early and dissolve themselves. Some of these may be seen by the general practitioner during the early stages or as they are in the process of breaking up. It is often helpful to provide each member of the marriage with an opportunity to express his feelings so that he may look more rationally and reasonably at his intended behavior and action in regard to the marriage. Perhaps he should consider the effects of divorce and separation. He should consider the feelings and attitudes of his spouse. In these situations it is necessary to let the couple make their decision as to what they wish to do about the marital problem and if separation and divorce, or in some instances, annulment, is strongly desired, it may be better not to persuade them otherwise. They may profit from this experience and go on to a later healthier and happier marriage.

Summary

In summary, I have pointed out that the psychotherapy of marital partners is a difficult and complex undertaking. One of the most important factors to be considered is the maturity, training, and attitude of the physician. Patients with marital discord come from many sources and are frequently found among the office patients of the general practitioner. If psychotherapy of marriage partners is to be considered, it is important to first evaluate the marital discord and the individual patients. Treatment must be considered from the point of view of needs of the individual and the marriage. It must be considered as therapy of an interactional process. There are many techniques that can be utilized in the effective treatment of marital discord by the general practitioner. Included among these are the giving of information, clarification of misconceptions, encouraging the establishment of better communication between the marital partners, and the giving of support to the feelings of one or the other partner. Where severely disturbed partners are found, referral to appropriate resources is advised. The question of seeing the partners separately or together or by different therapists has been discussed. It is recognized that psychotherapy of marriage partners is difficult to begin with and that when one attempts to see both partners, the situation may become more difficult and more complex. The joint interview may be extremely difficult but has its indications and advantages.

It seems that society has really given us a challenge when we realize that the quality of marriages is one of the most important determinants of the future mental health and behavior of our society, and yet marital discord seems to be one of the first reflections of disturbances in society and of maladjustments of individuals. This creates a vicious circle that will take the interest and skill of every professional person in order to preserve the heritages that we have so dearly cherished and loved in our country, in our state, in our communities, and in our homes. Maybe we are not all the superman that I seem to have said we should be in order to work with these disturbed marriages, but if we really want to help our fellow man, where is a better place to start?

Addendum

Since the presentation of this paper, other articles have appeared in the literature. Mr. Jay Haley [8] has written an excellent discussion of the techniques of marriage therapy. He describes the therapist role in the intervention in the marital conflict and he gives special attention to the resistance of the individual partners to change and their reaction to changes in each other. Mr. Haley has recommended specific areas of focus and techniques for the therapist that are wise and important considerations.

References

1. Ackerman, Nathan W. April, 1954. "The Diagnosis of Neurotic Marital Interaction," *Social Casework*, 35:139-47.
2. Alexander, Franz. 1953. "Principles and Techniques of Briefer Psychotherapeutic Procedures," *Proceedings of the Association for Research in Nervous and Mental Disease*. Reprinted in C. E. Vincent (ed.), *Readings in Marriage Counseling*. New York: Thomas Y. Crowell Company, 1957.
3. Bergler, Edmund. 1946. *Unhappy Marriage and Divorce*. New York: International Universities Press.
4. Busse, E. W. May, 1956. "Principles of Marital Counseling for the General Practitioner," *Med. Rec. Ann.*, 50:101-4.
5. Eisenberg, Sidney. Feb., 1953. "Can One Partner be Successfully Counseled Without the Other?" *Marriage and Family Living*, 15:59-64. Reprinted in Vincent, *Readings in Marriage Counseling*.
6. Flint, Arden A., Jr., and B. W. MacLennan. July, 1962. "Some Dynamic Factors in Marital Group Psychotherapy," *Int. J. Group Psychother.*, 12:355-61.
7. Fromm-Reichmann, Frieda. 1950. *Principles of Intensive Psychotherapy*, Chapters I, II, and III. Chicago: University of Chicago Press.
8. Haley, Jay. March, 1963. "Marriage Therapy," *Arch. Gen. Psychiat.* (Chic.), 8:213-34.
9. Herndon, C. Nash, and Ethel Nash. May, 1962. "Premarriage and Marriage Counseling," *J.A.M.A.*, 180:395-401.

10. Laidlaw, Robert W. April, 1960. "The Psychiatrist as Marriage Counselor," *Amer. J. Psychiat.*, 106:732-36. Reprinted in Vincent, *Readings in Marriage Counseling.*

11. Mace, David R. May, 1954. "What is a Marriage Counselor?" *Marriage and Family Living*, 16:135-38. Reprinted in Vincent, *Readings in Marriage Counseling.*

12. Martin, Peter A., and Waldo Bird. May, 1953. "An Approach to the Psychotherapy of Marriage Partners," *Psychiatry*, 16:123-27. Reprinted in Vincent, *Readings in Marriage Counseling.*

13. Mittelmann, Bela. April, 1948. "The Concurrent Analysis of Married Couples," *Psychoanal. Quart.*, 17:182-97. Reprinted in Vincent, *Readings in Marriage Counseling.*

14. Mudd, Emily H. June, 1955. "Psychiatry and Marital Problems," *Eugen. Quart.*, 2:110-17. Reprinted in Vincent, *Readings in Marriage Counseling.*

15. Patton, J. D., J. D. Bradley, and M. J. Hornowski. Dec., 1958. "Collaborative Treatment of Marital Partners," *N. Carolina Med. J.*, 19(12):523-28.

16. Perelman, J. S. April, 1960. "Problems Encountered in Group Psychotherapy of Married Couples," *Int. J. Group Psychother.*, 10:136.

17. Skidmore, Rex A., and Hulda Van S. Garrett. Nov., 1955. "The Joint Interview in Marriage Counseling," *Marriage and Family Living*, 17:349-54. Reprinted in Vincent, *Readings in Marriage Counseling.*

18. Stokes, W. R., and Robert A. Harper. Dec., 1954. "The Doctor as a Marriage Counselor," *Med. Ann. D.C.*, 23:670-72. Reprinted in Vincent, *Readings in Marriage Counseling.*

19. Stone, Abraham. Feb., 1953. "Can One Partner be Successfully Counseled Without the Other?" *Marriage and Family Living*, 15:59-64. Reprinted in Vincent, *Readings in Marriage Counseling.*

20. Thompson, Clara. 1959. "An Introduction to Minor Maladjustments," in S. Arieti (ed.), *American Handbook of Psychiatry*. New York: Basic Books, Inc.

PART FOUR

Marriage Counseling Instruction in the Medical School Curriculum

18

Sexual Attitudes and Behavior of Medical Students: Implications for Medical Practice

Harold I. Lief, M.D.

There is increasing recognition of the deficiences of physicians in dealing with the sexual and marital problems [6, 9, 12, 13, 17] of their patients; indeed, this book is an obvious reminder of the need for more and better instruction in these matters.* Other than the clergy, the physician is most often consulted by patients searching for greater fulfillment in their marital lives.[10] But because most physicians are not equipped by either experience or training to properly help their patients, more and more patients are turning to non-medical people for counsel and treatment.

Are these non-medical people adequately handling the vast demand for these clinical services? The answer is an unqualified "no." Mc-Hugh [15] reports that "according to experts in the field, only 15% of

* The data from which this report was culled were derived from the records of 150 medical students treated in the Hutchinson Memorial Psychiatric Clinic, Tulane School of Medicine, and from 100 "non-patient" students serially interviewed by our psychiatric research team, consisting of Dr. Harold Lief, principal investigator, Dr. Robert Lancaster, Dr. Vann Spruiell, and Dr. Victor F. Lief. The research was supported by a grant from the Commonwealth Fund.

the 228,000 ministers in America are doing counseling that can be called competent." He tested 451 of the most *modern* members of the ministry with his *Sex Inventory* and concluded, "It is disturbing to see the level of wrong sex information among even these modern ministers." He found that half the ministers in America are still preaching that sex is evil.

As for the competence of general marriage counselors, the number of counselors who are professionally qualified is extremely small. One survey [3] disclosed that "the incompetents and quacks outnumber the dedicated, competent professionals in the field." The February, 1962, Directory of the American Association of Marriage Counselors—the professional body in the field—contained fewer than 450 names, with many of these being non-clinical members.

Actually, the physician is in the best position to help those distressed by marital and sexual difficulties.[2, 11] The premarital medical examination offers an excellent opportunity for preventive and ameliorative marriage counseling. In addition, patients with certain categories of problems, such as infertility, frigidity, and impotence customarily seek the advice of a doctor.

Of the medical specialties, only the training afforded by obstetrics, gynecology, and psychiatry, according to the study of Herndon and Nash,[9] gave their members any degree of experience and hence of competence in handling the sexual and marital dilemmas of their patients. However even these specialists reported that their education in medical school was definitely deficient in this regard. General practitioners and specialists, other than the "Ob-Gyn" men (and women) and psychiatrists, are apparently not getting necessary training either in medical school or in their graduate or post graduate experience.

Can psychiatrists, who, presumably, are experts in the field of marriage and sex, handle the problem? Even if patients sought them out first, the 13,000 psychiatrists are insufficient in number to handle the load, while at the same time caring for the many thousands of patients with other emotional problems. But, in fact, patients go to psychiatrists last, not first,[8] despite a popular misconception of some sophisticates that most people would never discuss their private intimate affairs with anyone but a psychiatrist.

It seems clear then that the burden of caring for the symptoms and faulty adjustments caused by the most frequent of all inter-personal conflicts—marriage—has to be assumed by the non-psy-chiatric physician, but, with the exceptions noted above, they have not been trained for the job; they are not experts on marriage and certainly not on sex. Sex behavior is intimately involved with the psychological and emotional aspects of life, and in at least that sense, doctors seem to be woefully ignorant about sex. It may even be true that they are relatively ignorant about sex behavior from a purely descriptive or phenomenological point of view, although this is diffi-cult to determine with any degree of conviction. But when it comes to the psychology of sex, those facets of sex life involving feelings and attitudes, many doctors are not much better informed than the patients they counsel. Only when it comes to the anatomy and the physiology of the sex apparatus can doctors, at least relatively speak-ing, claim to be experts.

This is not enough. Knowledge of gross anatomy does not confer on the physician knowledge of how to help a teenager to manage strong sexual feelings; knowledge of the physiology of conception and procreation does not include methods of handling the problems of young married couples who are sexually frustrated; knowing how to deliver a baby does not mean that the doctor can rescue a middle-aged man who is panicky because of failing sexual powers.

The truth is that medical students bring to medical school the same conceptions and misconceptions, the same information and mis-information, the same confidences and anxieties regarding sex that any group of similarly educated people have; then in medical school, little is done to inform the students or to teach them new attitudes.

Striking confirmation of this is found in a recent study by Green-bank [5] of the 1959 graduates and a smaller number of faculty mem-bers of the five medical schools located in Philadelphia. One of the results of his survey of attitudes toward mental illness was that "half of the students have a feeling that mental illness is frequently caused by masturbation. Even one faculty member in five still believes in this old, and now discredited, idea."

What are medical students really like? In order to train them in the field of marital counseling, the medical educator has to have a good idea of the personalities of students and how these influence their sexual attitudes and behavior. If this is better known, it will be easier to devise educational methods that are more effective because they take into account the nature of the raw material that has to be shaped, prodded, challenged, stimulated and catalyzed and, in so doing, provide the proper atmosphere for appreciable growth and development. This is the primary significance of this report.

Personality Characteristics of the Medical Students

The young adult has two primary tasks in his personal development: an occupational identification and the growth of a capacity for intimate relationships with others, especially with those of the opposite sex.[4] The medical student is no exception; he has the same tasks. What is unusual, however, in his life, is the intense preoccupation with the task of becoming a physician, not only in acquiring the knowledge and skills of the physician but in its more subjective attributes: the inner feeling of becoming and then being a physician, the certainty that the role of physician fits him, and that society accepts and approves his newly acquired role behavior. In short he has to learn to *identify* with his new profession; this identification takes place not only directly in the classroom, laboratory, the clinic and ward, but in indirect places and ways made up of all the transactions that go on between himself and his peers, his instructors, and his patients. This whole process is so intense, so concentrated that it is accompanied by a narrowing of the range of interests and of outside pursuits. Medical school becomes almost as total or as closed an environment for its students as does the submarine for its crew.

This happens to nearly all students and as a consequence produces a different sort of life experience from that of the majority of young adults. Much of "outside" living escapes the medical student. Winnicott [18] has stated it well: "The doctor's long and arduous training does nothing to qualify him in psychology and does much to disqualify him. It keeps him so busy from 18 to 25 he finds he is middle-aged before he has the leisure in which to discover himself. It takes him years of medical practice and the struggle to find time to live his own life before he can catch up on his fellow creatures, many of whom have lived a lot by the time they are 25."

This picture is quite different from the usual sterotype offered by popular books and movies describing the life of medical students and interns, such as "The Interns" or the English "Doctor in the House" series. Students do not spend a lot of time cutting up, drinking, and whoring (the exceptions are very few) and thus learning about life, especially sex, by varied and direct experience. In general their sexual experiences are more limited and less varied than their counterparts in other walks of life. The number of "virgins" among the male students was at first surprising until it became clear that this pattern of sexual restraint, even of inhibition, was a dominant one.

That these sexual restraints are present to such a degree should not have been so unexpected when one considers that the personality type found most frequently in medical school (more than 50 per cent of our students) is the obsessive compulsive.[14] The obsessive compulsive personality is one in which mastery, control, thoroughness, safety, and self-restraint are dominant attributes. The obsessive is the sort of person who puts intellectual matters above emotions, security above pleasure, service to others above self service (at least at conscious levels), exactitude above fantasy. He is the student who works harder for good grades even in subjects he cares little about. The most frequent personality description given medical students by faculty members goes something like this: "He is a hard worker, extremely conscientious, is a little shy and retiring, doesn't let go of his feelings, is somewhat hard to draw out." We find this type of student in droves in medical school because (1) he is attracted to medical school since it is a way of serving others, gaining control over life and death, and satisfying his intellectual needs; (2) this sort of student is apt to get good grades in college and be highly eligible for medical school; and (3) he makes a good impression on medical school admission committees often composed of people with similar personalities.

Lest anyone think that these are disparaging remarks, it should be made clear that this type of student has an easier time in medical school than any other; there is a fit between the structure and organization of the school (at least most medical schools as far as can be determined), the demands placed on the students by the school, and and the obsessional student himself, to the extent that these character traits become even more prominent as the student goes through school. The school rewards and hence reinforces the very traits being described.

This is a far cry from the popular stereotype of the student, but it is in keeping with the public's view of the doctor. In this view the "good doctor" is "the old family doctor," educated, wise, thoughtful, patient, careful, dependable, and trustworthy. This conception has a long tradition beginning with the ancient oath of Hippocrates. Part of the oath reads: "Into whatever houses I will enter I will go into them for the benefit of the sick and will abstain from every voluntary act of mischief and corruption; and further, from the seduction of females or males or freemen and slaves." The patient expects the physician to be a model of decorum in sexual matters, that he will not only refrain from injuring his patients through injudicious sexual advances, but that he will not gossip or in any other way use information derived from the patient to injure the patient. The role of the good doctor receives such community support and fits in so well with the emotional needs of the doctor that it seems clear that the vast majority of the physicians act toward their patients in a way that is quite consistent with the oath of Hippocrates.

The student is quite aware of the image of the "good doctor" and as part of his identification with the medical profession tries to model his behavior on that image. This is another factor that limits direct gratification of his sexual drives.

The relative isolation from outside pursuits, his attempt to model his behavior on the image of the "good doctor," and his basic personality pattern, in which a degree of emotional isolation has been present anyway, not only interfere with sexual experimentation but likewise interfere with the development of intimacy, the other great task of this age period. The exchange of feelings, the sharing of goals and values, of attitudes and beliefs with a loved person, is inhibited unless there is *time* for meeting potential mates and developing such relationships. More and more students deal with this problem by marriage, sometimes premature contracts that provide a lot of strain on an already somewhat precarious adjustment. In the class that graduated from Tulane in 1959, 20 per cent of the students starting their freshman year were married. At the beginning of the senior year 57 per cent were married. The national figures show that 60 per cent of the students are married by the time they finish medical school, an astonishing figure when one recalls that only twenty years ago it was common practice for many hospitals to exclude married students from internship.

In view of the difficulties encountered in the marital adjustments of medical students and their wives, it is astonishing and a tribute to the flexibility of these young people that most of the marriages seem to be lasting ones. Even in the best of these, however, there are unusual stresses. The student has very little time to devote to his wife and children. (About half these student marriages produce children before the student graduates.) When he is home he often is torn between his desire to "play" with his family and his need to study, a conflict that frequently produces guilt and irritability. Either his studies or his family may be felt to be an intolerable burden.

Some recent studies [1] demonstrate that married women desire companionship from their husbands even more than love or affection or material things. The decreased time available for companionship as well as the conflicting feelings of the medical student which may interfere with his freely and joyously participating in family activities provide a source of stress for the wives. Add to this the fact that most of the wives work in order to help support their husbands through school, as well as a frequent need to postpone having children, and financial insecurity for the majority, and one has a recipe for a foundering marriage. We have seen students "gratefully" take the support offered by their wives through school and then discard them when they no longer need them, but as indicated above, despite the precarious course charted by these student marriages, a minority "go on the rocks." Nevertheless it seems to be true that many students are not in a position to counsel patients regarding sex and marriage on the basis of their own rich and satisfying sexual life, especially within the framework of a deeply felt shared intimacy with someone of the opposite sex.

Mental Health of Medical Students

We have attempted not only evaluations of personality types but of a global sort of mental health placed along a continuum, one end of which is "mature" and the other is "conflicted," a synonym for which might be "emotionally disturbed." Between are two groups; one we have labeled as "emergent," the other "normaloid." The student labeled "emergent" is on the road to maturity but is essentially still in late adolescence. His emotions, drives, defenses, and coping mechanisms are in such flux that his personality is rapidly changing, albeit in a healthy direction. The "normaloid" is so called because he makes a good social adjustment and his psychological difficulties are apparent only to skilled observers (and perhaps, over time, to an intimate, such as a spouse or close friend). Briefly, these difficulties involve emotional constriction or isolation. The "normaloid" is not very comfortable with his own feelings (or those of his patients); he tends to be outwardly directed and conformist, more anxious to please others than to act in accord with his inner standards or beliefs; not only is he not introspective but he tends to be suspicious and distrustful of the introspection of others, hence he dislikes dynamic psychiatry. These students are not unlike the "homoclites" described by Grinker [7] or the "normopaths" described by others. In our view, admittedly based on an ideal of mental health which may not be subscribed to by others, even by other psychiatrists, the "mature" student is not only "normaloid" in his social adjustment but is much more comfortable in his feelings, more introspective, and more creative.

The "conflicted" student may be slightly or seriously disturbed; in any case most of them have social and interpersonal conflicts as well as inner ones, but they are usually more introspective, and at least potentially more creative than the "normaloid" students.

Of our sample of sixty non-patient students studied intensively, ten or 16.7 per cent were "mature," ten or 16.7 per cent were "emergent," seventeen or 28.3 per cent were "normaloid," and twenty-three or 38.3 per cent were "conflicted." Roughly speaking one-third of the students are either "mature" or on the way to maturity, one-third are "normaloid," and one-third "conflicted."

The relationships between these mental health types and specific sexual responses will be taken up later in this paper. First attention is directed toward the more general characteristics of the students' sexual attitudes and behavior.

General Characteristics of Sex Behavior

Examining a representative cross-section of medical students, as we did in our study, we found a striking absence of "far out" aberrant behavior. There are very few students who would be willing clients for the sort of activities sponsored by Dr. Ward and Christine Keeler.

Although there are homosexual students and homosexual doctors, and almost every class has at least one, more exceptional behavior, such as fetishism, exhibitionism, peeping, cross-dressing, true sexual masochism, or the use of more than one mate at a time occurs only sporadically. For every student whose sexual behavior is undercontrolled, there are five students who are overcontrolled and sexually inhibited. From the standpoint of *behavioral characteristics alone,* the majority of medical students fall in the usual or "normal" (where "normal" is used in a statistical sense). Using the two most general categories of undercontrol and overcontrol, however, it might be useful to cite a few examples of each.

A student whom we shall call Arthur had a contemptuous disregard for the opposite sex. He took great delight in the conquest of girls and became an expert seducer. Needless to say, he had little ability to love, for sex and love were not fused as they are in a healthy person. He could never experience the complete enjoyment from coitus available to the person who can feel the full rapture of a relationship in which the mate's pleasure is as important as his own. Arthur enjoyed his reputation as a reprobate and lady killer among his classmates even though his fellow students, almost to a man, detested and shunned him.

Another student, whom we shall call Bernard, had a similar attitude and approach to women but disguised it under a façade of being a clean-cut and righteous youth, giving altogether the impression of being an "All-American Boy." Only a few of his close friends recognized the real character of this student. Bernard was married to an older woman who played a maternal role to her youthful husband. This is a variant of the madonna-prostitute theme, in which the man experiences sexual pleasure only with "degraded" women. A degraded woman, in the eyes of men like Bernard, is any woman who has sexual relations outside the marital bed. Behind this viewpoint is the attitude that sex is nasty and "dirty." One can enjoy sex only with "dirty" women, not with one's wife who, like mother, is "clean" and "pure." Accordingly Bernard tried to seduce the nurses who had a reputation around the hospital for being easy marks or "pushovers."

A third medical student whom we shall call Caesar came from a Latin American country in which the double standard of morality is even more in evidence than in the United States. In that culture it is expected that a man prove himself by having many affairs and by having a mistress even after his marriage. This cult of *machismo* or masculinity regards a man as weak who is celibate or who remains faithful to his wife. Caesar firmly believed in this value system and spent a lot of time that should have been devoted to his studies pursuing and seducing women in order to reassure himself that he was a man.

Dan is a pseudonym for a medical student whose father was aggressive, domineering, and sadistic. Dan felt intense hatred for his father and acted out his unconscious desires for revenge upon him by attempting to seduce as many married women as possible. After he succeeded in making one his mistress, he would abruptly leave her to begin the cycle over again with another married woman. Most of the time the women were the wives of his "friends." He carried out the pattern with another medical student and his wife. The latter, deeply depressed after Dan's desertion, had a severe psychotic reaction. Remorse over this caused Dan to seek psychiatric treatment.

From the viewpoint of the medical educator, the significant aspect of these case vignettes is not the aberrant sexual behavior per se but its effect on the doctor-patient relationship. How will these four men deal with the sexual problems of their patients? Before discussing this question, let us first turn to the much more frequently found type of medical student, the student who is overcontrolled and sexually inhibited.

Among medical students we find a surprising number of men who had not had coitus before marriage. Sometimes this is based on religious grounds; more frequently it is based on sexual fears and consequent internal restraints. An extreme example of the latter was described to me by a urologist. He reported that, in his hospital, two interns, of the opposite sex, of course, fell in love and wanted to get married. When they came to him for advice it turned out that neither of them had any idea of how to proceed with the sexual act. In retrospect, he feels that coming to him for advice was a courageous act on their part, since most students are deeply ashamed of admitting their ignorance of sex, so aware are they of the expectation of the public that they are experts in this field.

Let us call another student Edward. He got married when he was in college to a girl in a neighboring school. He had been very shy and had found it difficult to make friends with girls before he met his wife. Happily married, he nevertheless keeps on wondering whether he has missed something in life. He tries to bury these thoughts; when questioned he states that he feels it is wrong to have a different standard for men than for women. If he expected his wife to be a virgin, as he did, it was mandatory that he be one. He would expect that of any man in similar circumstances.

Fred was adversely affected in a somewhat different fashion by his sexual fears. Burdened by a chronic illness in childhood, and overprotected and dominated by his mother, he could never quite trust a woman. Each girl was unconsciously seen as a spider attempting to trap him in her web. He had no trouble finding girls, but each time it became serious he would find some excuse for leaving her, usually by provoking the girl into a fight or into the arms of another man. Sexual relations were too dangerous, for then he would be under the spell of the woman. It was not until he was far along in his residency training that he was able to have sexual relations; even then he was emotionally detached. The first time that he thoroughly enjoyed coitus was with a married woman. When she declared her love for Fred and her intention of seeking a divorce from her husband in order to marry him, he turned her down, saying that he would like to carry on the sexual affair with her but could not countenance divorce because of his Catholicism. He did have strong religious beliefs, but it is not surprising that they fitted in with his emotional needs and were used to rationalize them.

George was so guilty about sexual activities that he had enormous remorse after petting. On several occasions he was certain that the girl would become pregnant if an accidental ejaculation occurred while he was fully clothed and there was no chance that the seminal fluid could come into contact with the girl's vagina. He was also afraid that he would contract syphilis or develop a cancer of the penis. These fears are quite common among adolescents and it may be surprising to some to realize that they are present in medical students as well but they are not uncommon. Guilt over masturbation is so frequent as to be rather commonplace in the experience of psychiatrists treating medical students.

There are even more extreme cases of overcontrol. One student had so much guilt over sexual self-stimulation that he clamped off his penis to prevent ejaculation. He developed a prostatitis. Still terribly guilty, he told his roommate that he had to masturbate several times weekly in order to drain the prostate. Sexual pleasure was permissible as long as it was a treatment not a treat.

Guilty fears, with or without religious scruples, make many students adopt a moralistic attitude toward others. A professor in the department of public health and preventive medicine gave a lecture on health practices of certain pre-literate societies; he included examples of their sexual behavior, e.g., polygamy. On an examination, the students accurately described this behavior, but many appended notes such as "this is morally wrong" or "this is indecent."

Impact Upon Learning

How do the responses of students affect learning about sex and marriage? After all, this is the major reason for being interested in this side of the student's life, for the graduate physician's competence in this area is bound to be an amalgam of his own life experiences modified by what he has learned in medical school, in internship, in residency, and finally, in practice. The previous portion of this chapter has been largely concerned with the life experiences of the student. Now, the learning process itself will be examined.

Anxieties about sex are ubiquitous among medical students. Even mature students, otherwise self-confident and poised, are hesitant about discussing the intimate details of a patient's sex or married life. Some degree of embarrassment is found in each student, no matter how stable or integrated his personality, because our Hollywood-Madison Avenue culture overstimulates sexual appetites and, especially for our young people, surrounds it with tantalizing mystery creating strong tendencies toward exhibitionism and peeping, the end result of which is a feeling of shame. (Shame is even more frequent than guilt; the Victorian era of repression produced guilt; the modern era of sexual expression and performance evokes shame and humiliation, although the two affects are overlapping.) He has to *learn*, through practice, that his role as physician requires his obtaining sex information and that his efforts in this direction are sanctioned by the public. He has to *learn* through experience that these interviewing techniques are not akin to the furtive whisperings of adolescents behind closed doors. The normaloid student, who is less comfortable with his own feelings, has even more discomfiture with such material, especially in interaction with patients. He would be happier if he could deal with each patient as if the patient were a machine, rather than a person with feelings. This student, while demonstrating the outward poise and grace of good personal relations with his patients, often has trouble acquiring the proper amount of "detached concern" and, hence, is troubled by the show of emotions frequently evoked in patients during discussion of their marital and sexual lives. The range of reactions among conflicted students is great—from relatively mature responses when dealing with sex to the most disturbed. Extreme pathological reactions are generally found in this group.

In any event, nearly every student has some anxiety when dealing with sexual material, especially in taking a history from a patient. This often becomes most noticeable in the clerkship in psychiatry. "The initial encounter with psychiatry," states Miller,[16] "may trouble a student deeply as he is led to introspection about his own emotional problems and conflicts. It may become particularly evident as he meets the open expression of sexual problems that are found so frequently in disturbed psychiatric patients. This causes at least some discomfort to almost any student, and may produce great anxiety in the one who has some sexual problems of his own."

Sexual anxieties may make medical interviewing difficult. The student may communicate his own embarrassment to the patient, increasing the patient's own feelings of shame, making rapport difficult to establish or maintain, and he may never obtain information vital to the understanding of the patient's complaints.

More disturbed students, usually those with undercontrol of their sex drives, may be very brusque and tactless. Their questions may probe too far, too fast, and by increasing the patient's anxiety interfere with rapport and with communication. One student would steer every interview around to sex and, even in the first interview, ask for detailed descriptions of sexual behavior. His patients would squirm like fish at the end of a hook; many became enraged.

Such unusual interest is, in reality, a defense against sexual fears, as are certain emotional reactions to patients' sexual behavior. Disgust, contempt, and sarcasm are out of place in a physician's response;

yet, strong anxiety may produce such untoward emotional reactions, which are, in other circumstances, not evoked or are easily controlled.

Some of the defenses against sexual anxiety have been mentioned in passing, such as emotional isolation and grandiose attempts at repairing masculine pride. Other prominent defenses employed by students and physicians are overidentification (or introjection) and projection. In the former the doctor sees the patient's problems as his own and may lose his capacity for objectivity; in the latter, he sees his own problems and the patient's as being similar and may even suggest his own solutions to the patient. For example, it is not surprising to find that those with overcontrol of their sexual drives restrict the sexual activity of patients with coronary heart disease and healed tuberculosis far more than is necessary. The failure to release sexual tensions and the loss of the opportunities to share mutual pleasure with a loved person may be much more dangerous than the added "work" and expenditure of energy in coitus.

Another danger lies in the possibility that the student or doctor may suggest, either directly or by innuendo, his own distorted values to the patient. Fortunately, most value systems dealing with sex are long held and deeply entrenched by the constant reinforcement of the original conditioning stimuli and are given up, if at all, slowly over a long period of time. Thus, most patients are protected from any ill-considered or impulsive suggestions.*

The examination of patients provides additional sources of stress for students. Breast and pelvic examinations are not learned without blushes and trembling, fumbling hands. Some of those experiences remain in the student's memory for life. Who among us who saw it happen can forget the first day in the Gyn clinic when a student approached an immigrant lady placed in stirrups in the lithotomy position, only to see her take one look at his blushing countenance and leap off the examining table exclaiming, "Let me from here out; I do not want to be a guinea pig."

Despite these anxieties, all students learn these mechanical skills quite readily and it is a rare physician who is troubled by the physical examination, though there are a few who are not quite as "detached" as they should be.

* For a discussion of techniques of interviewing patients about the topic of sex, see Ian Stevenson's book, *Medical History Taking*, (New York: Paul B. Hoeber, 1960), pp. 201-2.

Another indication that the topic of sex elicits anxiety is in the frequency with which humor is employed to deal with it. One junior student, an older man, put it this way:

The only way sex is discussed by the class is to make a joke of it. No one can be serious about it except when he is by himself. A student bought the book, *Sexual Deviants;* when a number of students were looking at it they could only joke about it. That was their way of responding to it. The private beliefs of students about sex are really not known because they won't be serious about it. No one in the class has discussed sex, that is, no lecturer has discussed it, except in anatomy. Oh yes, Dr. B. gave us a lecture on the physiology of sex, but it turned into a big laugh session. I thought it was immature. The students' ignorance of sex is colossal. Only in jokes will they consider sexual deviations. What you know from years of experience is unknown to them. They think that you put words in the patients' mouths by your manner of interviewing. They don't realize that it is experience that leads you to ask questions in certain directions. The students can't act shocked, although they are; so they respond with humor.

Students tend to over-react, as well, to the teaching of sexual material. They may show great interest, even become absorbed, but in large groups they are afraid to reveal what they consider to be undue concern so they pretend to be casual or "sophisticated." Actually, they may be shocked by information new to them because of their lack of experience but are careful not to "let on" that they feel the way they do.

At other times they demonstrate strange resistances; they may claim that a relatively normal or frequent form of sex behavior is perverse or that a genuine perversion is normal, depending on the relative strength of their beliefs and guilty fears. They may object to case presentations of sexual material because they feel the presence of a patient before a medical group is damaging or "traumatic" to the patient. In one such instance, in a seventeen-year-old boy with delayed sexual maturation, the students thought that a testicular biopsy was preferable to a case presentation in which the boy's feelings about his "small penis" would be revealed, completely disregarding the potential reassurance that could be given the patient by the psychiatrist. The discussion with the students in this and in a very similar incident indicated that their resistances could be attributed to an overidentification with the patient.

Resistances decrease sharply in small group discussions and in informal bull sessions in which the students feel less threatened and defensive and are reassured by finding that their areas of ignorance, doubts, and fears are shared by others.

During internship and residency young doctors are more open to experience than are students, but, since there are practically no formal programs of sex education for them, their experiences are extremely varied. Only in psychiatry and in obstetrics and gynecology do the majority of residents obtain enough instruction and experience to make them feel competent to deal adequately with their patients' sexual and marital problems.

Implications for Medical Education

The substance of this report is that: (1) many more students are overcontrolled and somewhat inhibited sexually than undercontrolled and sexually casual or promiscuous; (2) many students (even if considered from the viewpoint of mental health to be, statistically speaking, within the "normal" range) have a significant amount of anxiety about sexual matters; and (3) these anxieties interfere in a variety of ways with their ability to manage the sexual problems of their patients.

Although there is increasing recognition of the need for better methods of education in the field of marital and sexual adjustment, not enough is being done to teach medical students how to deal properly with these problems as they are encountered in medical practice. Part of the difficulty can be traced to a reluctance to discuss sex on the part of the faculty in much the same way that parents find it embarrassing to discuss sex with their children. Why is this so? Many teachers feel that such an intimate topic is too personal or that discussion will make too many students too anxious—in essence it signifies the projection of inhibitory feelings of the faculty onto the teaching situation. Another reason this matter has not been raised as an issue for discussion among medical educators is its controversial nature, and most people avoid controversy, especially if it is apt to involve strong feelings and cherished beliefs.

Still another possible cause for the failure of medical educators to realize the inadequacy of sexual education resides in the vast impact of specialization not only on the practice of medicine but on teaching. Minor sexual adjustments that may lead to major consequences in the lives of people do not come to the attention of the specialist teachers of medical students. Most teachers simply are not aware of this as an important area of practice, or if they are, they deny or disregard it.

The time is now ripe for conferences among medical educators and more research in order to determine means of counteracting the deficiencies in medical education indicated in this paper so that graduate physicians will be confident of their ability in responding to the enormous demand for services by patients asking for help with the most delicate and, potentially, the most satisfying of all human relationships—marriage.

References

1. Blood, Robert O., Jr. 1962. *Marriage*. Glencoe, Ill.: The Free Press.
2. Christensen, H. T. 1958. *Marriage Analysis*. New York: Ronald Press Company.
3. Davidson, William. Jan. 5, 1963. "Quack Marriage Counselors: A Growing National Scandal," *Saturday Evening Post*, p. 17.
4. Erikson, Erik H. Jan., 1956. "The Problem of Ego Identity," *J. Amer. Psychoanal. Ass.*, 4:56-121.
5. Greenbank, Richard K. August, 1961. "Are Medical Students Learning Psychiatry?" *Penn. Med. J.*, 64:989-92.
6. Greene, Bernard L., Alfred P. Solomon, and Noel Lustig. March, 1963. "The Psychotherapies of Marital Disharmony," *Med. Times*, 91:243-56.
7. Grinker, Roy R., Sr., and R. R. Grinker, Jr. June, 1962. " 'Mentally Healthy' Young Males (Homoclites)," *Arch. Gen. Psychiat.* (Chic.), 6:405-53.
8. Gurin, Gerald, Joseph Veroff, and Sheila Feld. 1960. *Americans View Their Mental Health*. New York: Basic Books, Inc.
9. Herndon, C. Nash, and Ethel M. Nash. May, 1962. "Premarriage and Marriage Counseling," *J.A.M.A.*, 180:395-401.
10. Joint Commission on Mental Illness and Health. 1961. *Final Report: Action for Mental Health*. New York: Basic Books, Inc.
11. Kavinoky, Nadina R. Oct., 1954. "The Premarital Medical Examination," *J.A.M.A.*, 156:692-95.

12. Lief, Harold I. 1963. "Orientation of Future Physicians in Psychosexual Attitudes," in Mary S. Calderone (ed.), *Psychosexual Attitudes and Contraceptive Practice.* Baltimore: Williams & Wilkins Company.

13. ———. May, 1963. "What Medical Schools Teach About Sex," *Bull. Tulane Med. Fac.,* 22:161-68.

14. ———, Katherine Young, Vann Spruiell, Robert Lancaster, and Victor F. Lief. July, 1960. "A Psychodynamic Study of Medical Students and Their Adaptational Problems," *J. Med. Educ.,* 35:696-704.

15. McHugh, Gelolo, and J. Robert Maskin. Dec. 1, 1958. "What Ministers Are Learning About Sex," *Look,* p. 79.

16. Miller, G. E. 1961. *Teaching and Learning in Medical Schools.* Cambridge: Harvard University Press.

17. Sandler, Bernard. April, 1957. "The Student and Sex Education," *The Lancet,* 272:832.

18. Winnicott, D. W. 1957. *The Child in the Outside World.* New York: Basic Books, Inc.

19

Marriage Counseling Instruction in the

School of Medicine Curriculum,

University of Pennsylvania

Emily H. Mudd, Ph.D.

The Division of Family Study (Marriage Council) of the Department of Psychiatry, School of Medicine, University of Pennsylvania, offers five programs dealing with the relationship between family attitudes, heterosexual behavior, and health or illness. Emphasis is on what the doctor or other professional person can do to be of assistance in counseling men and women preparing for marriage or in marital conflict. Three of these programs are offered through the Department of Psychiatry, School of Medicine, one through the Veterans Administration, and one jointly with the Graduate School of Education and the Department of Psychiatry.

Program A, Family Attitudes, Sexual Behavior, and Marriage Counseling

This course, continued since 1952, is listed yearly in the catalogue of the School of Medicine under electives as "A series of 12 to 14 lectures and discussions, open to entire fourth-year class, Drs. Mudd,

Goldberg, Peltz and others." The course subject matter includes discussion of young marriages; the impact of the three major religions on sex, marriage, and divorce; legal aspects of marriage problems; fidelity and infidelity; the meaning of love and pre- and postmarital sex adjustment.*

Comments from students vary from the specific to the more general.

"The lectures stimulated thinking and informal discussion in and outside the classroom, which brought out new ideas: that no two couples can have their problems solved in one way, but each problem is individual; better understanding of need for anyone giving marriage counseling not to give advice."

"The lectures presented a sampling of experienced opinion on a subject of considerable importance in medical practice which is ignored by the formal schedule and attended to only occasionally by the teaching faculty as a whole."

"Whether such a course should be compulsory is doubtful, but I feel that it has helped me better prepare myself to face and handle these social problems that will come up in practice."

Registration

This averages 35 to 50 students yearly. Approximately 450 senior medical students have taken this course during the eleven years it has been offered.

Evaluation

On the basis of our experience, we believe that there is a body of scientific data on family attitudes, sexual behavior, and marriage counseling sufficiently developed for communication to medical students as part of the regular medical curriculum. Student response indicates interest and receptivity, which become correlated not only with the theory and practice of medicine but also with the personal needs of the students. These electives make a contribution to the medical student's vocabulary, to his concepts of the personality in social interactions, and to his grasp of many symptomatic configura-

* The 1963 course outline is appended. This outline is modified yearly after evaluation by teachers and students.

tions expressive of the tensions of our times, particularly in the area of marriage.[1]

Program B, Orientation to Marriage Counseling

Since 1959, case study utilizing a one-way screen to observe interviews of marriage counseling cases has been an integral part of the fourth-year required course in Outpatient Clinical Psychiatry in Psychiatric Outpatient Department, Hospital of the University of Pennsylvania. The School of Medicine Bulletin states: "Weekly conferences on patient care integrate the teaching of the students in the Psychiatric Outpatient Department and medical clinics. Marriage Council techniques are demonstrated by members of the Division of Family Study through screen interviews and discussions." The following procedure is used:

A staff counselor (psychiatric social worker) from the Division of Family Study and Marriage Council interviews a husband and wife individually and then jointly in application interviews and on-going marriage counseling cases. A staff member of the Department of Psychiatry, who formerly had six months supervised training at Marriage Council as a V.A. resident, sits in the observation room with the senior medical students and answers questions as to the how and why of the counseling process.

Registration

To hold the student observation groups to a reasonable seminar size, the senior class is divided into eight groups, each with approximately 12 to 18 students who observe at different intervals. Each year approximately 80 out of 125 seniors participate in the marriage counseling discussions. During the four years of this program about 300 senior medical students have been included in this aspect of the required psychiatric sequence.

Evaluation

Evaluation is made yearly by the medical students of all courses offered by the Department of Psychiatry. The marriage counseling interviews and case discussions have continuously been rated highest of the courses by the senior students. Some comments indicate student reaction:

"This was very interesting. I felt, though, that more emphasis and time should be devoted to this type of Rx since we will see a lot of marital problems in our future private practice."

"Excellent from the point of view of acquaintance with marital problems and the opportunity to see two people interviewed simultaneously and the interaction between the two."

"Very excellent, should be continued."

"One of the best parts of the program."

"Could there be more than one demonstration during the 12-week period?"

Program C, Orientation to Research in Marriage

Since 1956, the Department of Psychiatry has offered placement to Medical School students who have received USPHS, Smith, Kline and French, or other fellowships for supervised activity in a variety of on-going research projects. Students may select the department and the research project they prefer.

Registration

The Division of Family Study and Marriage Council have been selected during the past seven years by ten such students. Curricula are planned individually with each student in accordance with his expressed interest and the potentials of the current research.

Evaluation

These students varied in their research ability, as would be expected. Three students made important contributions resulting in papers; one was awarded three consecutive fellowships; two were awarded two consecutive summer fellowships. This continuing time permitted them to complete their studies, one of which won the UMA Day Psychiatric Prize for the paper presented and was subsequently published.[2] Another presented his work at the Annual Meeting of the American

Psychological Society. This material and that of the third student is being incorporated into a book in preparation by Drs. Emily Mudd and Howard Mitchell, to be published by Association Press.

Program D, Training of Psychiatric Residents

In 1947, the Dean's Committee of the Veterans Administration Neuropsychiatric Postgraduate Training Program invited the Marriage Council of Philadelphia to be one of six clinical resources in the Philadelphia area to be utilized for the training of their residents. The purpose as stated by the V.A. was "to orient residents to marriage counseling through seminar discussions, case conferences, didactic presentations and supervised counseling in marriage problems." Residents spend one day weekly for six to twelve months at Marriage Council.

Registration

During the sixteen years since the inception of this program, thirty-seven neuropsychiatric residents have completed it. Since 1959, four residents from the Department of Psychiatry at the University of Pennsylvania have asked to be assigned for this same training and have completed it successfully.

Evaluation

Many of these men continued work on a volunteer basis after their assignment was completed. Follow-up reports indicate they are using the approaches learned during this program in their current psychiatric practice and teaching and that they feel these enable them to save important time and render constructive assistance in certain of their cases.

Program E, Doctor of Education—Specialization Counselor

The purpose of this interdisciplinary doctoral program is to bring new perspective, new knowledge, and new skills for the promotion of mental health to the professional persons with whom children, young people, and their parents naturally have contact: teachers, ministers, physicians, and school counselors.[3] It includes courses and seminars in the Department of Psychiatry, School of Medicine, the Division of Family Study, and the Graduate School of Education. Additional courses may be selected at the School of Social Work and the Graduate School of Arts and Sciences. Initiated in 1959, it is listed in the Bulletin of the Graduate School of Education, University of Pennsylvania as follows:

A special program in counseling for the Doctorate in Education, in cooperation with the Division of Family Study, Department of Psychiatry of the School of Medicine and the Marriage Council, is available for properly qualified students. Courses in this program include: Education 780, Systematic Psychiatry and Human Behavior, Part I (combining Education 780 and 782), 1 c. u.; Education 781, Human Behavior, Part II (Methods of Clinical Diagnosis and Literature Seminar for Residents, combining Education 781, 783, 785), 1 c. u.; Education 786, Case Seminars and Family Attitudes, Part I, Term I (combining Education 784, 787, 788), 1. c. u.; Education 787, Case Seminars and Family Attitudes, Part II, Term II (combining Education 784, 787, 788), 1 c. u.; Education 788, Supervised Marriage Counseling, Part I, Term I (combining Education 789), 1 c. u.; Education 789, Supervised Marriage Counseling, Part II, Term II, 1 c. u. Interested students should apply at the Division of Family Study and Marriage Council, 3828-30 Locust Street, Philadelphia 4, Pa., as well as The Graduate School of Education.

Seminars at the Division of Family Study and Marriage Council concentrate on the following five areas:

Personality Growth and the Dynamics of Behavior

Emphasis is not on acquiring an intellectual understanding only, but on the utilization of this knowledge as a basis for acceptance and understanding of the troubled persons with whom the trainee may work.

The Counselor's Therapeutic Use of Self

Emphasis is on helping the trainee develop sufficient self-understanding and discipline so that he may think and act appropriately within a helping situation.

The Process of Counseling

The basic principles underlying a helping process are discussed, questioned, and evaluated. Through the actual experience of counseling under supervision, the trainee gradually accepts and incorporates these principles as part of his own counseling philosophy.

Socio-Cultural Factors

Perspective is gained as the trainee sees how early life patterns, emotional motivations, and cultural roles are intermingled, and as he comes to recognize, understand, and accept the many diverse ways that individuals have of meeting their own and others' needs.

Supervision

Focus in supervision is limited to the manner in which the trainee uses himself within the counseling relationship and does not at all attempt to deal with the total personality of the trainee. Effort is made to help the individual professional person transfer and integrate his new-found knowledge and skills into his own discipline.

Registration

A maximum of fourteen students per year can be accommodated. In the five years this new specialization has been offered, forty-one graduate students have registered, thirty-seven of whom have completed the marriage counseling seminars and supervised counseling and are in process of finishing their doctoral degree requirements. In this continuing group, three have received their doctoral degrees, five have passed their preliminary doctoral examinations and are currently writing dissertations in some area of marriage relationships or marriage counseling, and twelve have passed their qualifying examinations.

Evaluation

During the process of completing their doctoral degrees in Education with a specialization in mental health and counseling, these thirty-four men and seven women are using their training experience in the following professional activities: teaching human relations and counseling in various university departments; counseling with increased numbers of individuals and groups in social agencies, courts, churches, clinics, and the U.S. Navy; and conducting family life education in schools, colleges, churches, and community groups. The continuing applications for training and the recommendations of the 1961 Joint Commission on Mental Health for the training of personnel auxiliary to psychiatry as counselors and teachers all lead to the conclusion that such a program can fulfill a professional, social, and community need.

FAMILY ATTITUDES, SEXUAL BEHAVIOR, AND MARRIAGE COUNSELING
Elective for Senior Students, School of Medicine, University of Pennsylvania

A course furnishing practical information on these subjects as encountered in medical practice. Emphasis is placed on actual case material and techniques for the physician in general or specialty practice. Recommended text: Emily H. Mudd and Aaron Krich, *Man and Wife* (New York: W. W. Norton & Co., 1957).

Outline of Lectures—1963

Unwanted Pregnancy and Teen-age Marriage
Sexual Adjustment before Marriage
Religious Viewpoints on Sex, Marriage, and Divorce
Divorce and Its Repercussions
Premarital, Marital, and Family Problems in General Practice
Sexual Adjustment during Marriage
Heterosexuality and Homosexuality
The Meanings of Love
Live Interview with Marriage Counseling Clients
Fidelity and Infidelity in Marriage

References

1. Appel, Kenneth E., Emily H. Mudd, and Philip Roche. July, 1955. "Medical School Electives on Family Attitudes, Sexual Behavior, and Marriage Counseling," *Amer. J. Psychiat.*, 112(1):36-40.

2. Mitchell, Howard E., James W. Bullard, and Emily H. Mudd. 1962. "Areas of Marital Conflict in Successfully and Unsuccessfully Functioning Families," *Journal of Health and Human Behavior,* 3:88-93.
3. Mudd, Emily H., Hilda M. Goodwin, and Donald R. Young. Jan., 1962. "Mental Health Teaching in Professional Education," *J. Med. Educ.,* 37(1):36-43.

20

Marriage Counseling Instruction in the Bowman Gray School of Medicine Curriculum

Ethel M. Nash, M.A.

For the past seven years instruction in the accumulated scientific data on family adjustment, normal sex behavior, and marriage counseling techniques has been included in the required curriculum of the Bowman Gray School of Medicine. The aim is to equip graduates to deal with this aspect of patient care at an individual and at the community level, and in terms of prevention as well as salvage. Particular emphasis is placed upon the counseling technique which is based on listening rather than telling the patient, on enabling patients to sift through their patterns of reaction and interaction and to arrive at their own decisions about next steps rather than following directives issued by the physician.

A three-pronged approach is used. (See the accompanying figure.)

The First Prong: Classroom Instruction

First-Year Class

We have moved away from the didactic method of lectures alone to one in which student participation is primary. This is initially

THREE-PRONGED APPROACH

I. Classroom Instruction

    A. First Year—Marital Interaction

        Marital Problems Quiz
        Marriage: Problems and Possibilities
        Pre-marital Pregnancy
        Teen-age Marriages
        Physiology of Sex
        Development of Sexual Satisfaction in Marriage
        Marital Problems in Pediatric Practice
        Marital Problems in Surgical Practice
        Masked Marital Problems Seen by the Internists
        Counseling Help for the Alcoholic Marriage
        Marriage: Fidelity and Infidelity
        Co-operation in Treatment of Disturbed Marriages

    B. Second Year—Family Reaction to Crisis

        Divorce
        Long-term Hospitalization

    C. Third Year—Marriage Counseling Techniques

II. Third and Fourth Years—Clinical Experience in Diagnosis of Marital Stress Symptomatology

III. Availability of:

Premarital Consultation to:
    Medical Students and House Officers
    Their Fiancées

Marital Counseling to:
    Medical Students and House Officers
    Wives of Medical Students and House Officers

achieved in the first year by a quiz about marital difficulties with which patients, either directly by questioning or indirectly through their symptoms, confront their physicians. A series of brief marital case histories, revolving around the subjects that will be brought up during the course, are presented. The students write answers indicating what, in each case, as physicians they would do, suggest, and think. Each case history is designed to provide an opportunity to broaden the class's knowledge of the scientific data about sex and marriage. At the same time, in relating lectures and discussions to the class's answers to the quiz problems an attempt is made to replace the embarrassment that many of them feel in talking about sex (an embarrassment so often concealed under an attitude of pseudo-sophistication) with the confidence that comes from knowledge and familiarity. The following cases selected from the quiz illustrate the use of this method.

CASE 1: SEXUAL FRUSTRATION. Mrs. P. is twenty-nine, college educated, has three children. After her routine annual physical examination she says: "Doctor, during our eight years of marriage, I have never experienced orgasm. My husband is despondent. He thinks it proves that he is no good as a lover. I am frustrated. Otherwise, we have a good marriage. We decided to ask you to help us." The much-discussed subject and often-presented problem of orgasm incapacity provides the opening for a series of discussions, reading assignments, and lectures on sexual preparation and malpreparation for marriage as it takes place in the family, at home, in church, and through peers. This leads into the lectures on the physiology of the sexual response, with explanations about the techniques that may make the difference between sexual frustration and satisfaction. Understanding of the significance of sex in human life is stressed as is recognition of the differing sexual desires of husbands and wives. These differing needs are often expressed in unequal frequency of desire for coitus, in the male's readiness for intercourse as soon as the idea occurs to him in contrast with the female's desire for a long-term work-up which may be best begun in the morning with an endearing remark, furthered perhaps by a phone call "just to say I love you," by help with the dinner dishes or the children, and by any words of appreciation. Specific maladjustments as revealed in "the fatigue symptom" or seen in the varying degrees of frigidity and impotence are studied.

CASE 2: PREMARITAL PREGNANCY. Illegitimacy is a problem causing concern in all twentieth-century affluent societies. Attitudes towards it vary from a relatively permissive attitude toward abortion with minimum stigma placed on illegitimacy, to the United States' attitude of very strict regulation of legal abortion with considerable stigma attached to illegitimacy. No matter whether the social and legal attitudes are tolerant or intolerant, the unmarried pair who find themselves in the position of having conceived a child are faced with a problem of far-reaching consequences. The case of "Lou, eighteen, the daughter of well-to-do and highly respected church-going parents, whose pregnancy test is positive but who no longer loves or is loved by nineteen-year-old Hank, father of the child-to-be," is one in which student involvement is immediate. They know that as physicians they will be confronted by such patients.

Research findings on the problems of the unwed mother are presented.[1]

Physicians from various specialties lead small discussion groups in which they outline their ways of working with such a patient. The pros and cons of the alternatives of marriage, of concealed pregnancy followed by adoption, and of the baby's being reared by Lou or her parents are considered. Emphasis is placed on the need for supportive attitudes on the part of the parents. Even more stress is placed on the acceptance of responsibility by both Hank and Lou for working through the consequences of whatever course of action is chosen.

CASE 3: TEEN-AGE MARRIAGE. The frequency of marriages in which both bride and groom are under twenty years of age is increasing every year. At least four factors can be identified which contribute to the increased rate. First, there is the culturally indoctrinated illusion that to fall in love, or a reasonable facsimile thereof, implies readiness for marriage. Second, there is a common illusion that marriage now constitutes less of an economic commitment for the man because of the prevalence of working wives and the widespread knowledge of birth control methods. However, birth control methods are seldom used consistently by young couples. Third, the social stigma attached to a first divorce is rapidly decreasing, with the result that many young people are encouraged to enter marriage on a trial basis. Fourth, teen-age marriages carry a disproportionately high load of premarital pregnancy. Premarital pregnancy is statistically associated with a high divorce rate. Fifty per cent of teen-age marriages break up within five years. Ninety per cent of today's divorcees and deserters themselves come from divorced, separated, or early bereaved homes. Yet some of these young marriages, which during the early period seem headed for divorce may, because of the elasticity and potential for growth of this age group, become satisfying with minimum therapy. "Mary, aged eighteen, has been married to nineteen-year-old Bob for a year. Both are working in the local mill but she has been absent from work frequently because of repeated stomach upsets and diarrhea. You, her physician, find insufficient organic cause for her malaise and therefore inquire whether she is happy in her marriage. She bursts into tears and sobs that 'Bob won't spend any time with me. He spends every evening with his buddies. He is so stingy, too. He says his money is for him. He complains about everything. My cooking doesn't suit him. When I ask him to pick up his clothes he calls it nagging. He even forgot my birthday.'" Usually the class decides that the physician should talk with Bob to get his viewpoint and to find out whether this couple could be helped to understand the nature of the marriage relationship with its acceptance of responsibilities. The concept is developed, from class discussion and study, of a marital framework that includes the need to develop household routines and schedules acceptable to both, a satisfying sex life, a merging of values about expenditures, anniversaries, in-laws, and all other facets of paired living, the development of a recreational pattern mainly within the married pair set, and the acceptance of some responsibility for the on-going life of the community.

CASE 4: A PROBLEM OF COMMUNICATION. "Pete, aged forty, has developed episodic hypertension. You, his physician, discover that this is triggered by resentment of his wife's widowed mother living with them. His wife, an only child, refuses to consider asking her mother to live near but not with them. Says Pete: 'Her mother is a good woman. She doesn't really interfere but we cannot make any plans at all without considering mother. She's been with us for six years now and she's only sixty-four and in good health. I see no near end to this situation. She could get a job and a small apartment nearby, but Mary won't even let me discuss this idea with her. Yet I feel unable to keep on indefinitely this way.' "

The problem of the ever-increasing number of aged persons is one that needs to be faced on a national level. Pete and Mary are representative of countless couples in a similar dilemma. Their predicament is complicated, as it is in many similar cases, by being unable to communicate, argue, quarrel if necessary, and in the end arrive through these means at a constructive solution.

The class comprehension of the nature of marital and sexual adjustment is now sufficient to make it advantageous to have physicians representative of various specialties discuss marital stress symptomatology. Marital problems crop up among the patients of all specialties but not all physicians feel competent to treat them. We vary the specialties to utilize the marriage counseling interests and competencies of available physicians. In a typical year an internist may discuss the frequent necessity for concurrent marital therapy in the treatment of patients whose symptoms are obesity, ulcerative colitis, bronchial asthma, peptic ulcer, and various psychosomatic dermatoses. A gynecologist may discuss treatment, when organic causes are insufficient for the symptomatology of pelvic pain, menstrual difficulties, and premenstrual tension, through a re-appraisal of attitudes towards sex, in-laws, career desires, or whatever may seem to be the basic emotional difficulty. A surgeon may discuss the patient who will return for more and more operations unless the marital stress is alleviated. A pediatrician may review the problems of children whose multitudinous ailments stem from the poor relationship between the parents.

Second-Year Class

Family Reactions to Crisis. The course in Preventive Medicine emphasizes the holistic concept of the patient and includes discussions of the principles of preventive measures applied at the levels of the individual patient, the family, and the community. The discussions at the family level include certain sociologic aspects of medical problems, one of these being that of family reactions to crisis. The students are introduced to the known emotional sequences in crises—the crisis, disruption, nadir of disorganization, and subsequent re-organization. Two types of crises are outlined. The first is the alienation process that leads to the divorce crisis. The process is always the same. A disturbance takes place in the affectional-sexual life of the pair. Mention of the possibility of divorce takes place. This is a moment as significant as the declaration of love in courtship. Ordinarily both have thought of divorce, but now, one has spoken of it. Next the appearance of solidarity is broken by one or the other speaking of their troubles to a friend, to a parent, or in a group. This is a master symptom of alienation that destroys even the fiction of solidarity. Now the process has entered a new phase. Next comes the decision to divorce, the crisis of separation with the liquidation of the household and the relationship and then the final severance—divorce. This is followed by a period of mental and emotional conflict and then the work of reconstruction has to begin.[2] Knowing this process students are alerted to the possibility of intervention and also to the necessity of helping the recently divorced patient do some re-evaluation before remarriage.

The second type of crisis discussed is that of the low-income, well-adjusted family when the breadwinner becomes seriously ill. The aim is to enable the student to see his medical vocation as involving preventive family and community action so that facilities are available to help such families survive and re-organize.

The Second Prong: Clinical Experience in Diagnosis of Marital Stress Symptomatology

Third- and Fourth-Year Classes

When students begin ward work with patients they are introduced to the idea of the counseling relationship as being based on empathic listening, on the establishment of rapport with the patient, and on unqualified assurance that any subject discussed will be treated confidentially. The concepts of marriage counseling described in Chapters 12, 15, and 16 form the content of the preliminary lectures.

On the wards the students are now taking histories, learning to listen to the patient's description of the onset of symptoms, to ask systematic and clarifying questions, and to sift the information obtained to make a preliminary diagnosis. They are told to apply the same techniques of investigative listening and sifting to obtain a marital history. Their tool is a marital history form.[3] Becoming familiar with this they use it to explore with the patient (and with the spouse whenever possible) their ways of interaction as revealed in the many facets of married life. The form besides providing the student with a social and marital history is a means of enabling a couple to recognize where they pull together smoothly and where friction occurs.

Medical students are always surprised by the eagerness of patients to talk with them about problems related to sex and marriage. Encouraged by this, they are not hesitant to present marital case histories to the class. These case histories are examined diagnostically first in terms of the type of marital interaction present. Is it one that is normally satisfying but which has been temporarily disrupted by a contingency factor or by some specific problem for which a solution has been hitherto avoided? Is it a marriage in which a neurotic type of interaction is unconsciously gratifying to both and will therefore be continued? Or is it a marriage in which one or both now find the tensions intolerable so that the relationship will be terminated if no improvement takes place? Secondly, in either partner, is there evidence of a psychosis, severe neurosis, or character disorder? If so, should referral be made to a psychiatrist? What other possible disposition can be considered? The prognosis for the marriage is discussed in terms of varied methods of working with these patients.

We are uncomfortably aware that as yet our medical students do not have the opportunity to get experience in marriage counseling beyond diagnosis but hope soon to provide opportunities for therapy and follow-up of patients in the out-patient clinic.

Many students find themselves thinking preventively. One student had as a patient a young man, aged twenty-six, with a bleeding duodenal ulcer who repeatedly expressed great concern because this would automatically prevent him from obtaining permanent employment at a local tobacco plant. This, he explained, threatened his approaching marriage. Before hospitalization he had been holding two part-time jobs, one at the tobacco plant when extra help was needed and the other driving an ambulance. His fiancee disliked the latter. He described an incident in which, while driving past his fiancee's home in the ambulance, he had forgotten to sound the siren and had nearly run her down. She became very angry with him. The student's first idea was to see whether anything could be done to persuade the company to accept the patient for permanent employment despite his ulcer. Then he recalled how the patient's eyes had shone with excitement when talking of driving the ambulance. It could be that this patient really wanted to drive the ambulance but could not face his fiancee's disapproval. Perhaps this was why he had "accidentally" nearly run her down. A further talk with the patient confirmed the student's hunch. To students who have had such experiences the desirability of the extended type of premarital medical examination and counseling is evident.

Further experience in diagnosis and in preventive marital counseling is provided through the Department of Obstetrics and Gynecology. Students in their third year take and report on a marital history in which they have looked for indications of gynecologic repercussions of marital stress. In their senior year, when on obstetrics, through again taking such a history and reporting it to the section group they begin to recognize that pregnancy may be a source of or even an attempt to solve serious marital stress.

It is suggested to these students that optimally the physician would talk with the husband at least twice during the pregnancy. As a marriage counselor I consider that this should be regarded as essential in a first pregnancy and very desirable in all subsequent ones. The first visit should be soon after the pregnancy is confirmed so that the husband becomes a knowledgeable part of the team from the beginning. The primigravida usually alternates between pleasurable anticipation of and anxiety about the birth process and her impending new status of "mother." The physician, by explaining to the husband what is happening to his wife physiologically and emotionally, can help him empathize with her mood swings, recognize that she may welcome or reject coitus, and understand that she may wish to continue with or withdraw from her outside activities as she adjusts to her new shape and to the required diet and exercise. Such an interview, if the husband is happy about the pregnancy, will reassure him.

Should the physician learn from the wife or the husband that he is unhappy about the pregnancy then the physician is warned that further inquiry is indicated since therapy may be required. If the physician learns that the baby was conceived as a means of trying to improve the marital relationship, referral for professional counseling should always be considered and almost always suggested. The time to effect repairs on such a marriage is during pregnancy.

The second talk should come during the third trimester of pregnancy, when the wife's needs to be taken care of and to be dependent reach a peak. These needs should be interpreted to the husband together with an explanation of his role during labor. He needs to know how to help; for how long he may stay with his wife; what she will be experiencing during these hours. Some husbands do not realize the importance of the traditional gift of flowers following the birth and mention of this can be casually included along with the suggestion that his wife's well-being will be greatly furthered by his frequent visits in the hospital.

Insecure husbands may feel that the duties of diapering and other aspects of baby care will result in loss of identity. Such husbands tend to be unnecessarily absent from the hospital, and in extreme cases even have to be hospitalized themselves with organically inexplicable symptoms. Obstetricians and pediatricians need to be cognizant of a husband's behavior at this time because of its implications for the marriage.

The Third Prong: The Availability of Premarriage and Marriage Counseling to Medical Students

A marriage counselor is associated with the Student Health Service. Counseling service is provided on request for students and house officers, and for their wives and fiancees. The value of the method of clinical teaching by the study of the individual case is generally recognized. If we consider that a student has a stimulus to learn from a hospital patient assigned to him then this stimulus should be very much reinforced if the student himself is the patient. The experience of being a counselee can be made valuable training for becoming a counselor.

Further, it should be obvious that the academic development of the medical student can be enhanced if his own marriage is given the maximum opportunity for optimum development.

References

1. Vincent, Clark, Jr. 1961. *Unmarried Mothers*. Glencoe, Ill.; The Free Press.
   The most comprehensive recent research available.
2. Waller, Willard, and Reuben Hill. 1951. Rev. ed. *The Family*. New York: The Dryden Press.
   This is a summary of pages 513-15.
3. See Appendix A.

21

Afterword

Frank R. Lock, M.D.

Within this text is a statement referring to why "unhappy" couples stay together. It is that, "social values and duties to children apart, there is a need in each partner to wring out of the other the response which signifies to the unconscious the typical interaction model with the internal object or objects which has come to be vested in the marital relationship." Taken out of context, it would dissuade any prospective reader from a thoughtful study of the wealth of material available to them in this volume.

Early in my experience as a resident, I encountered a devout newlywed of Catholic faith who was in an emotional turmoil because of her failure to respond in the sexual consummation of her marriage. No physical abnormalities were found. Inquiry led to a statement of guilt because Saint Peter observed this intimate personal experience from the vantage point of a holy motif on the wall of the bedroom. The suggestion that this religious influence could be resolved by turning the picture to the wall at appropriate times was accepted with immediate improvement in the situation and prompt resolution of the whole problem. With this experience, a young physician became an expert on marriage and sexual counseling. When the next opportunity to use this skill appeared in the crowded outpatient clinic, it was in the person of an angular woman with close-cropped hair, who invariably wore slacks with a center vent, and broad low-heeled shoes, complaining of frigidity. She came with, and at the insistence of, her husband, a small man who was a clerk in a women's clothing store. There were no physical abnormalities in either partner. Unfortunately, there were no holy pictures which might be turned to the wall in the bedroom, and the expert failed abysmally since he did not have the slightest concept of covert or latent homosexuality.

Relatively few physicians will have the time or inclination to acquire the knowledge that is essential to doing competent marriage counseling in their medical practice. However, every competent physician is aware of the direct influence of emotional homeostasis upon physiologic and pathologic states in medical practice. In one-third of the patients seen in a referred gynecologic and obstetric consultation practice, the symptoms were present when no pathologic changes were found or minor changes that were insufficient to explain the situation. Although no documentation was made of the exact incidence of marital conflict as the primary factor in the large group of patients suffering from functional disease, it was an obvious factor in a large segment of this group.

A relatively complex terminology has been developed in the area of marital relationships and in the description of the complex problems of interpersonal relationships encountered in a "sick" or "dead" marriage. Nearly all of the research and practice in marriage counseling has been done by psychiatrists, clinical psychologists, and sociologists. The terminology is explicit but it is not generally used or known by physicians oriented to ordinary medical practice. Little or nothing is given to the medical student or in residency training of physicians in fields other than psychiatry and obstetrics and gynecology. This volume presents an orderly, understandable basis for an interested physician to acquire a fundamental concept of prophylactic and therapeutic measures that are applicable in daily medical practice. That sexual incompatibilities result from faulty techniques is true occasionally, and any comprehending reader will appreciate that the problem is much more apt to be the result of inherent inhibitions or stressful interpersonal situations. For the majority, superficial or petty misunderstandings exist which can be solved easily before they lead to more complicated personal conflicts.

The physician is the individual most often consulted, other than the minister, by patients searching for greater fulfillment of their marital lives. The studies of sexual attitudes and behavior of medical students by Lief reveal fundamental deficiencies applicable to most physicians in medical practice. It may stimulate an introspective self-appraisal that could enrich the life of the reader, and will probably broaden his understanding of his personal responsibilities in medical practice.

Medical men cannot ignore their responsibility to the patient in the area of family life or confine their professional treatment to overt organic diseases if they are to meet the minimum requirements of adequate patient care. However, the qualities instilled in the student with great care during his undergraduate medical education may be the ones that create attitudes that tend to make him an unsatisfactory counselor. He first learns normal anatomical, biological, and physiological states in the human. He then acquires a large body of facts concerning pathological conditions, their effect upon the functional adequacy of the individual, and what to do about them. He is encouraged to develop confidence in himself and to obtain in exchange the confidence of his patients in his integrity and ability to solve their problems. He learns to make decisions promptly and precisely and to direct patients explicitly in what they must do to obtain a given result. He may develop an M.D. (magnus deus) complex. In the area of stressful interpersonal relationships, it is particularly difficult to avoid interpretation on a basis of personal experience and prejudices. Qualified counselors recognize their inability to make decisions for their patients and attempt to help them develop enough objectivity to understand their own problems and reach a decision about the solution.

The opportunity for prophylactic counseling in medical practice is enormous. Some reasonable guide lines are herewith provided in premarital counseling. The physician can allay the fears of a couple anticipating marriage, or he may precipitate an emotional panic from which the couple may never recover. He may provide nothing beyond a cursory physical examination or a mature discussion of the personal adjustments that must be made and how to avoid some of the pitfalls that frequently cause heartbreaks and disappointments. How often can a working woman make the transition from her role with personal and financial independence to the role of housewife and mother who is completely dependent upon her husband without severe emotional stress? How many women find that they cannot make this adjustment and are confused by their inability to make a decision to begin their family?

How many physicians are thoroughly oriented in the fundamental psychological attitudes of women and able to interpret the problems relating to their attitudes toward marriage, environmental change, sex, motherhood, and many similar major changes that will occur during the course of any normal life span?

Although no one will become an expert in the field of family life through absorption of fundamental principles and techniques offered in this volume, many will be provided with new perspectives and methodology that will assist them in meeting the needs of many patients with relatively simple problems. The application of common sense and mature judgment in medical practice is of great value for the average patient. Very few can read this volume without acquiring a great deal of new knowledge in this extremely important area.

Appendices

Annotated Book List

Index

Marital History Forms

Ethel M. Nash, M.A.

Patient: Name _____ Age _____ Occupation _____

 Religious preference _____

Health: Before marriage: Good ☐ Average ☐ Poor ☐

  Comments _____

  Since marriage: Good ☐ Average ☐ Poor ☐

  Comments _____

Age at marriage _____ Is this a first marriage for you? Yes ☐ No ☐

If not, was former marriage(s) broken by death ☐ divorce ☐ desertion ☐

Spouse: Name _____ Age _____ Occupation _____

 Religious preference _____

Health: Before marriage: Good ☐ Average ☐ Poor ☐

  Comments _____

  Since marriage: Good ☐ Average ☐ Poor ☐

  Comments _____

Age at marriage _____ Is this a first marriage for spouse? Yes ☐ No ☐

If not was former marriage(s) broken by death ☐ divorce ☐ desertion ☐

Children

AGE	SEX	AGE	SEX	AGE	SEX

Marriage of Patient's Parents

Father: Age _____ Occupation _____ Education _____

    Religious preference _____

Mother: Age _____ Occupation _____ Education _____

    Religious preference _____

Siblings of patient: Number _____

Parental marriage is (was) happy ☐ average ☐ unhappy ☐

Who is (was) dominant? Father ☐ Mother ☐ Neither ☐

To which parent did you feel closer? Father ☐ Mother ☐

Are parents living together? Yes ☐ No ☐

If not was marriage broken by death ☐ divorce ☐ desertion ☐

Marriage of Spouse's Parents

Father: Age _____ Occupation _____ Education _____

    Religious preference _____

Mother: Age _____ Occupation _____ Education _____

    Religious preference _____

Siblings of spouse: Number _____

Parental marriage is (was) happy ☐ average ☐ unhappy ☐

Who is (was) dominant? Father ☐ Mother ☐ Neither ☐

To which parent is spouse closer? Father ☐ Mother ☐

Are parents living together? Yes ☐ No ☐

If not was marriage broken by death ☐ divorce ☐ desertion ☐

Marital Framework

Household Routines and Schedules Are Set Up Acceptably to:

Both ☐   Neither ☐   Spouse only ☐   You only ☐

Comments _____

Child Rearing:

You and spouse agree about methods?   Yes ☐   No ☐

Comments _____

Finances:

You regard the available income as: Sufficient ☐   Insufficient ☐

You and spouse agree ☐   disagree ☐   about expenditures. The checking ac-

count is joint ☐   separate ☐. You give spouse ☐   receive from spouse ☐

an allowance.

Comments _____

In-Laws

Do ☐   do not ☐   constitute a problem in your marriage. If yes, difficulty is

caused by: Spouse's mother ☐   father ☐   brother ☐   sister ☐

Your mother ☐   father ☐   brother ☐   sister ☐

Comments _____

Religious Beliefs

Do ☐   do not ☐   cause difficulty. **Comments** _____

Personal Habits of Spouse I Dislike:

Poor table manners ☐   Driving habits ☐   Monopolization of auto ☐   Sleep-

ing habits ☐   Temperature at which house is kept ☐   Extravagance ☐

Stinginess ☐   Nagging ☐   Sulking ☐   Pouting ☐   Unhelpful in

house ☐   Neglects yard ☐   Omits courtesies ☐   Over-Punctual ☐

Unpunctual ☐   Jealous ☐   Bad temper ☐   Explosive outbursts ☐

Treatment of guests ☐   Use of alcohol ☐   Behavior at parties ☐

Quarrelsome ☐ Unfaithful ☐ Excessive emphasis on cleanliness ☐
On neatness ☐ Under-emphasis on cleanliness ☐ On neatness ☐

Pattern of Quarreling includes Physical Attack? Yes ☐ No ☐ By both ☐
Spouse only ☐ Only I do this ☐ Both bring up previous disagreements ☐
Only spouse does ☐ Only I do this ☐

Appreciation and Communication:

I do ☐ do not ☐ receive adequate praise and appreciation. I think I do ☐
do not ☐ give this to spouse. We communicate easily ☐ with difficulty ☐
cannot ☐

Onset of Marital Difficulties:

Marital difficulties became obvious during which year of marriage? _____
Onset did ☐ did not ☐ follow conception of first child. Onset did ☐
did not ☐ follow birth of first child. Do ☐ did ☐ you enjoy being
pregnant? Comment _____
Did your husband share your feelings _____ did he visit you in the
hospital? Yes ☐ No ☐ Did you enjoy his visits? ☐ Why? _____
If not, why? _____

Sex Education in Parental Home:

No discussion of sex ☐ Questions answered antiseptically ☐ Premarital
intercourse was much feared ☐ Tacitly encouraged ☐
Mother's attitude toward sex was _____
Father's attitude toward sex was _____

Sex Education Outside Parental Home:

Church teachings did ☐ did not ☐ create a sense of guilt. Practice of
masturbation you regard as highly dangerous ☐ Arouses strong guilt
feelings ☐ Some guilt feelings ☐ Natural and acceptable ☐ Not
thought about ☐

Main Sources of Sexual Information Were:

Parents ☐ Siblings ☐ Friends ☐ Spouse ☐ Books ☐ School ☐ College ☐ Church ☐

Dating Pattern:

Dated Frequently ☐ Infrequently ☐

Petting: Did not pet ☐ with spouse only ☐ spouse and others ☐ only others ☐

Premarital Intercourse: With spouse only ☐ others only ☐ spouse and others ☐ with prostitutes or pick-ups ☐ Did not have sexual intercourse prior to marriage ☐ I am glad of this ☐ I regret this ☐ I did ☐ did not ☐ have an earlier broken love relationship. Spouse did ☐ did not ☐ have an earlier broken love relationship.

Wedding Ceremony:

Took place in church ☐ home ☐ before justice ☐

Honeymoon:

Length: Less than a week ☐ one week ☐ two or more weeks ☐

Spent: Alone ☐ Visiting friends ☐ Relatives ☐ You regard it as a happy experience ☐ Satisfactory ☐ Unhappy ☐ *Wife* experienced orgasm? Yes ☐ No ☐ *Husband* experienced: Always adequate erection and ejaculation ☐ some premature ejaculation ☐ some impotence ☐ total impotence ☐

Present Marital Sex Life:

Satisfactory to: Both ☐ Husband only ☐ Wife only ☐ Neither ☐

Reasons for Dissatisfaction:

Spouse's techniques are: dull ☐ distasteful ☐ disgusting ☐

Spouse rejects frequently ☐ rejects totally ☐ is too passive ☐ Personally am disinterested in intercourse ☐ Infidelity has occurred: Yes ☐ No ☐ This is known to spouse: Yes ☐ No ☐

Coitus was at some time in the marriage satisfactory: To you ☐ To spouse only ☐ To both ☐ Never to either ☐

* * * * * *

A copy of the above form can be given to the patient after the first interview to take home and fill out. When spouse also comes for counseling it is often helpful to have each fill one out, with the instruction that neither should allow the other to see what has been checked. These can be brought to the next session or mailed in.

Should more detailed discussion of sexual attitudes and practices seem desirable it often helps to use a form which can be purchased, *by professional personnel only,* from the Marriage Council of Philadelphia, 3828 Locust Street, Philadelphia 4, Pennsylvania. This is "Marriage Adjustment Schedule 1B." This is used in *the counseling of married couples only* and *is always used by the counselor within the counseling period.* It is *never* given to the patient to complete by himself. It is usual to hand one to the patient. The physician then fills out the answers as they are given on his copy. This schedule does not try to find out the extent of a person's knowledge of sex, but rather to furnish information about his or her feelings and attitudes.

APPENDIX B

The American Association of
Marriage Counselors

The purpose of the American Association of Marriage Counselors is the establishment and maintenance of high professional standards in marriage counseling. Clinical membership is given only to screened applicants who have completed a minimum of at least two years of acceptable graduate study, with concentration in areas related to marriage, counseling, or marriage counseling. They must hold whatever degree or diploma is necessary for the practice of the recognized profession for which they have been trained and be in good standing in that profession.

To qualify for membership in the American Association of Marriage Counselors they must in addition have had a minimum of five years of professional experience in marriage counseling; for associate membership, two years. Further they are bound by the Association's Code of Ethics. Thus far those accepted for membership number approximately 500.

Any physician who would like to receive a list of marriage counselors in his area may obtain this by writing to the Executive Director's Office, 27 Woodcliff Drive, Madison, New Jersey.

Annotated Book List

For Physicians:

Ackerman, Nathan W. 1958. *Psychodynamics of Family Life*. New York: Basic Books, Inc. $6.75
Pioneer work by a psychiatrist in counseling with the family as a group.

Calderone, Mary S. (ed.). 1964. *Manual of Contraceptive Practice*. Baltimore: Williams & Wilkins Co. $10.00
Written for physicians this book is almost a "must" to be aware of the most recent research findings.

De Martino, Manfred F. (ed.). 1963. *Sexual Behavior and Personality Characteristics*. New York: Citadel Press. $7.50
Valuable papers on some basic concepts involved in sexual behavior, orgasm adequacy in women, impotence, and on the effect of self-esteem on sexual behavior.

Dickinson, Robert Latou. 1949. *Atlas of Human Sex Anatomy*. Baltimore: Williams & Wilkins Co. $10.00
Incomparable material for premarital instruction or sex education.

Eisenstein, Victor W. 1956. *Neurotic Interaction in Marriage*. New York: Basic Books, Inc. $6.50
Marital interaction patterns of neurotic partners.

Ellis, Albert and Albert Abarbanel (eds.). 1961. *Encyclopedia of Sexual Behavior*. New York: Hawthorn Books, Inc. $30.00
For those who want to follow Dr. Lansing's counsel to "read up on the subject of sex."

Johnson, Dean. 1961. *Marriage Counseling: Theory and Practice*. Englewood Cliffs, N.J.: Prentice-Hall, Inc. $5.75
Describes techniques frequently used by trained marriage counselors.

Kirkendall, Lester A. 1961. *Premarital Intercourse and Interpersonal Relations.* New York: Julian Press, Inc. $7.00
Author's thesis: "A relationship that is already a lie will not be improved by sex; a good relationship will probably be able to handle the results of premarital sex."

Mudd, Emily H., M. Karpf, A. Stone, and J. Nelson (eds.). 1959. *Marriage Counseling: A Casebook.* New York: Association Press, $6.50
Selected members of the American Association of Marriage Counselors use case histories to illustrate techniques of marriage counseling.

Mudd, Emily H., and Aron Krich (eds.). 1956. *Man and Wife.* New York: W. W. Norton & Co. $4.95
Based on lectures re family attitudes, sexual behavior, and marriage counseling given to medical students in the elective course on marriage counseling, sponsored by the Division of Family Study, Department of Psychiatry, University of Pennsylvania Medical School.

Oliven, John S. 1955. *Sexual Hygiene and Pathology.* Philadelphia: J. B. Lippincott Co. $12.00
A useful presentation of these subjects.

Stone, Abraham, and Lena Levine. 1956. *The Premarital Consultation.* New York: Grune & Stratton. $3.25
A manual for physicians. It describes the content and methods of an extended type of premarital medical examination.

Van de Velde, Theodoor H. 1950. *Ideal Marriage.* New York: Random House. $7.50
A classic. Useful for those instructing in sexual adjustment.

Vincent, Clark. 1961. *Unmarried Mothers.* Glencoe, Ill.: The Free Press. $6.00
Examines the problems of illegitimacy. A "must" for all physicians who are concerned with prevention and treatment.

For Patients Also:

Baruch, Dorothy W., and Hyman Miller. 1962. *Sex in Marriage: New Understanding.* New York: Hoeber Medicial Div., Harper & Row. $4.95
Useful to professionals and laymen although written in everyday language. Illustrates how attitudes about sex go back to childhood influences. Includes frank discussion of sexual techniques. Describes the kinds of interpersonal relationships that are needed throughout marriage.

Bergler, Edmund. 1948. *Divorce Won't Help.* New York: Harper & Brothers. $3.95

Thesis is that neurotics choose each other as marriage partners. To avoid getting on the conveyor belt of divorce, each must resolve his own neurotic needs.

Butterfield, Oliver M. 1953. *Sexual Harmony in Marriage.* New York: Emerson Books, Inc. $1.50
Offers sexual information helpful to premarital couples.

Calderone, Mary S. 1960. *Release from Sexual Tension.* New York: Random House. $4.95
Readable and informative book that covers many aspects of sexual adjustment.

Davis, Maxine. 1963. *Sexual Responsibility in Marriage.* New York: Dial Press, Inc. $7.50
Written with the usual Davis vivacity.

Despert, J. Louise. 1953. *Children of Divorce.* New York: Doubleday & Company, Inc. $3.50
Suggestions by a psychiatrist of ways in which divorced parents can act to minimize the disadvantages to their children. Very practical.

Duvall, Evelyn M. 1956. *Facts of Life and Love.* Rev. ed. New York: Association Press. $3.50 (also available under the title *Facts of Life and Love for Teen-agers* in paperback)
For the thirteen- to sixteen-year group.

Fishbein, Morris, and E. W. Burgess (eds.). 1955. *Successful Marriage.* New York: Doubleday & Co., Inc. $6.00
One of the best sources of information available.

Fishbein, Morris, and R. J. R. Kennedy (eds.). 1957. *Modern Marriage and Family Living.* New York: Oxford University Press. $5.50
Prepared as a college course book, it is an excellent interdisciplinary study.

Genne, William H. 1956. *Husbands and Pregnancy.* New York: Association Press. $2.50
As far as I know this is the only "Handbook for Expectant Fathers."

Greene, Carol. 1964. *Sex and the College Girl.* New York: Dial Press, Inc. $4.95
The introduction is by Max Lerner. A journalistic report on love and sex.

Guttmacher, Alan F., W. Best, and F. S. Jaffe. 1961. *Planning Your Family.* New York: Macmillan Co. $5.95
A concise but complete book covering all aspects of family planning in simple language.

Hastings, Donald W. 1963. *Impotence and Frigidity.* Little, Brown & Co. $5.50
This book presents much of the known medical information about impotence and frigidity. Patient and counselor are guided towards the

genuine therapy—the discovery and resolution of the inner conflicts in-hibiting a natural and spontaneous married life.

Haussamen, Florence, and Mary A. Gurtin. 1960. *The Divorce Handbook.* New York: G. P. Putnam's Sons. $3.95

Provides necessary information about the variety of serious and often overlooked legal problems that people face in divorcing.

Havermann, Ernest. 1962. *Men, Women, and Marriage.* New York: Double-day & Company, Inc. $3.95

A book especially suited for young married and about-to-be married couples and those who talk with them. Resulted from the author's four-part series on love and marriage in *Life* magazine. Excellent.

Hilliard, Marion A. 1958. *Women and Fatigue.* New York: Doubleday & Company, Inc. $2.95

Men seem to understand their wives better after reading this!

————. 1957. *A Woman Doctor Looks at Love and Life.* New York: Doubleday & Company, Inc. $2.95

Readable book about women's fears, fatigue, the menopause, and sex as these relate to marital adjustment.

Hunt, Morton M. 1962. *Her Infinite Variety.* New York: Harper & Row, Publishers. $5.95

A "must" for all educated people who seek to understand the conflicting cultural values in which the American woman is enmeshed. The insights are refreshing. It is of equal significance for both men and women.

Kling, Samuel G. 1963. *The Complete Guide to Divorce.* New York: Bernard Geis Associates. $6.95

Presented in concise question and answer form. Covers every possible legal aspect of divorce.

Levy, John and Ruth Monroe. 1938. *The Happy Family.* New York: Alfred A. Knopf, Inc. $4.00

A classic that seems to be as applicable in the sixties as it was in the thirties.

Meares, Ainslie. 1957. *Marriage and Personality.* Springfield, Ill.: Charles C. Thomas, Publisher. $3.95

Describes how different personality types interact in marriage.

Peterson, James A. 1960. *Toward a Successful Marriage.* New York: Charles Scribner's Sons. $3.95

Addressed to those individuals who can profit from greater understanding of special areas of marriage such as sex and finance.

Pilpel, Harriet and Theodora Zavin. 1952. *Your Marriage and the Law.* New York: Holt, Rinehart and Winston, Inc. $3.95

Useful information and perspective.

Polatin, Phillip, and Ellen C. Philtine. 1956. *Marriage in the Modern World.*
Philadelphia: J. B. Lippincott Co. $3.95
A psychiatrist and a psychologist collaborate to provide information and
insights about marriage in modern America.

Poponoe, Paul. 1956. *Marriage is What You Make It.* New York: Macmillan
Co. $3.95
Thesis is that many marriages fail because husbands and wives do not
know how, or are unwilling, to give to their life together the same study
and determination that they give to their jobs in the business world. Highly
practical.

Robinson, Marie N. 1959. *The Power of Sexual Surrender.* New York:
Doubleday & Company, Inc. $4.95 (also available in paperback)
A leading psychoanalyst discusses sexual frigidity in the light of the
myths and taboos under which women are reared. She believes that women
can regain and safeguard their femininity by learning "the power of
surrender."

Simon, A. W. 1964. *Stepchild in the Family.* New York: Odyssey Press, Inc.
$5.00

Spock, Benjamin. 1962. *Problems of Parents.* Boston: Houghton Mifflin Co.
$5.00
The Spock insights brought to bear in the problems of divorce, desertion,
bereavement, and remarriage as they may affect children.

Stokes, Walter. 1962. *Married Love in Today's World.* New York: Citadel
Press. $3.95
Dr. Stokes, a pioneer among physicians in marriage counseling, is liberal in
his approach.

Stone, Hannah M., and Abraham. 1952. *A Marriage Manual.* Rev. ed. New
York: Simon and Schuster, Inc. $4.95
Answers frequently raised questions about sex.

Sussman, Marvin B. 1963. *Source Book in Marriage and the Family.* Boston:
Houghton Mifflin Co. $3.75
A sourcebook of recent research findings.

Pamphlets for Patients:

Public Affairs Pamphlets: There are about forty on various aspects of family
relations and of marriage counseling. They are accurate and readable. 25
cents each from: 22 East 38th Street, New York 16, N. Y.

Beck, Joan. 1964. "Our Unwed Fathers." Chicago: Florence Crittenton Associates of America, Inc. 50 cents.

Excellent in its suggestions of how to help the unwed father carry responsibility for the future of his child and himself.

Greenblatt, Bernard R. 1962. "A Doctor's Marital Guide for Patients." Chicago: Budlong Press Co.

Comes in two editions, one for patients wishing general contraceptive information, the other for those who wish to use the rhythm method only. Offers common-sense advice to husbands and wives about developing sexual satisfaction. A little out-of-date concerning contraception and can best be used along with the Planned Parenthood booklet "Modern Methods of Birth Control." (10 cents)

Kelly, G. Lombard. 1962. "A Doctor Discusses Menopause." Chicago: Budlong Press Co.

Informative and reassuring for husbands and wives.

Levinsohn, Florence, and G. L. Kelly. 1962. "What Every Teenager Wants to Know." Chicago: Budlong Press Co.

Well-written sexual information for this age group.

These last three pamphlets are $1.50 for a single copy but obtainable by physicians in lots of twenty-five at 75 cents.

Journals for Physicians:

Family Life. This is the monthly service bulletin of the American Institute of Family Relations. $1.00 annually. Send to 4287 Sunset Boulevard, Los Angeles 27, California.

Family Process. Published semi-annually by the Mental Research Institute and the Family Institute. Subscriptions $5.00 a year to *Family Process,* 428 East Preston Street, Baltimore 2, Maryland.

Journal of Marriage and the Family. Published quarterly. Subscription $12.00 annually, includes membership in the National Council on Family Relations. Applications to N.C.F.R., 1219 University Avenue S.E., Minneapolis, Minnesota.

This list is far from exhaustive considering the resources available. To it should be added others suggested by many of the contributors at the close of the individual chapters. The list was originally prepared for the use of students at the Bowman Gray School of Medicine.

ETHEL M. NASH

Index